DATE DUE		

Prescription
for Excellence

Michael Rachlis, M.D.

PRESCRIPTION FOR EXCELLENCE

How Innovation is Saving Canada's Health Care System

HarperCollins*PublishersLtd*

HarperCollins books may be purchased for educational, business, or sales promotional use through our Special Markets Department.

HarperCollins Publishers Ltd
2 Bloor Street East, 20th Floor
Toronto, Ontario, Canada
M4W 1A8

www.harpercollins.ca

National Library of Canada Cataloguing in Publication

Rachlis, Michael
Prescription for excellence : how innovation is saving Canada's health care system / Michael Rachlis.
— 1st ed.

Includes index.
ISBN 0-00-200661-8

1. Health care reform—Canada.   I. Title.

RA395.C3R3195 2004   362.1'0971
C2003-900501-1

TC 9 8 7 6 5 4 3 2 1

Printed and bound in Canada
Set in Times

This book is dedicated to my parents, Harry and Ruth Rachlis, my partner, Debby, and our children, Linus and Leila. Thanks to Debby for taking on an even more disproportionate share of household management during the past eighteen months. Thanks to Linus and Leila for understanding that their dad has an unusual job.

Contents

Preface

It was late on November 28, 2002, as I settled into the back seat of a taxi at Pearson Airport. After I gave my address, the driver asked me what I had been doing that day. I replied that I had been in Ottawa for the release of the final report of Roy Romanow's Royal Commission on the Future of Health Care. The driver immediately responded, "Romanow, Romanow. He says we have to spend more money! We don't have to spend more money."

I reassured him that Romanow had made a lot of recommendations other than spending money, but he was adamant. "We don't have to spend more money, just stop wasting money!" I didn't have to encourage him to tell me more.

"I took my wife to the doctor four days ago. She had a cold. The doctor ordered an X-ray and prescribed her antibiotics. The medicine cost us over fifty dollars. Then he asked her to come back today. She's feeling fine, so I phone the office to find out about the X-ray, but the secretary says she has to come in to get the result. So I have to get off work and drive her. It costs us more money. Then he tells her the X-ray is fine and she should finish the medication. I don't think she needed the X-ray. I don't think she needed medicine. And I don't think she needed to come back to see him."

I tried to suggest that there might have been good reasons for the doctor's course of action, but by this time he was in full flight. "You have to go one place to get your blood taken and somewhere else to see a specialist. The doctors should have their offices together in the hospital so all of your visits and tests could be in one place. And we don't need so many prescriptions."

This driver's views aren't dissimilar from those of others that I have heard in my travels across the country. Taxi drivers often ask what I do and why I'm in town. When I explain that I am a public health physician who subspecializes in health system problems, the floodgates are opened.

First, they mention their adoration of medicare. Canada's taxi drivers are disproportionately not Canadian-born and several have claimed to me that medicare was part of their decision to emigrate to Canada instead of the United States. Medicare symbolizes to them that Canada is a more caring country than the United States. Canadians, new and old, tend to be passionate about medicare.

Then the drivers often express their debt to people who work in the health care system—a wise doctor, a skilled nurse, a compassionate paramedic. A person, a team, a place that made a difference.

The finale is a litany of complaints about the health care system. There are the complaints you read on the front page of the paper—access, funding, coverage. Then there are the ones you don't usually read. Concerns about mismanagement, lots of stories about waste, and, too often, tales of miscommunication. I hear a lot of common-sense recommendations for reform, as well as some not so sensible recommendations.

Canadians want to keep medicare and they want to fix the health care system. But what does that better-quality and more efficient system look like? How do we get there? This book attempts to answer these questions.

There are solutions to medicare's problems. They have been developed somewhere across this great country by some of the hundreds of thousands of Canadians who work in health care. This book was inspired by the innovators I have been fortunate to meet as I have travelled across Canada. It tells their stories. These are the people who are truly saving medicare.

Canadians are opposed to market medicine, but, like my taxi driver, they don't believe that the cure is a lot of new money. When Romanow's commission wound down, so did much of the informed public debate. One day we hear high-powered misinformation generated by Canadian free-marketers, sometimes paid for by their American friends. The next day, it's media-savvy pressure tactics from health care's powerful interest groups. We seldom hear from average Canadian patients or providers. This book is an attempt to refocus the dialogue on them. Let's design the system around quality care for patients and high-quality work environments for providers. This approach is also our best strategy to control costs and ensure medicare's sustainability.

A quick point about style. When a name is used with an initial for the last name, it means that a patient has requested anonymity or that the profile is really a composite case. When full names are used, it is with the patient's permission or when the case was already a matter of public discussion.

The book uses stories to lead the reader through the analysis. However, I have provided references for important statements of fact. The book's general approach is, in tribute to Neil Postman, evidence-based storytelling.

I would like to sincerely thank everyone who has taken time to contribute to my broader education in the last ten years. I would especially like to thank the many Canadian communities that have invited me to talk about health care. I have felt the passion that burns for medicare throughout our country. Thanks as well to the staff in government departments and health organizations who so willingly helped me with my research.

After all this research, I was left with a major problem. The book includes a lot of material—50 per cent more than HarperCollins originally expected. But even at this length, I couldn't include every worthy program and innovator. I apologize to those who gave me their time but don't see their stories in print. I also apologize that there may be more examples from some places than others. I have seen a lot of Canada, but I certainly haven't been everywhere. I also haven't seen everything of possible interest in the places I have visited.

I would like to thank Rick Hudson, Joel Lexchin, Steven Lewis, and Debby Copes, who read portions of the text and made helpful suggestions. Thanks to my editor at HarperCollins, Chris Bucci. Thanks also to Iris Tupholme, Kevin Hanson, Neil Erickson, Noelle Zitzer, Shona Cook, and Rob Firing at HarperCollins, freelance editors Stephanie Fysh and Ian MacKenzie, and indexer Gillian Watts. I owe a special debt to my agent, Dean Cooke. I hope that this product continues to justify the trust that all of you have placed in me.

It is a particular delight for me, and I hope for readers as well, that my son, Linus Rachlis, took the author photo and made a significant contribution to the cover design.

Finally, I would like to thank the readers of *Second Opinion* and *Strong Medicine*, which I co-authored with my friend Carol Kushner.

You have been an endless source of support and strength during the past year and a half. I sincerely hope that this volume vindicates your loyalty and provides you with the tools you need to modernize medicare for the twenty-first century.

Part I

Introduction

Chapter 1

The Gathering Storm

In December 1999, Canada was enjoying an economic boom. Nortel, Canada's gift to high technology, hit $70 a share; and business leaders were heaping praise on Finance Minister Paul Martin for slaying the deficit dragon. In the US, *Entertainment Weekly* voted swivel-hipped singer Ricky Martin entertainer of the year. Representatives of highbrow culture reacted with glee to the news that TV ratings and share prices for the World Wrestling Federation had fallen to all-time lows. Evidently they were losing advertisers like Coca-Cola because the programming was deemed "unacceptably crude."

Of course there were possible dangers on the horizon: some claimed that the Y2K monster would devour us all once the clocks hit midnight on December 31, while others asserted that the stock market was creating a bubble that would soon burst. In spite of these warning signs, the national mood was generally upbeat as Canadians prepared for the party of the millennium.

Things were also looking up for an eighteen-year-old Toronto boy, Joshua Fleuelling. In the summer, Joshua wasn't really getting along at home. He had spent the summer sleeping in parks or his parents' garage. But by December he had his life together. He was working as a landscaper, living with his parents, and spending a lot of time with his long-time girlfriend, Melissa Page. Joshua had had asthma since he was three years old, but it wasn't troubling him much now and he always had his blue puffer in case he had trouble breathing.

However, storm clouds were moving in. Nortel hit $120 a share in August 2000; by Christmas it would slide to $50 on its way to becoming a penny stock. Ricky Martin would soon eschew *la vida loca*, and wrestling would be as popular and tasteless as ever. And a perfect storm was gathering that would sweep Joshua, his family, and Toronto's health care system into the abyss.

Crowded ERs: Portent of Doom

Emergency rooms in Toronto and many other parts of the country were particularly crowded in December 1999. It seemed that everyone had his or her own version of the cause of the problem. Toronto ambulance supervisor John Whalley noted that ERs were overflowing with people with mild flus or other minor problems: "Mostly the folks that are walking into emergency off the streets load them up so there's no room for ambulances." Ambulance spokesperson Rick Boustead also pointed out that doctors' offices and walk-in clinics were operating on holiday hours.[1]

Other observers noted that patients with minor illnesses don't clog ERs. Gridlock ensues only when ERs cannot move really sick patients who require admission up to inpatient wards. Patients with minor problems might inconvenience themselves with long waits, but really sick people are seen first.* Besides, someone with a sprained finger doesn't take much nursing time. Unstable sick patients, who require active treatment and monitoring, do need a lot of nursing time and rapidly use up the limited number of heart monitors.

One has to look closely to find the true cause of the problem

---

* Of course, apparently minor problems can, in fact, be serious or can become serious. And minor problems can be uncomfortable. But, in general, patients with ambulatory problems don't clog the system while they wait.

during ER gridlock. Sometimes it may appear that there are too few ambulances on the roads because paramedics are not able to transfer their sickest patients to overworked ER staff in a timely fashion. The true causes of ER gridlock, however, are always downstream.

When ERs are overcrowded with sick patients requiring monitoring, it is often because the intensive care unit (ICU) is full. But the problem may not be in the ICU, either. Often ICUs are not be able to move their patients out because the regular wards are full. In turn, the wards may be saturated with patients who should go to long-term care facilities that are themselves crowded. Finally, there may be a large number of hospital and nursing home patients who could be treated at home, except for a lack of available home care.

On December 21, 1999, Ontario health minister Elizabeth Witmer announced a ten-point plan to reduce ER crowding. It included measures to improve patient flow in ERs and ICUs. The government promised money for "flex beds" that would be opened at busy times, as well as better discharge planning and temporary long-term care facility beds. The government did have plans to build another twenty thousand long-term care beds, but they wouldn't be ready for a while. This was essentially the same plan that the provincial government had promised for at least two years. There was little extra funding for home care. In the meantime, the *Toronto Star* advised its readers to "stay well."

Besides these problems, the boom-bust cycle for nurses had left Toronto hospitals particularly short staffed. When governments have money, they give it to health care. When they run out of money, they cut health care funding. The Ontario economy boomed from 1984 until 1990 and the province increased hospital budgets. Hospitals expanded programs and hired more nurses. In the early 1990s, the economy fell apart and then Mike Harris arrived and needed money for his tax cuts. As they say on Bay Street, Ontario hospitals got a close haircut. From 1992/93 to 1997/98, the province cut hospital budgets by 10 per cent, resulting in the layoffs of thousands of nurses.

When he was premier, Bob Rae had focused on getting nurses to accept wage concessions for job security, but Mike Harris's solution was layoffs. When the opposition challenged him, he compared nurses to Hula Hoop workers who lost their jobs when the fad faded in popularity.[2] Harris claimed that in the private sector, industries had to continually restructure their workforces.

The thought of re-election turned on the taps. The province increased hospital budgets by 10 per cent in the year prior to the June 1999 election. But by December 1999, when hospitals had some money, they couldn't find nurses to take jobs. Many nurses had left the country; many more had simply given up nursing. Nursing is a tough job made more difficult by shift work and a dangerous work-place. Nurses have the highest injury rates* and the highest absentee rates of any class of worker—it's more than a bit ironic that hospitals are some of the unhealthiest workplaces. With a booming economy, there were lots of other jobs for bright nurses. If you didn't mind irregular hours, you could sell real estate and make a bundle. If you wanted regular hours, you could work for a pharmaceutical or medical supply company. At the same time, many of the hospital nursing jobs available were casual or part-time. In fact, only half of all nursing positions were full-time. As a result, Toronto hospitals, like some in other provinces, were paying bonuses to attract nurses two years after paying millions in severance to lay them off.

While the lack of hospital nurses created serious problems, the lack of community nurses was at least as devastating. On December 31, Doris Grinspun, the outspoken executive director of the Registered Nurses Association of Ontario, lamented that there was a shortage of two thousand community nurses. The lack of full-time positions and wages 15 to 20 per cent lower than in hospital discouraged nurses from working in home care. Stephen Handler, executive director of a Toronto home care agency, noted that after a period of

---

* Primarily back and other musculoskeletal injuries.

layoffs, nurses had many job opportunities but that the least attractive of these were in home care. Many home care nurses had to accept casual employment. Understandably, they turned down assignments over the holidays to spend time with their families. This left more patients in hospital who could have been treated elsewhere. Finally, long-term care facilities cut back their admissions over the holidays, building up even more patients in hospital.

In Toronto's hospitals, 10 to 20 per cent of patients were waiting to be transferred to a long-term care facility, and a like number could have been discharged into home care if there had been the programs and staff for them. If Toronto hospitals had been able to discharge these five hundred to one thousand patients, there would have been lots of room for patients like Joshua Fleuelling if they ever got sick.

Crowded ERs are merely a symptom. When there is an obstruction to patient flow, it will always be manifested by full ERs, but the real problem might be a long way from the hospital. As Doris Grinspun put it, "ERs are the Grand Central Station of railways, except the trains have nowhere to go."

Influenza: The Surge That Soaks Up All Remaining Capacity

Toronto's ERs had been under severe pressure for several years. After winning the 1995 provincial election, Mike Harris appointed former Queen's University dean of medicine Dr. Duncan Sinclair to head up the Health Services Restructuring Commission. The commission had the legal authority to close or merge hospitals, and it did so with gusto. Much to Dr. Sinclair's chagrin, there was no similar power to reinvest in community care. That was up to the provincial government—and they preferred tax cuts.

As a result, by December 1999, over five thousand hospital beds had been taken out of service in Ontario, but few of the savings had been reinvested in nursing homes and home care services.

Canadian hospitals operate at over 90 per cent capacity most of the time. Many industries, like the airlines and movie theatres, would love to operate at such capacities. Above 85 to 90 per cent capacity, however, there is no tolerance for surges in demand. Up until fifty to seventy years ago, there were regular epidemics of polio, diphtheria, and whooping cough. Now these and many other illnesses have mainly been relegated to history. Today, influenza is the most deadly regular source of demand surge.

Most people consider influenza a minor problem—maybe a touch more serious than having the sniffles—nothing to get worried about. However, influenza can be a deadly illness. Beginning at the end of the First World War in 1918 and continuing for nearly two years, influenza travelled the planet and killed millions. In fact, that epidemic killed more people than did all of the Great War's battles.

The 1918–20 flu epidemic was unusual because it struck down young, healthy people. This was partly because there were no antibiotics at that time to treat complications such as pneumonia. Today, influenza's main danger is to older people and people with weak immune systems. Even now, in an average year, influenza sends seventy thousand to seventy-five thousand Canadians to hospital and over six thousand to their graves.[3] And 1999 was not an average year.

Almost every year, influenza causes a two- to four-week surge in demand. This period coincides with most serious ER crowding as well as with peaks in emergency admissions.[4] These periods also coincide with the highest admission rates for congestive heart failure and chronic respiratory disorders.

In the first three weeks of December 1999, there were more cases of influenza for that month alone than the whole of the previous three years combined. Approximately every ten years, the influenza virus mutates so that people who have previously been exposed are no longer immune. However, it was an old version (technical name, A/Sydney/5/97-like) that had been around for two years that caused the problem that winter.

In late November, there was a deadly outbreak in a Dutch long-term care facility that killed ten residents. Then several outbreaks were reported in the south of France. By early December, the flu was hitting Ontario, BC, Quebec, Saskatchewan, and many parts of the

US. On December 22, Dr. Lori Kiefer, with the Toronto Department of Public Health, reported that there were outbreaks in nine long-term care facilities, sending many residents to hospital. Dr. Allison McGeer, director of infectious diseases at downtown Toronto's Mt. Sinai Hospital, prophetically predicted that the flu would soon wreak havoc in emergency wards: "We were on critical care bypass at 23 out of 25 emergency departments in Toronto before the flu season hit—wait for January to come."[5]

By December 28, the crisis had escalated to the point where all twenty-four adult emergency rooms had closed their doors to ambulances.[6] Half were on critical care redirect consideration, which asked ambulances to go elsewhere with all but the most critically ill persons. The other half of the ERs were on critical care bypass, meaning that ambulances were not to bring any patients under any circumstances. At one point that day, only the Hospital for Sick Children was accepting all ambulances.

Hospitals already had problems discharging patients to long-term care facilities, but the flu made things much worse. Nursing homes with flu outbreaks weren't admitting patients. They weren't even taking their own residents back from hospitals. Hospital wards were filling up with nursing home patients. Most hospitals were now reporting over 100 per cent occupancy.

Many countries were in dire straits. US officials claimed that the outbreak on the East Coast was the worst in recent history. On January 5, 2000, UK officials said that there were only eleven ER beds left for the whole country.

On New Year's Eve, while tens of thousands of partiers filled Toronto's Yonge Street, a deadly drama unfolded 400 metres away. At 11:45 p.m., Henry Musuka brought his young baby to St. Michael's hospital. He thought she was having trouble breathing. Musuka became extremely agitated, terrified that his child wouldn't be seen quickly. Fearing that the delay could be fatal, Musuka took Dr. Richard Yu hostage and held a pellet gun to his neck. Staff called the police and the situation spiralled out of control. As the fireworks burst celebrating the new millennium, police shot the young father dead. Now ER staff had reason to fear for themselves as well as for their patients.

Elective Admissions: The Final Straw

By the second week of January 2000, the situation was fully unravelling. The final straw was the resumption of elective admissions. Hospitals typically trim these procedures during time of low staffing, such as over the holidays. After New Year's, operating rooms gear up. Certain elective surgical patients, such as heart patients, inevitably require a minimum of one to two days of intensive care after their operations. A percentage of the others will also need some time in intensive care. But Toronto hospitals ran out of ICU beds, forcing ERs to manage critically ill patients for days instead of hours.

On top of everything else, the first week of January 2000 was the worst week for influenza in Toronto in over ten years. By January 14, twenty-four out of twenty-five area ERs were regularly on some form of ambulance diversion.

Joshua's Story

Toronto had had a relatively mild winter up until January 12, 2000. On that day, there was snow, and by the next day the wind chill dipped to –27 degrees Celsius, very cold for southern Ontario. Senior climatologist David Phillips counselled, "Even with what you hear about global warming . . . Canada is still the land of ice and snow." Toronto public health administrator Liz Janzen issued the winter's first cold-weather alert. This mobilized dozens of groups to help street people stay warm or, even better, to get out of the cold.

The wintry weather was a boon to Joshua Fleuelling. He spent most of Wednesday the twelfth and Thursday the thirteenth clearing snow from sidewalks and driveways. He finally quit at 4:30 p.m. on Thursday. He went to his girlfriend Melissa Page's house and made dinner for her and her mother. Melissa was concerned about Josh because he was having difficulty breathing. After dinner, he lay down for a nap, but Melissa woke him at 8:00 p.m., concerned that he was "breathing funny." She knew about Joshua's asthma. She suffered from it herself.

Some diseases, such as smallpox, have disappeared. Others, such as stomach cancer, are a lot less common than they used to be. But asthma is now two to three times more common than it was forty years ago.[7] No one really knows why. The latest speculation focuses on the lack of immune stimulation for children because of our increasingly sanitized world. It is suggested that this lack of early immune stimulation leads to autoimmune disease in later life. There is also some research that suggests that decreased breast-feeding makes children more susceptible to respiratory allergies. Asthma drugs are worth tens of billions of dollars worldwide, but there are only a few millions spent on researching why the epidemic has developed.

Wheeze or Breathe: Asthma Is Badly Managed

Josh had another big problem: he wasn't treating his asthma properly. He had had his first asthma attack when he was three years old. All told, he had been treated over twenty times in ERs. Joshua's family doctor for eight years, Dr. Thomas Kerlow, did map out an action plan for Joshua's disease management. In particular, Dr. Kerlow stressed the importance of using prophylactic, or "preventer," medication instead of relying upon so-called rescue medication. But Joshua apparently was using the prophylactic medication only intermittently. As a result, he was much more likely to have an attack, and a severe one at that.

This problem is not unique to Joshua or to asthma. The drive for medicare in the early twentieth century was based on ensuring hospital treatment for acute illnesses, like appendicitis or diphtheria, and for accidents. But over the middle part of the last century, the pattern of Canadian health and illness changed. Now many more

Canadians suffer from chronic illnesses, such as asthma, coronary heart disease, cancer, and diabetes. Chronic diseases account for 70 per cent of all deaths and over 60 per cent of health care costs.[8]

While the Canadian health care system does an excellent job with acute health problems such as heart attacks and car-accident injuries, it does a poor job of managing chronic illnesses. As a result, too many people get sick with complications that could have been prevented. Dr. Ronald Grossman, head of respirology at Mt. Sinai, notes, "It's clear the deaths are largely preventable. If they managed their asthma properly they wouldn't have to endure such severe attacks."[9]

A British Columbia study of asthma showed that only 20 per cent of patients had appropriate medication management.[10] A national survey showed that 60 per cent of Canadian asthmatics did not have their disease properly controlled.[11] Sometimes patients aren't compliant with therapy. Sometimes the health care system does a poor job of educating patients on self-management. All told, five hundred Canadians die every year from asthma, and almost all of these deaths are preventable.

Melissa Page telephoned Marjorie Fleuelling and said that her son, Joshua, wasn't feeling well. Marjorie came over immediately and took him home. Joshua said good night to his father, Bradley, at 9:00 p.m. and went to bed. Joshua was a fit eighteen-year-old, but he had worked very hard and by the time he went to bed he had been up for over thirty hours.

About 1:30 Friday morning, Marjorie heard a loud crash in the bathroom and ran upstairs. Joshua was struggling to breathe. She helped him with his medication but it didn't seem to provide any relief. Finally, at 1:48 a.m., Marjorie called 911.

At 1:55 a.m., firefighters arrived as the first emergency response and administered oxygen. At 1:57, Toronto paramedics Tony Smith and Gary Lewis arrived at the Fleuellings' house. Smith and Lewis were Level 2 paramedics, meaning that while they could insert intravenous lines and read cardiograms, they could not provide certain advanced life-support care. In particular, they couldn't intubate—

place a tube through a patient's larynx directly into the trachea. This procedure is a prerequisite for other advanced life support, such as mechanical ventilation.

Normally, a call about a possible breathing emergency would lead to the dispatch of a Level 3 paramedic. But in the early morning hours of January 14, the four Level 3 paramedics on shift were working together in two pairs. Neither of the two advanced teams was available at 1:55 a.m. One was on standby to the police emergency task force, and the other was on preceptor duty, assisting in the training of other paramedics. If the Level 3 paramedics had been paired with Level 2s, there would have been four advanced life-support units instead of just two.

As Smith and Lewis began to assess Joshua, he suddenly collapsed with full body convulsions. Joshua's brain had become so deprived of oxygen that he had suffered a seizure. Then his heart stopped. While firefighters administered CPR and oxygen, the paramedics called for an advanced life-support crew but were told none was available. The paramedics gave Joshua an electric shock but his heart was still silent. This time it was the firefighters who asked for an advanced life-support crew, but they too were told there was still none available. As the emergency personnel prepared Joshua for transportation, they were told that the nearest ER, Scarborough General, which was only 4 kilometres away, was on critical care bypass, so the dispatcher ordered them to Markham Stouffville Hospital, 7 kilometres farther away. They left the Fleuelling home at 2:11, with one paramedic driving and the other doing CPR with a firefighter on Joshua. They finally arrived at Markham Stouffville ER at 2:23. Working feverishly, the ER personnel re-established Joshua's heart and airway and commenced mechanical ventilation. However, after the passage of so much time, Joshua had sustained irreversible brain damage. He was taken off life support at 9:12 a.m. on Sunday, January 16.

Fortunately, the rest of Joshua's body was healthy enough, and his family generously gave his organs for transplant. Joshua's untimely death did have some upside. However, there was no getting around the tragedy of the loss of one so young to such a preventable cause.

Who Was Responsible?

After Joshua's death and through the subsequent coroner's inquest, a number of assertions were made as to the true cause of Joshua's death. The ambulance department recommended more ambulances and paramedics as well as more hospital funding, nursing home beds, and nurses. The hospitals recommended more funding for hospitals as well as for ambulances, nursing homes, nurses, and other good things. Nursing groups recommended more nurses. It was somewhat predictable.

By the time the ambulance was called, it's not clear that even immediate advanced life-support assistance and a hospital across the street would have saved Joshua. But a more effective health care system response might have made a difference. Joshua's family and friends would have done anything to find out.

Joshua's case was reported widely in the US as a failure of Canadian medicare. Major reports from the *Washington Post*, the *New York Times*, and ABC News focused on the disaster in Canada's emergency rooms but either did not mention influenza or suggested that it was simply a Canadian excuse to minimize medicare's failure.[12] At the same time, for almost ten days, sixty of the eighty-one ERs in Los Angeles diverted ambulances. Reports by *Time* and *USA Today* attributed the problem to the flu epidemic.

We do know that bad air can aggravate asthma, and Toronto has some of the worst air in North America. The city sits downwind from dozens of coal-fired generating plants in the Ohio Valley. The millions of automobiles in the Toronto area daily spew tonnes more pollutants. It has been estimated that in the city of Toronto alone there are one thousand premature deaths, five thousand five hundred hospital admissions, and over sixty thousand cases of bronchitis in children every year due to bad air.[13]

Cigarette smoking aggravates asthma. At the inquest into Joshua's death, Dr. Kerlow remembered admonishing Joshua about his smoking: "He'd come in with a pack of cigarettes in his top left pocket and I'd say, 'Josh, you've got to quit smoking.'" Later in the inquest, the lawyer representing the Ontario Ministry of Health claimed that "the cause of Joshua's death was not ER overcrowding but rather certain lifestyle choices that he made."

At eighteen, Joshua had already been a smoker for several years. Tobacco addiction is tough to break. It's even harder if you start as a kid. In early 1994, when Joshua was a vulnerable twelve-year-old, the newly elected federal Liberal government claimed that it had to cut tobacco taxes to deal with massive smuggling activities. The government cut taxes, and smuggling fell. But teen tobacco use rose sharply for the first time in three decades. Teenagers were being offered a "starter rate."* It turned out later that tobacco companies facilitated much of the smuggling.[14] Instead of going after the tobacco companies, the federal government had cut taxes. Tobacco taxes take in $5 billion, but tobacco costs nearly $10 billion—$3 billion for health care costs and $7 billion through lost productivity and expenses such as disability pensions.[15]

In 1996, when Joshua was a suggestive fourteen-year-old, RJR-MacDonald launched a series of billboards featuring rock guitars and the enigmatic but "cool" tag line, "Either you like it or you don't." Of course, they claimed not to be targeting young people. But tobacco companies have to recruit underage smokers because forty-five thousand smokers die every year from their habit.[16]

Smoking was clearly a lot more than just a lifestyle choice for Joshua Fleuelling. Joshua's smoking was as much due to government negligence and tobacco company malfeasance as to any free choice on his part.

---

* The rate of smoking is coming back down again mainly because of the recent increases in taxes.

Influenza Denouement

Within hours of Joshua's death, the Toronto Emergency Medical Services (EMS), which administers Toronto's ambulance service, ordered paramedics to take critically ill patients to the nearest ER despite any posting of critical care bypass. The EMS also split up the Level 3 paramedics to double the number of advanced life-support teams available.

By the end of January 2000, Toronto hospitals were relatively quiet. In the first half of the month, hospitals were operating at a normal status only 40 per cent of the time. On many occasions nearly all hospitals were diverting patients. But by the end of the month, they were operating normally over 80 per cent of the time and there was no more gridlock. The flu had receded quickly. Long-term care facilities and home care agencies started taking clients out of hospital again. ICUs and regular wards were able to move their patients, albeit haltingly, through the system.

At its peak, influenza had increased the demand for medical beds by 10 to 20 per cent. With beds already clogged with patients who should have been in nursing homes or treated at home, the resumption of elective surgery tipped the Toronto hospital system over the brink.

Quietly Something Different Was Happening out West

Saskatoon was also hit hard by the flu epidemic of December 1999 and January 2000, but the hospital system there was never gridlocked. Starting in 1992, Saskatoon had consolidated all its health facilities and most of its personnel under one regional board. The Saskatoon District Health Board* (now called the Saskatoon Regional Health Authority) administered the funding for hospital care as well as home care, long-term care facilities, public health,

---

* The district health boards have been reconfigured into regional health authorities, or RHAs, the most common designation in English Canada.

and mental health. The regional structure is no panacea, but it did allow for better co-ordination of the different sectors than was permitted in Toronto. In Toronto, each hospital and each nursing home acts quite independently; home care and public health are completely separate entities.

In Saskatoon there was a high flu vaccination rate for the elderly, but no higher than Toronto's. If anything, Toronto might have had higher vaccination rates for employees in long-term care facilities. In both locations, public health officials tracked the progression of the flu. However, there were some key differences that spared Saskatoon the worst of Toronto's problems.

One of the major problems in Ontario was the number of outbreaks in long-term care facilities. The vast majority of facility residents had been vaccinated, but 40 per cent of the frail elderly don't have strong enough immune systems for the vaccination to take. Consequently, it is important to identify influenza outbreaks quickly when they occur in long-term care and to take preventive action. This should have included the administration of an antiviral drug, amantadine, to all residents of a home at the first sign of an outbreak.

In Saskatchewan, health officials considered one case of influenza-like illness (ILI) to be an outbreak, while Ontario officials tended to wait for two cases of ILI or one laboratory-confirmed case before declaring an outbreak. Amantadine is a tricky drug to use properly. It can be toxic, so it is important to calculate the right dose depending upon the patient's weight and kidney function. In Saskatoon, the health district had co-ordinated a region-wide campaign to get standing orders for the correct dose of amantadine on every resident's chart by October, before influenza season. Within hours of one resident's being diagnosed with probable influenza, staff gave all residents the correct dose of amantadine, and the whole institution was protected. As a result there were few outbreaks in Saskatoon long-term care facilities, and those that did occur were very small.

Ontario nursing home physicians were supposed to inform public health officials about influenza cases so they could identify outbreaks early. But it wasn't happening routinely.[17] There were dozens of institutional influenza outbreaks in the Toronto area, and several involved over 25 per cent of the residents. This poor communication between different parts of the system was also a predominant feature of the 2003 SARS outbreak in Toronto and may well have caused many of the additional cases.[18]

Saskatoon doubly benefited from its adept management of influenza outbreaks in long-term care. Fewer long-term care patients needed hospital care. And because the long-term care facilities were mainly free of influenza, hospitals could still discharge patients to them.

Communities usually get two weeks' warning before a surge of influenza cases hits. By early December 1999, Dr. Cory Neudorf, Saskatoon's medical officer of health, had seen the flu strike in BC, Alberta, and then Regina. He knew he had short period of time to take action. He worked with his hospital colleagues around the senior management table to scale back elective surgery so new post-surgical patients wouldn't hit already full ICUs.

The integrated management system led to other initiatives. The home care department hired more temporary staff to reduce new pressure on ERs and to take every referral they could from hospitals. In Saskatoon, the home care nurses had the same wages and benefits as the hospital nurses. The health district even worked with private-practice doctors to encourage them to keep some offices open over the holidays to see minor cases.

Saskatoon had another advantage. It started flu season with many fewer alternate level of care* patients in acute care beds than did Toronto. The Saskatoon region had made a priority of ensuring that patients were in the correct location. By the winter of 2000, less than 5 per cent of hospital patients were waiting for long-term care or home care. Now it's less than 1 per cent. That's an extra 10 to 20 per

---

* Alternate level of care or ALC patients are those who could be cared for in rehabilitation or long-term care facilities or at home.

cent of capacity that Saskatoon has over Toronto because ALC patients aren't occupying acute care beds. If there had been the extra beds available, Toronto could have got through the flu season without hostage dramas or critical care bypass postings.

Saskatoon wasn't alone in its success. Edmonton and Calgary also escaped the winter 2000 influenza season without experiencing gridlock.[19] In each case there was an integrated approach keyed by public health within a regionalized system. Dr. Brent Friesen, the medical officer of health for Calgary, claimed that the secret to his community's success was the focus on long-term care facilities. Dr. Friesen noted that the combination of complete immunization and immediate administration of prophylactic amantadine had greatly decreased the number and size of outbreaks.[20]

In Edmonton, the regional authority identified when the flu surge was likely to hit and then, like the other two cities, mounted a comprehensive system response. The command team representing ERs, hospital wards, nursing homes, home care, and public health met every day at 7:30 a.m. and 2:00 p.m. to co-ordinate their response. When it seemed that the system might face gridlock, the team cancelled some elective surgery to prevent a crisis from developing. Whenever one ER was overwhelmed, the administrators ensured there was another that would take emergencies. The authority placed extra home care staff in ERs and arranged to send patients home instead of having to admit them to hospital. Dr. Robert Bear, the executive vice-president of the Edmonton Capital Health Authority, said this plan prevented the hospitalization of dozens of patients.

A Regionalized System Paved the Way for Comprehensive Influenza Management

It is hard to draw absolutely firm conclusions from this uncontrolled experiment of different approaches to an influenza epidemic. But Saskatoon, Calgary, and Edmonton managed to keep their health systems flowing while Toronto's became gridlocked. The key factors appear to be better control of outbreaks in long-term care institutions and the timely ramping up of home care services in combination with the scaling back of elective surgery. This required an integrated working relationship among public health, acute care, home care, and long-term care. As Dr. Bear says, "We have had the capacity to problem-solve right across the system and that has made manageable what would have been a disastrous situation."[21]

Dr. Bear previously worked at St. Michael's Hospital in Toronto. Ontario is the only province without some sort of regional authority,* which Dr. Bear says is "a very powerful organizational model."

Things Aren't as Bad as They Seem

In January 2000, the Toronto hospital system melted down during a bad flu outbreak. Many Canadians (and Americans) wrongly blamed the problems on medicare. Further analysis shows that the problems were a result of lack of system management. The Toronto ER crisis was not an indictment of the notion that health care should be provided according to need. Some parts of the country, far away from media central in Toronto, did take the appropriate management strategies, and their ERs kept operating.

This isn't unusual. When something goes wrong with our health care system, medicare's enemies and friends have differing views as to the causes. Enemies say governments can't do anything right, while friends of medicare say governments need to spend more money. When Roy Romanow started the fact-finding phase of his royal commission in 2001, he noted that he saw the debate shaping around three distinct perspectives on the health care system.[22]

The first perspective he noted might be called the *Globe and Mail* or centre-right view:

---

* The exact model varies considerably across the country, but that in Saskatchewan and Alberta is the most integrated.

- We established medicare in the post-war period when we were young and healthy and when the economy was growing rapidly. It worked pretty well then.
- Now we are old and decrepit and the economy is stagnant. Medicare doesn't work very well anymore. People are on wait lists that start north of 60 and go to the US border. Health care costs are shooting through the roof. The public sector is too inefficient to make it work right.
- We now have to be cruel to be kind. To save medicare, we should allow some privatization of finance and more for-profit delivery.

The second perspective he noted might be called the *Toronto Star* or centre-left view:

- At the beginning of medicare, the federal government paid half the bills and everything worked pretty well.
- The federal government gave up 50-50 cost-sharing in 1977 and then slashed funding over the next twenty years. The provinces have been cutting too, and medicare is starved of funds. As a result, we've got poorer services, privatization of finance, and more reliance on for-profit delivery.
- Now we need much more federal and provincial money and more federal enforcement of the Canada Health Act to save medicare.

The third perspective might be called the *National Post* or far-right view:

- Medicare was always a bad idea.
- Services are terrible. Health care costs are out of control. What do you expect from a government-run system?
- We should do what we always should have done: we should privatize the financing and encourage for-profit firms to enter the

delivery system. The invisible hand of the market will soon fix our problems.

Romanow found that none of these three perspectives really resonated with Canadians.* He said that he would be looking for a "Fourth Way," a more compelling story that Canadians would take for their own. Unfortunately, he never did present the vision Canadians were really looking for. His final report was interpreted as fitting the second scenario—calling for more money without a fundamental restructuring of the delivery system.

The fourth way that Canadians are looking for can be summarized like this:

- Public finance still makes sense. It provides for services to be delivered according to people's needs, reduces administrative overhead, and dramatically reduces costs to business.
- Money isn't the main issue. Medicare does need adequate, predictable, sustainable funding, but the main issue is the poor organization and management of services.
- Innovation in service delivery can provide better quality care without breaking the bank.

Canadians still believe in the values of medicare. We still want health care to be provided according to need. But we are all worried that the system may not be there for us when we need it.

Canadians have repeatedly told public opinion surveyors that they don't think that a lot more money is needed to fix medicare's problem. In November 2002, just before the Romanow Commission released its findings, 88 per cent of Canadians told Ipsos-Reid pollsters that "we would not need to raise taxes to pay for improving health care if we just did a better job of spending money that's being

---

* Although public opinion polls favour the second.

spent now."[23] The poll confirmed that Canadians prefer a public system: 65 per cent rejected user fees or private spending.

The influenza example demonstrates that Canadian instincts are right on. The ER crowding in Toronto that may have led to Joshua Fleuelling's death was not caused by medicare. A commitment to care being provided according to people's needs does not mean that ERs have to be overcrowded. The Ontario government had cut back the Toronto system over the previous seven years. But the chaos appeared to be due as much to lack of overall planning and co-ordination as a lack of resources.

Usually we don't get enough information to accurately diagnose the health care system's problems. The media prominently play up health care disaster stories, but reporters' and editors' eyes glaze over when presented with a story about an innovative solution.

The enemies of medicare in Canada and the US monitor the media for gory stories that make our health care system look bad. Furthermore, doctors, administrators, drug companies, nurses, universities, and unions will all at different times claim that the sky is falling somewhere in order to gain political or economic advantage.*

Throughout most of the past thousand years, many wars have been fought on Polish soil because it lies between Western Europe and Russia. In Canada, our health care system is the political battleground between right and left. Too frequently, this ritual combat squeezes out evidence-based dialogue.

This book agrees with Canadians that there are solutions to our health care woes that don't require either a lot of money or the rejection of the values upon which we founded medicare. The following pages analyze the common problems that afflict our health care system and then outline examples of innovative programs that can solve them.

The best government report on health care in recent years (and the least publicized) was the Fyke Report, released by Saskatchewan in

---

* Sometimes they're right.

April 2001. It was the only report to highlight the fact that the system's real problems were related to poor organization and consequent poor-quality care. Kenneth Fyke, a long-time senior health care administrator, noted, "Many attribute the quality problems to a lack of money. Evidence and analysis have convincingly refuted this claim. In health care, good quality often costs considerably less than poor quality."

The US Institute of Medicine has also championed this issue. Its 2001 report *Crossing the Quality Chasm*[24] derived its title from the report's emphasis on the immense gap between the present level of quality and the potential that could be attained. The authors were careful to clarify that individual doctors, nurses, or other providers did not cause the problems. The vast majority of people who work in health care are dedicated to their patients. Rather, the organization of the system typically obstructs good quality. In fact, often it is only because of individual providers that patients survive a too frequently deadly system.

The Key Is Innovation

It is said that every system is perfectly designed to achieve its outcomes. In January 2000, the Toronto health system was perfectly designed to achieve gridlock, and it did. The governors and administrators in Saskatoon and some other cities worked hard to redesign their systems so it would achieve smoother patient flow, and they forestalled gridlock.

After the Second World War, some Pacific islanders built ramshackle airstrips and used mock radios in an attempt to bring in cargo—the Western manufactured goods they had come to treasure during the war. Anthropologists referred to these groups as "cargo cults." In our case, we continue to pour resources and political attention into our health care system hoping this will make us feel as good as when we first implemented medicare.

Medicare is a tremendous Canadian achievement. Prior to medicare, many Canadians died because they could not afford care. Canadian families suffered grinding poverty because of unpaid medical bills. Young Tommy Douglas had osteomyelitis, a serious bone infection in his leg. The Winnipeg doctors told Douglas that he had to have his leg amputated, but, at the last moment, Dr. Robert Smith, a prominent Winnipeg surgeon, volunteered his expert services if Tommy agreed to be a teaching patient. These events left Douglas with the view that if he hadn't been considered an "interesting case," he would have lost his leg. He vowed that no Canadian family should ever have to choose between health care and impoverishment.

Right-wing ideologues and commercial interests have put the majority of Canadians on the defensive about medicare. "See, it doesn't work!" they say. "Look at all the wonderful achievements from user fees in Sweden and medical savings accounts in Singapore." Of course, these are false solutions. User fees cause problems with access in Sweden just like in Saskatchewan.[25] Medical savings accounts have dramatically increased costs in Singapore.[26]

With the many months that Douglas spent in hospital, it is a good bet that his clever eye saw waste and poor-quality care. Douglas was adamant that public health insurance was just the first step in the health system's transformation. "Removing the financial barriers between the provider of health care and the recipient is a minor matter," he said, "a matter of law, a matter of taxation. The real problem is how do we reorganize the health delivery system. We have a health delivery system that is lamentably out of date."

If we really wish to save medicare, we must all become advocates for innovation. Of course we must maintain public payment for hospitals and doctors, and we should also phase in home care and pharmacare. But to save medicare, we must tackle its problems head on. We must roll up our sleeves and restructure our health care system to improve the quality it provides. As we improve quality, we will also protect medicare's Achilles heels by improving access and controlling costs.

But we can't do this by looking to the past. We tend to always do things just as we always have done them in health care, and then we are surprised that we always get the same results. Douglas knew this too. Some of his final public words were direct advice from James Russell Lowell, to not "attempt the Future's portal / With the Past's blood-rusted key."

Chapter 2

Setting the Table

Joshua Fleuelling's untimely death fed the fire of medicare criticism, but medicare had nothing to do with Toronto's ER debacle. This chapter will dispel other myths about our health care system. First, we briefly review the history of medicare and conclude that despite a few potholes, medicare was the right road to have taken. Then we look at how much money we spend on health care and conclude that we aren't spending too much and we probably don't need to spend a lot more. Innovation will be the true saviour of our health system.

We Took the Right Road with Medicare

Canadians love their medicare. But what is medicare? To some, it is the whole health care system. To others, it is just the part of the system that is paid for publicly. To still others, it is just the hospital and medical insurance plan pioneered in Saskatchewan and then spread nationwide. This book shamelessly uses medicare to mean both the whole health system and the timeless aspiration for Canada's health policy described in the Canada Health Act:

> *. . . to protect, promote and restore the physical and mental*
> *well-being of residents of Canada and to facilitate reasonable*
> *access to health services without financial or other barriers.*

A Brief History of Medicare

Although people think that medicare debates are a recent phenomenon, they go back at least one hundred years.[1] In 1919, new Liberal leader Mackenzie King convinced his party to include a plan for health insurance in their election platform. However, the federal government took no action until Saskatchewan made the first move. As described in chapter 1, Saskatchewan premier Tommy Douglas's burning desire for medicare was fuelled by his own experiences with sickness as a child in Winnipeg. Douglas's Co-operative Commonwealth Federation, or CCF,* came to power in 1944 when Saskatchewan was struggling out of the Depression. Douglas took on the health portfolio himself, and on January 1, 1947, the province inaugurated its hospital insurance plan. This was the first universal health insurance program introduced in North America.

Prior to public insurance, many patients couldn't pay their bills. Now government paid for everyone. Prior to medicare, people suffered terrible tragedies. They either avoided health care because they couldn't afford it, or they sought care and were ruined financially. The program was soon popular with Saskatchewan's hospitals and doctors because now they got paid. Prior to medicare, 10 per cent or more of hospital bills went unpaid.

Some other provinces began to experiment with their own programs, and in 1957 the federal government passed the Hospital Insurance and Diagnostic Services Act. The act laid down the template for future federal health programs. It did not take over provincial jurisdiction for health care. Rather, the federal government

---

* The CCF was the predecessor of the New Democratic Party, or NDP.

promised to pay 50 per cent of the costs of a province's hospital insurance program if the province agreed to abide by the program criteria.

Because the feds were now paying half of Saskatchewan's hospital insurance program, Douglas had the money for the next step, insurance for physicians' services. This time Douglas faced major opposition.

The Canadian Medical Association (CMA) had supported public medical insurance during the Second World War. But with the advent of the cold war, many doctors and some average Canadians equated public insurance with socialism. In the United States, the American Medical Association was unalterably opposed to public health insurance. The irascible Dr. Morris Fishbein, long-time editor of the *Journal of the American Medical Association*, even referred to medical group practices as "communist cells."[2]

The hawks in Douglas's cabinet wanted government-run health services, like Britain's National Health Service. But the doves won the day with an insurance plan. The opposition was still very bitter. When Saskatchewan launched its medical insurance plan on July 1, 1962, over 90 per cent of the province's doctors went on strike, refusing to see patients even in an emergency. While the physicians started with a fair degree of support, the first reports that patients were being harmed changed public opinion. The government recruited British doctors as strikebreakers, and several communities hired them for their community clinics. The American Medical Association, meanwhile, provided support to the strikers. Hundreds of reporters descended on Regina from all over the globe.

On July 17, the government brought in Lord Stephen Taylor from Britain as a consultant. The English peer was an enigmatic figure. He was an active member of the Labour party, a midwife of the much-vaunted National Health Service, and a practising physician. Even though he started his Saskatchewan stint working for the government, true to his complicated character he soon became the mediator. His Lordship shuttled between the provincial cabinet in Saskatoon's

Bessborough Hotel and the Saskatchewan College of Physicians at the Medical Arts building three blocks away. He finally achieved an agreement on July 23. He then took his reward, a week's fishing in northern Saskatchewan.

This truce came to be known as the Saskatoon Agreement. It permitted medicare to go forward, but it also allowed doctors to charge patients small amounts above the tariff negotiated with the provincial government.

In 1961, as the storm was developing in Saskatchewan, the CMA petitioned Prime Minister John Diefenbaker to appoint a royal commission to investigate health care. Many within the CMA hoped that a dispassionate review of the facts would scuttle medicare's ships before they launched. However, Justice Emmett Hall's commission surprised many by not only supporting national medical insurance but also recommending coverage for home care, mental health, pharmaceuticals, and dental and optical programs for children.

Dief was no longer the chief by the time Justice Hall submitted his report in 1964. He was now the Opposition leader facing Prime Minister Lester Pearson and his Liberals. They had a fragile minority government and were supported alternately by the smaller parties—the Douglas-led NDP and the Social Credit party. The Liberals—*plus ça change*—were badly split. Some wanted to implement all of Hall's report and some wanted none of it.

Parliament passed the eventual compromise, the Medical Care Act, in 1966. It was to have its royal proclamation on July 1, 1967, as a Centennial present to Canadians, but the Liberal right wing wasn't through yet. Mitchell Sharp was finance minister, and he didn't like public health insurance. The Finance Department didn't like it much either.

On September 8, 1966, Lester Pearson was attending a Commonwealth Prime Ministers' meeting in London, and Sharp was acting prime minister. In a plot worthy of Shakespeare, the finance minister shocked Health Minister Allan MacEachen and the rest of his front bench by announcing to the House of Commons that the medicare proclamation was to be delayed until July 1, 1968. This was ostensibly because of fear of inflation and increasing deficits. Of course, Sharp wanted more than just delay—he wanted to use the time to cancel the proclamation altogether. As medicare advocate and cabinet minister Judy LaMarsh said, "The opponents of medicare smelled an ally. They came out of their lairs again."

However, the pro-medicare forces eventually prevailed. The legislation was implemented in time for Canada's 101st birthday on July 1, 1968. Pearson was no longer the prime minister. He had passed the reins of office to his young justice minister, Pierre Elliott Trudeau.

The new act was a compromise. It covered only physicians' services. Home care, drugs, and other issues would wait on the shelf. As with the hospital insurance legislation in 1957, Ottawa promised to cover 50 per cent of the bills if the province's programs obeyed the federal criteria. While most provinces signed up within the first year, Ontario stood opposed. Premier John Robarts wanted a US-style system where government would provide medical insurance only to those who could not purchase it from the private market. However, Trudeau stood firm. Robarts had to accept the federal criteria or forget the cash. Finally, in 1971, Ontario joined the other provinces, and medicare was in place from sea to sea.

By 1969 it was clear that there would be some sort of national program. The country's deputy ministers of health commissioned Dr. John Hastings, professor of public health and health administration at the University of Toronto, to examine options for the reorganization of medical practice under medicare. In 1972, Dr. Hastings's commission recommended a new model with group medical practice; non-fee-for-service payment; doctors working in teams with nurses, social workers, and other providers; and more focus on prevention. Some provinces were interested. Nursing associations, public health groups, and others were very keen. But the medical profession was cool. Doctors were already facing more change than most of them wished just in accommodating themselves to public insurance. The provinces had their hands full implementing medicare and were wary of more fights with doctors. As a result, there was little change in the delivery system even though it was now publicly funded.

The Feds Break Their Promises and Cut the Cash

During the 1970s the federal government and several provinces wanted to change the funding rules. The feds were concerned about their open-ended funding obligations. At the end of the year, the provinces simply told Ottawa how much they had spent on doctors and hospitals, and the feds cut a cheque for half. This made it hard for the feds to plan their own budgets.

Some of the provinces were also dissatisfied. For example, Manitoba began covering most nursing home costs in 1973 and home care bills the year after, but the province received little federal support for these programs. After several years of negotiations, the federal government passed the Established Programs Financing Act (EPF) in 1977. EPF replaced the so-called 50-50 cost-sharing with a new block fund. The federal payments for hospitals, medical care, and post-secondary education were put into one pot with the promise that the funding would grow at the same rate as the economy (the gross domestic product, or GDP).

But the federal government didn't put all its new money into the EPF fund. The feds and the provinces also massively rearranged the country's finances. The federal government cut its income tax rates by 16 per cent, and the provinces raised theirs by 16 per cent.* There was no impact on taxpayers from this reshuffling of national income, but it gave the provinces greatly increased revenue to fund health care and universities.

After 1977, the feds counted these transferred tax points as part of their health care transfer but the provinces didn't. This set up decades of interminable federal–provincial wrangling, which continues today,

---

* The details were slightly different in Quebec, *bien sûr.*

about how much each side pays. The two parties look like the prover-
bial couple who divorced twenty-five years ago but still fight over the
furniture.

The Trudeau government soon broke the original deal when it uni-
laterally cut back its EPF cash contribution in 1983. At the same
time, there was other strife between the federal government and the
provinces.

Doctors did well financially with the introduction of medicare in
the late 1960s. They were being paid for all their work for the first
time. Prior to medicare, at least 10 per cent of medical bills went
unpaid. Now, some doctors in poor communities saw their incomes
jump by 30 per cent or more. However, with inflation at over 10 per
cent, by 1975 doctors' incomes were slipping. It took doctors a while
to accommodate themselves to negotiating with government. But
now they were becoming more militant.

During the 1974 election, Trudeau had dismissed Conservative
leader Bob Stanfield's call for wage and price controls to counter
inflation. In fact, that was probably why he won the election. But the
following year, he decided they were a good policy after all. Starting
in October 1975, doctors—and millions of other Canadians—had to
dampen their dreams and live with income controls. Trudeau
removed the cap in October 1978.

In 1978 in Ontario, less than 10 per cent of doctors had taken
advantage of the Saskatoon Agreement to extra-bill their patients.
The Ontario Medical Association schedule was only 10 per cent
higher than the medicare tariff paid by the province's Ontario Health
Insurance Plan (OHIP), so extra-billing would add only 10 per cent
to a doctor's income. But in October 1978, the OMA raised its fee
schedule by 30 per cent. Now there was a big incentive to extra-bill.
Doctors had to give three months' notice to OHIP before they could
start to extra-bill. By January 1979, the numbers of extra-billing
Ontario doctors jumped. By June 1979, 20 per cent of the province's
physicians were extra-billing patients, and in some areas all of certain specialists were levying extra charges.

Ontario doctors pointed out that a higher proportion of Alberta doctors extra-billed. Alberta's laws allowed doctors to bill medicare for some patients while extra-billing others. In Ontario, doctors had to formally opt out of medicare to extra-bill. The political turmoil was focused in Ontario where federal elections are won and lost.

A Brief History of Canadian Medicare

1919 Federal Liberal leader William Lyon Mackenzie King promises medicare in the federal election.

1947 Tommy Douglas's Saskatchewan Co-operative Commonwealth Federation government implements hospital insurance in Saskatchewan.

1957 Louis St. Laurent's Liberal government passes the Hospital Insurance and Diagnostic Services Act. The federal government pays 50 per cent of the bills.

1962 Saskatchewan implements medical insurance.

1964 Justice Emmett Hall's federal royal commission recommends medical insurance as well as coverage for home care, pharmacare, and coverage of other services.

1966 Lester Pearson's Liberal government passes the Medical Care Act, which covers doctors only. The federal government pays 50 per cent of the bills.

1971 All provinces sign on to the medicare plan.

1972 Dr. John Hastings's report on the Community Health Centre in Canada for the Council of Deputy Ministers of Health recommends the reorganization of medical practice to complement public medical insurance.

1977 The federal government passes the Established Programs Financing Act (EPF). The federal government combines its support for health care with its transfer for post-secondary education. The feds promise that the funding will grow at the same rate as economic growth.

1983 The Trudeau Liberal government cuts the EPF transfer payment.

1984 The Trudeau Liberals pass the Canada Health Act, which codifies the criteria for the federal transfers and explicitly penalizes those provinces that permit hospital or physician user charges.

1986, 1989, 1991 The Mulroney Conservative government makes further cuts to the transfer payments to the provinces.

1994 Liberal prime minister Jean Chrétien appoints the National Forum on Health to advise on the direction of the federal government's health policy.

1995 The federal government implements a new block fund, the Canadian Health and Social Transfer (CHST), which unites the funding for health care, post-secondary education, and social services. The funding is cut further.

1997 The National Forum reports and recommends increased federal funding and the coverage of home care and pharmacare. The federal government restores a little funding and promises home care and pharmacare.

2000 The federal government increases funding for the CHST and provides some targeted funding for primary health care, home care, and diagnostic and medical equipment.

2002 The Romanow Commission recommends more federal funding, more provincial accountability, and limited coverage for home care and pharmacare.

2003 The federal government and the provinces sign a new five-year funding agreement. The federal government creates separate health and social transfers. The feds increase overall financing and create new targeted funds for primary health care, home care, catastrophic drug coverage, and diagnostic and medical equipment.

Adding to the controversy, some provinces also began allowing hospitals to charge their patients. In 1979, Trudeau and the Liberals were temporarily out of power, and Joe Clark was prime minster of a minority government. Monique Bégin had been the federal minister of health and welfare and was now a fiery Opposition health critic. She was upset that Health Minister David Crombie was taking such a permissive line with the provinces. She demanded an inquiry into what the provinces were doing with the funding the federal government gave them for health, and she called for controls over extra-billing and hospital user fees. Crombie brought Emmett Hall back from retirement to chair an inquiry. Clark's government was short lived, so, once again, Hall issued his report to a Liberal government. And Bégin was once again in the health portfolio.

Justice Hall's review concluded that extra-billing and user fees were not congruent with Canadians' values, which favoured access unimpeded by user charges. He suggested that the feds take measures to eliminate these practices. He also recommended some changes in the delivery system, including better community health services and the enhanced use of nurses.

It took four more years of tumultuous political debate, but in 1984, Parliament unanimously voted for the Canada Health Act. It was one of the last pieces of legislation that the Trudeau government passed. The act slightly better defined the criteria the provinces had to meet to be eligible for federal health funding. It explicitly labelled extra charges for hospital and physicians services as verboten. The provinces would now lose one dollar of their federal grant for every dollar of physicians' or hospital user fees that was permitted within their borders.

Brian Mulroney cleverly had his Conservative MPs vote for the Canada Health Act, not wanting to give the Liberals any edge in the upcoming federal election. But after winning the election, the Mulroney government never developed the regulations necessary for the act to properly function. Mulroney also took his own sharp

The Five Principles of Medicare

1. *Universality of coverage.* The provinces have to cover 100 per cent of their residents for hospital and physicians' services.
2. *Portability of coverage.* The provinces have to cover their residents for care in other provinces at the rates that pertains in other provinces. They are supposed to cover their residents while out of the country at least at the rates that would have pertained in their home province.
3. *Reasonable accessibility to services.* The provinces are to ensure that services are "reasonably accessible" and that financial charges or other barriers do not impede access. This criterion also requires the provinces to pay reasonable compensation to their health professionals.
4. *Comprehensiveness of services.* The provinces are supposed to cover all "medically necessary" services provided by doctors or within hospitals. This criterion is actually a misnomer because community services (such as home care) are not covered and neither are the services of other providers (except dental services within hospitals—a rare event these days).
5. *Public administration.* The provinces have to administer their health insurance programs either themselves or through a body that is accountable to the provincial government. This criterion is also a bit of a misnomer because it expressly forbids neither for-profit insurers acting on contract with a province nor for-profit providers of services.

knife to transfers to the provinces, making cuts to provincial transfers in 1986, 1989, and 1991.

In 1993 Jean Chrétien's Liberals stormed back into power. They took an axe to the transfer payments in 1995 and replaced the EPF block fund with the Canadian Health and Social Transfer (CHST), which combined the transfers for health, post-secondary education, and social services. They cut $6 billion from cash transfers in the process. Eventually, the feds were forced to up their payments slightly, prior to the 1997 election. After running large budget surpluses for several years and facing an election in the fall of 2000, Chrétien gave the provinces $23 billion in new funding over a five-year period.

The September 2000 health accord with the provinces helped the Liberals win another large majority, but within months the provinces were crying poverty again. They claimed that the federal government wasn't paying its fair share. Some provinces threatened to privatize their systems. The premiers and the feds filled the airwaves with advertisements, each blaming the other for medicare's problems.

The history of medicare lent itself to misrepresentation. The provinces claimed that the feds were paying only 14 per cent of their health costs while the feds claimed it was nearly 40 per cent. The provinces calculated their figures using the federal cash as the numerator and their total health care expenditures as the denominator. The feds crunched their numbers using the CHST health cash *plus* the calculated value of the tax points they transferred in 1977 as the numerator. To make their case even better, the federal government used only the costs of hospital and physicians' services as the denominator. The feds' rationale is that the Canada Health Act requires the provinces to cover only these services. But the federal calculation leaves out the provincial expenditures on home care, long-term care, drugs, and so on.

Though the feds cut the cash, they also eased up on the whip. According to Auditor General Sheila Fraser, the federal government doesn't even have the information it needs to monitor whether the provinces are adhering to the Canada Health Act.[3] The *Globe and Mail* revealed that the federal government has identified potential violations of the act by every province. The feds are moving so slowly to investigate, though, that some suspected infringements have been on the books for nearly twenty years.[4]

In 2000, Premier Roy Romanow of Saskatchewan lobbied his old friend Chrétien to establish a royal commission to take a comprehensive look at the country's health care system, but the prime minister rebuffed him. However, by spring 2001, the prime minister was fresh out of rabbits. On April 4, 2001 he asked Romanow to chair the Royal Commission on the Future of Health Care in Canada.

Post-Romanow Malaise

In 2000, the federal government wanted to use new cash to leverage change in the provinces. It wanted the money to be used for primary health care, home care, and medical equipment. But by the time the federal government and the provinces inked the September 2000 agreement, only 7 per cent of the new money was tied to specific reform purposes. The agreement targeted roughly 4 per cent of the new funds for new medical equipment and 3 per cent for primary health care reform. The rest ended up in the provinces' general revenues accounts, where it could be used for any purpose.

The provinces paid a big price for their "win" over the federal government. Most of the money wasn't targeted, so doctors, nurses, and other health workers immediately strong-armed their provinces for large pay increases to do the same work as before. The raises were overdue, but innovation was sidelined in favour of political grease. Even the funds for high technology and primary health care weren't really targeted. Some provinces used the high-tech funds to buy lawn mowers, ice makers, and woodworking tools.[5] Initially, the feds wanted five criteria for primary health-care pilot projects, but after a series of negotiations, the provinces forced the feds to fund them if they met only one. Romanow warned the feds not to make the same mistake again. He recommended targeted funds over two years with strict accountability for expenditures. These funds would include a rural and remote-access fund, a diagnostic services fund, a primary health care transfer, and envelopes for limited home care and pharmacare programs. Romanow recommended a total of $3.5 billion in 2003/4 and $5 billion in 2004/5. He further recommended that the federal government raise the transfer to $6.5 billion in 2005/6 and then grow it at a pace slightly greater than the growth in the gross domestic product (GDP) in a series of five-year plans. The federal funding would be sequestered to separate health care funding from other transfers.

Some claimed that Romanow had advocated eliminating for-profit providers. In fact, Romanow did not make such a specific recommendation, though he did expound at length on his concerns about for-profit care. But Romanow did suggest two policies that would inhibit profit-making health care businesses. First, he suggested that the Canada Health Act explicitly identify diagnostic services such as MRI and CAT scans as medically necessary under the Canada Health Act. This would thwart the plans of some provinces to allow for-profit operators to sell some of their scans at market prices while having their base expenses covered by public patients. Second, Romanow recommended that the federal government close a loophole in the Canada Health Act that allows workers' compensation boards to buy services outside of medicare. For-profit surgical clinics depend upon these contracts for the majority of their income.

Romanow endorsed the creation of a National Health Council, which would have an extensive mandate including everything from approving new drugs and assessing new medical technologies to monitoring the system, reporting on its performance, and facilitating program improvements. Somewhat mysteriously, the report recommended eliminating public insurance for out-of-country care.* There was no mention of long-term care even though this sector represents 10 per cent of health costs, and there was almost no mention of public health. The proposed home care and pharmacare programs are considerably less comprehensive than those recommended by the National Forum on Health in 1997.

Prime Minister Chrétien and the premiers continued their dysfunctional relationship when they came together in February 2003 to

---

* Out-of-country costs amount to less than 0.2 per cent of health care expenditures.

fashion a post-Romanow agreement. It was classic Canadiana. The feds claimed they had reached an agreement on an accord. Some of the premiers, notably Alberta's Ralph Klein, claimed there was no agreement, but they were taking the money. There wasn't even agreement on how much money was involved. The federal government claimed that it was providing $34.8 billion over five years. But the provinces pointed out that some of this new money was "old" money because it had already been promised in the 2000 agreement. The prime minister waxed rhapsodic about the difference between "new money" and "new, new money."

The February 18, 2003, budget enshrined the 2003 (dis)agreement to include

- an immediate investment of $2.5 billion into the Canada Health and Social Transfer;
- the creation of separate health and social transfers to increase transparency (the feds will increase these transfers to the provinces and territories by $9.5 billion over the next five years);
- $16.0 billion over five years to provinces and territories for a Health Reform Fund targeted to primary health care, home care, and catastrophic drug coverage;
- $5.5 billion over five years for diagnostic and medical equipment, health information technology, and the creation of a six-week compassionate family care leave benefit under Employment Insurance; and
- $1.3 billion over five years to support health programs for First Nations and Inuit people.

The feds and the provinces will fight over the criteria for the targeted funds for months to come, guaranteeing federal and provincial political analysts continued employment. But the promise of Romanow's cross-country treks seems destined to be unfulfilled. The commission held twenty-one days of public hearings and heard six hundred presentations from individuals or organizations. Two thousand other Canadians sent the commission formal submissions, and over ten thousand forwarded e-mails or letters. Over twenty thousand completed on-line surveys. Canadians said passionately that they wanted to keep a public system and modernize it. But there is no room for democracy, and even less for evidence once the first ministers start jawing.

Romanow attempted to craft his own political deal with the premiers. Not surprisingly, the premiers failed to see his report as the final word. They took it simply as the feds' opening gambit in a new game in a long-running match.

The biggest disappointment is that Romanow failed to articulate an overall vision for the health care system. This lack of vision left Romanow open to the criticism that he had closed his mind to new ideas. Of course, most of his opponents were proposing the oldest idea of all—taking money out of our own pockets to pay the doctor. Canadians wanted Romanow to defend medicare. They wanted someone with his pro-medicare credentials and record of integrity to admit that the health system is replete with waste and poor patient care. Most Canadians are still left between two uncomfortable positions: one advocates the erosion of public coverage and more for-profit delivery, and the other claims that medicare can be fixed with more money, more enforcement of the Canada Health Act, and a little tinkering with the delivery system.

History Demonstrates
That Medicare Was the Right Choice

When Tommy Douglas started the continent's first universal public health care program, Saskatchewan hospital insurance, over fifty years ago, Canada and the US spent similar proportions of their national economies on health care and had similar health statistics. Now we spend 50 per cent less of our GDP on health care,[6] 58 million Americans either have no insurance or live with someone who lacks coverage,[7] and tens of millions have such inadequate coverage that half a million people annually declare personal bankruptcy because of health care bills.[8]

In addition, medicare greatly lowers the cost of doing business in Canada and is one of the most important components of our national competitiveness. It is estimated that in the auto industry, medicare amounts to an $8 per hour per employee economic advantage.[9]

Harvard researchers recently calculated that in 1999 the costs of administration throughout the health care system were $1,059 (US) per capita in the United States but only $307 in Canada.[10] In fact, half of the huge difference in costs between the American and Canadian systems is due to higher paper-shuffling costs in the US private system.

While spending less, we actually get more. Canadians have more doctor visits[11] and more days in hospital.[12] We do have fewer MRIs and get fewer open-heart surgeries, but we get more of some high-tech services, including bone marrow transplants.[13] Finally, US infant mortality is now 34 per cent higher, while life expectancy is 2.4 years lower.[14]

Over the past fifty years, our economies, national defence, and culture have become more integrated. But Canadians have fashioned a unique health care system. Clearly, we took the right turn at the fork in the road with public health insurance.

Money Isn't the Main Issue

Sometimes it seems that all health care stories concern money. "We don't have enough of this." "Someone died because of lack of that." "Health care is becoming unaffordable." "Pay doctors more or they will leave the country." "Pay nurses more or they will leave." Etcetera, etcetera.

Sometimes it is stated simultaneously that "health costs are spiralling out of control" and that "our health care system is dangerously underfunded." It seems unlikely that we could be simultaneously spending too much *and* too little. The *National Post* and the Canadian Conservatives claim that our federal government is a free spender and has little reserve to pay for health care, even if more is needed.

This section reviews Canadian health costs and the federal government's financial picture. It looks as though we aren't overspending, but neither have we slashed health care budgets to the bone. And if we do need extra cash, the federal government has lots to spare. Maybe if we focused more on what we get for our spending instead of on how much money we spend, we could fix our health care system's real problems.

And the Oscar for Out-of-Control Health Care Costs Goes to . . . the USA

It is true that Canadian costs have increased in the last five years, but this followed five years of restraint. Canada actually spends less of its GDP on health care now than it did in 1992. And health care costs in Canada appear to be under better control than those of our major trading partner, the United States. It is forecast that the difference between the two countries for 2002 (9.8 per cent of GDP in Canada and 14.7 per cent in the US) will be larger than ever. Figure 1 shows that the difference between US and Canadian health care spending as a share of GDP has increased from zero at medicare's establishment in 1971 to over 4 per cent now. That's almost as much as our entire spending on education.

But the System Hasn't Been Starved of Cash Either

Canada has not slashed the health care system either. As Figure 2 shows, during the past ten years, per capita, real government funding for health (controlled for inflation) has increased by 20 per cent. But governments whipsawed the system. In a completely unprecedented fashion, governments cut costs from 1991 to 1997 by 6 per cent. Since then, governments played catch-up and increased their expenditures by nearly 30 per cent. We are nearly back on to the trend line

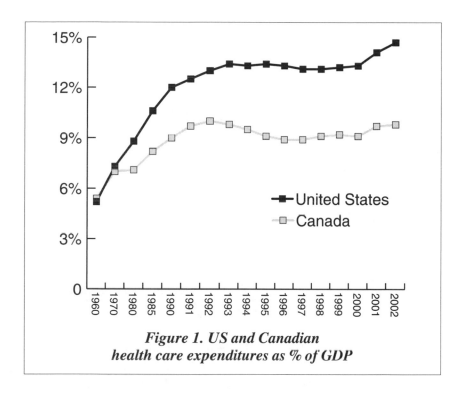

Figure 1. US and Canadian
health care expenditures as % of GDP

from 1978 to 1992, when provincial government health care costs were increasing at 2.5 per cent per year (compounded). Furthermore, in 1999, only four out of thirty OECD countries spent more of their GDP on health care than Canada.[15]

Of course, there are significant differences between provinces. Ontario cut its funding from 1991 to 1997 by 4 per cent* and then increased it by 28 per cent from 1997 to 2003 for a paltry net gain of 16 per cent over the period.[16] On the other hand, Newfoundland and Labrador increased its spending by 14 per cent from 1991 to 1997

---

* In current or non-inflation-adjusted dollars.

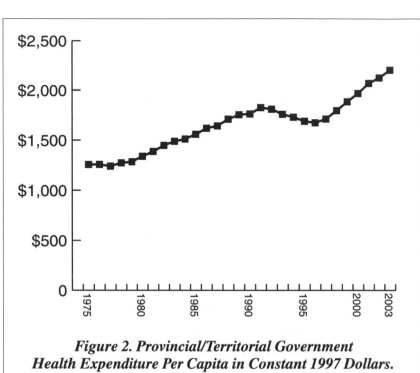

***Figure 2. Provincial/Territorial Government
Health Expenditure Per Capita in Constant 1997 Dollars.
From Canadian Institute for Health Research.***

and then increased it another 42 per cent from 1997 to 2003 for a 62 per cent increase. Manitoba and Saskatchewan are two other provinces that didn't do much cutting in this period. Alberta wins the yo-yo award. It cut per capita spending by 20 per cent from 1991 to 1995 and then increased spending by 53 per cent per capita in the next eight years. However, it's remarkable that whatever the specific provincial situation, the rhetoric is the same: governments claim that health care costs are rising rapidly, while the opposition parties and providers claim health care is being strangled.

The health care system does need some new money for certain goods and services (such as MRI scanners and home care nurses) and to re-establish federal leadership for health policy. But just because parts of the health system do need more funding does not mean that the whole system is grossly underfunded.

The Federal Government Does Have the Money, If We Do Need It

Prime Minister Paul Martin claims government cupboards are bare. Conservatives claim government is out of control and warns that we must cut taxes. But are the federal coffers really empty? Is the federal government really such a profligate spender? A closer examination reveals that the federal government has immense fiscal capacity. Furthermore, the Liberals have cut the federal government by one-third since they came back into power in 1993. In its last full year in power, the Mulroney government spent 22.7 per cent of the country's GDP, but that had fallen to 14.8 per cent by 2002.[17] This represents the lowest share of GDP spent by the federal government in over fifty years.

Of course, the federal government has off-loaded some of its responsibilities to the provinces. But the provinces are not suffering unduly either. Total provincial and territorial spending has fallen to 17.3 per cent of GDP from an average of 20.4 per cent during the Mulroney years.

During the 1990s, the federal department of finance appeared to be deliberately lowballing its budget estimates. Ministers Martin and then Manley would routinely sketch out tight budgets and at the end of the year there would be a large surplus, which would be used to pay down the national debt. From fiscal year 1999/2000 to 2002/2003, the federal department of finance estimated collective surpluses of only $10.5 billion in its budgets. But the collective surpluses were actually $46.7 billion. Since the Liberals have come to power, the total surplus comes to almost $100 billion.

Some economists did accurately forecast these surpluses.[18] Jim Stanford and his colleagues in the Alternative Federal Budget project claim that if there is any fiscal squeeze in this country, it is "entirely self-inflicted." It looks as if the Liberals are purposely trying to dull our demand for government spending.

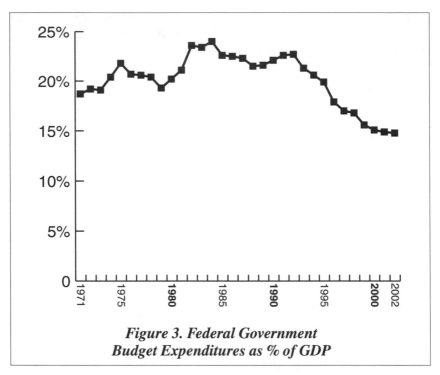

Figure 3. Federal Government
Budget Expenditures as % of GDP

Unfortunately, there are many who would like to shrink government even more. In 2000, the federal government announced plans
to cut taxes by $100 billion over five years. In fact, the true value of
the tax cuts will likely be over $120 billion. All told, the federal and
provincial governments have cut taxes collectively to the tune of
nearly $50 billion per year. That's enough to pay for all of the
Canadian military—four times over.

Of course, the vast majority of the tax cuts go to people who pay a
lot of taxes. In Canada, the rich are getting richer and the poor are getting poorer. As of 1999, the poorest 10 per cent of Canadian families
collectively held –0.4 per cent of the country's wealth—they owed
more than they possessed.[19] In the meantime, the top 10 per cent held
53 per cent. The poorest 50 per cent of Canadians collectively held

only 6 per cent of Canada's assets. Why is it that we fervently believe that the best way to make poor people productive is to pay them less but the best way to make rich people productive is to pay them more, in advance?

During their first term, the Liberals consistently claimed that they were cutting spending to balance the books so we could afford our social programs. Now it's truth-telling time. Even with federal spending at a fifty-four-year low, we could still afford a whole menu of social policy reforms, *as long as the government doesn't cut taxes any more*.

Of course, a main theme for this book is that we don't need to spend a lot more on health care to give Canadians a much more effective system. But it is patently false to claim that governments are broke and that Canadians must wait indefinitely for the fulfillment of the promises the Liberals made in the last three election campaigns.

Conclusion

It is clear that we made the right choice at the correct fork in the road fifty years ago when we started on the medicare path. We had a health care system very similar to the American one then, and without medicare, we would have a US-style system today. We owe our current good fortune to farsighted people such as Tommy Douglas, Emmett Hall, and Monique Bégin. We also owe it to ourselves. Without Canadians' strong political support for medicare, the privileged interests who take 20 per cent of the dollars out of the US system for their private profit would have plundered medicare too.

The medicare debate features endless cacophony about cash, from "We're spending too little" to "Costs are out of control." Adequate sustainable funding is important but focusing on money distracts us from fixing the system.

If we need more resources for health care, there's lots to be had. Despite the right's rantings about government's being out of control, the federal government is a smaller part of our economy than it has been for over fifty years. The Liberals continue to run large surpluses and cut taxes while claiming that Canadian aspirations for a just society should sit on the shelf indefinitely. If we had had such gutless politicians in the 1860s, there would never have been a Canada.

Part II

Fixing the System's Problems—
From Crowded ERs to High Drug Costs

Chapter 3

Focus on Quality and Watch Other Problems Melt Away

On February 20, 2000, Esther Winckler, a sharp seventy-seven-year-old, was admitted to Chilliwack General Hospital. She had been treated for lung cancer successfully in 1986, had quit smoking, and had very much enjoyed the succeeding years. The previous week she had taken advantage of the balmy west-coast winter weather to work in her garden. She was suffering chronic pain from a degenerative left hip and was looking forward to the improved quality of life promised by her upcoming hip replacement. However, within two weeks she would be dead and her family's faith in the health care system would be shattered.*

The first portent of doom was confusion about anesthesia. Prior to admission, an anesthetist had told her that she could have a spinal anesthetic, which would allow her to stay awake during the procedure. But when she was admitted, another anesthetist told her that she had to have a general anesthetic. After surgery, staff were concerned that she was dehydrated and she was given at least 2 litres of intravenous fluids. However, because of poor record-keeping and probably poor communication, staff continued to give her more fluids, overloading her heart and triggering congestive heart failure.

---

* Further information on Esther Winckler can be found at a Web site maintained by her family, http://www.esthersvoice.com.

But the doctors didn't diagnose her heart failure for twelve hours, during which time her blood did not have enough oxygen to sustain her brain and other vital organs.

After a few days, Winckler was still very unstable, but the hospital transferred her from the intensive care unit (ICU) to another ward, which coroner Margaret Turner later described as understaffed. During her time on the ward, Esther Winckler had at least two serious falls. The staff failed to diagnose a critical head injury and three fractured ribs, despite such signs as slurred speech, dilated pupils, and bruising. She didn't have a bowel movement during the last fifteen days of her life, but such records were not kept. Neither was there any documentation of her nutrition. Eventually she died because of lack of oxygen to her brain and bowel.

How could a vigorous person like Esther Winckler die in a system from which she had sought care? Chapter 2 highlighted that the real problems with Canada's health care system relate to quality of care. This chapter introduces Part II of the book, which showcases successful examples of innovation, the true remedies for medicare's malaise. We will learn about the origins of our quality problems and be introduced to a powerful framework for developing solutions.

Killing Medicare: Shooting at the Wrong Target

The *Globe*'s crusty columnist Christie Blatchford is angry with medicare.[1] In a column for her former employer, the *National Post*, Blatchford gave full spleen to her fury with the health care system. She recalled "crying with rage in emergency rooms" and fighting back tears at nursing stations, "waiting for someone to acknowledge my presence." She relived unhappy occasions when she found her relatives lying in their own excrement. And she sadly recollected "walking in to find a food tray sitting untouched, its lid still on, because no one had or found the time to help a starving old man get his false teeth in so he could eat." Blatchford is appalled that Canadians regard medicare as a national icon. She resolutely refuses to be defined by mediocre medicare.

It certainly sounds as though her mother got poor-quality care, but Blatchford is shooting at the wrong target. We tend to think of medicare as a government system, but it is still really more of an insurance program or, as University of Toronto dean of medicine Dr. David Naylor describes it, "public payment for private practice."[2] The quality problems Blatchford describes are not a result of government involvement with health insurance. In fact, medicare has enabled many Canadians to get health care who could otherwise never have afforded it.

Blatchford rejects the values behind our health care system, but most Canadians strongly support the concept that we should have access to high-quality health care services without financial or other barriers. The quality problems that Blatchford identifies in Canada's system are endemic to other health care systems as well. This is true whether they are publicly or privately funded or whether they favour for-profit or not-for-profit delivery. Simply privatizing medicare's finance and selling hospitals to multinational conglomerates would do little to eliminate the appalling problems that Blatchford has described in her columns. In fact, these problems are more common in for-profit care* and are rampant in the US.

The Main Problem with Medicare Is That It Was Designed for Another Time

There has been a major change in the pattern of illness since we first started debating medicare over a hundred years ago. At that time, most health problems were acute illnesses, such as tuberculosis and

---

* See chapter 12 for more details.

diphtheria, and accidents and injuries. However, today most health problems are chronic illnesses such as heart disease, cancer, and diabetes. Our health care system copes poorly with chronic illness. This problem stems directly from the way we implemented medicare. First the public purse covered hospital care because it was the most expensive part of the system. Then we covered physicians' services because they were the next expensive and deemed the next most important. But these policy successes left us with the legacy of inadequate community and chronic care. As a result, thousands of Canadians die every year and tens of thousands are hospitalized from heart attacks, strokes, kidney failure, and other preventable complications of their chronic illnesses.[3]

At the beginning of medicare, almost all care for complicated conditions was provided in hospitals. Patients were often admitted to hospital for "investigations," a rarity today when administrators watch their case severity indices more closely than your broker watches the TSX. The case severity index indicates the average sickness of the patients and, therefore, the resources that are needed to manage them. Hospitals strive to have the highest case severity index to demonstrate that they have the sickest patients who need the most resources.

And the sheer number of possible tests and investigations has grown exponentially. At one time, X-rays were considered high-tech, but they were supplanted for some tests by CAT scans* in the 1970s and by MRI† in the 1990s. Now, just as we are buying MRI scans by the dozen, some high-tech companies are pushing PET scans‡ as the new standard of diagnosis for certain problems.

---

* Co-axial tomography takes X-ray pictures in a 360° scan and then reproduces the image with computer assistance.
† Magnetic resonance imaging uses powerful magnetic fields to detect subtle differences in electrical charges.
‡ Positron emission tomography detects the emission of positrons from an imbibed, labelled sugar solution to detect metabolic activity. PET scans are particularly useful at demonstrating the functioning of brain and heart tissues.

Preventive medicine used to be limited to a history, a physical examination, vaccinations, and a few simple urine and blood tests. Now the possibilities for further information on our health are almost limitless. Why not get a PSA test for prostate cancer? Or, if you don't have a prostate, how about a BRCA test for ovarian cancer? In the United States, commercial interests carpet bomb the airways with the urgent need to get tested for this, know your number for that, and ask your doctor about the other thing. The multimedia message is that health is simply a state of inadequate diagnosis.

To make things more difficult, medicine has fractured into more and more specialties. Up until 1937, there were only two classes of specialists in Canada: surgery and internal medicine. By the end of the Second World War, there were still only eighteen, but today the Royal College of Physicians and Surgeons of Canada* recognizes over seventy specialties and subspecialties.[4] And more are being created all the time.

In the 1960s, general surgeons did orthopedics, cancer surgery, and even removed tonsils and adenoids. Now, in urban areas, general surgeons are pretty much limited to the abdomen while subspecialists have taken over the rest of the body. In the 1960s, general specialists in internal medicine handled heart attacks and strokes, as well as complicated diagnostic problems that crossed several body systems. However, today in urban areas, general internists find themselves mainly managing elderly patients with multi-system pathology.

The fracturing of medicine into dozens of new specialties means that patients are increasingly shunted around on an endless series of merry-go-rounds. Patients frequently find that it takes them months to get all their tests and see the right specialists. The Canadian system has become known—unfairly in many ways—as being riddled with waits and delays.

---

* The College is the national body responsible for certifying medical specialists.

It's the Quality

Poor management of chronic illness and needless waits and delays are only the tip of the quality iceberg. The stories of Esther Winckler and of Christie Blatchford's mother remind us that quality problems are pervasive. But poor quality is not a result of a series of individual mistakes. Remember, Joshua Fleuelling's untimely death had nothing to do with the performance of any of the individual heath care workers who were involved with his care. Rather, the structure of the Toronto system prevented Joshua from getting the care he needed. And there are other glaring quality problems that are only occasionally brought to light.

Dangerous Health Care
The US health system has more problems than those of most other countries, but the Americans have led the world in carefully documenting quality problems. In 1999, the key US scientific advisory body on health care issues, the National Institute of Medicine, published a landmark report, *To Err Is Human: Building a Safer Health System*, which described a litany of serious quality problems.[5] Interestingly, the key research had actually been done several years earlier but had no impact until the National Institute of Medicine's report threw a spotlight on it.

In the mid- to late 1980s, some of the world's best-known health services researchers from Harvard University painstakingly went through 30,000 hospital charts that represented a scientific sample of all the patients who had sought care from New York State hospitals in 1984.[6] The results were damning:

- Four per cent of patients had suffered an adverse event from their hospital care.
- One per cent of patients suffered frankly negligent care.
- One out of every 200 patients admitted to hospital died from the adverse consequences of his or her care.

• One out of every 500 patients suffered a permanent disability from the consequences of his or her hospital care.

The investigators estimated that every year in New York State there were 7,000 deaths and 1,700 permanent disabilities caused by negligent hospital care. Studies in Britain and Australia found even higher rates of adverse events.[7] In Canada, this would work out to over 10,000 deaths and 3,000 permanent disabilities annually.

In Canada, the Royal College of Physicians and Surgeons established a National Steering Committee on Patient Safety on September 22, 2001, after a forum they held at their annual meeting in Ottawa. Dr. John Wade, an anesthetist and former Manitoba deputy minister of health, chaired the committee, which included four doctors, an academic, a nurse, a pharmacist, and a public representative. The committee presented its report to the college's next meeting on September 28, 2002.

The Canadian Institutes of Health Research and the Canadian Institute for Health Information are co-operating on a study of Canadian hospital adverse events that will report in early 2004. It is overwhelmingly likely that it will show the same pattern as the one that emerged from other countries. But what will happen then, when Canadians are finally told officially that their health care system kills thousands of patients every year?

The February 2003 federal budget quietly provided $10 million annually to establish a new Canadian Patient Safety Institute. The specific mandate, membership, and activities of the Edmonton-based institute will be developed by federal, provincial, and territorial ministers of health, in collaboration with health professional organizations and other stakeholders.

In the US, the National Institute of Medicine has continued to push the envelope. In 2001, it released another groundbreaking report, *Crossing the Quality Chasm: A New Health System for the 21st Century*.[8] The authors chose to use the word *chasm* because they wanted to emphasize that the gap between the quality the system provides and what it should deliver is not small. It is yawning. And poor quality goes well beyond the simple errors documented in *To Err Is Human*. To quote the institute, "Serious and widespread quality problems exist throughout American medicine." As Esther Winckler's case testifies, they exist north of the border too.

Classifying Quality Problems

We are most familiar with the type of quality problem referred to as "misuse" or the failure to execute properly, as in the case of Esther Winckler. Misuse is also what killed Jeffrey Brown on July 30, 1996. On that day, the thirty-three-year-old Brown was in southwestern Ontario's Leamington District Memorial Hospital being treated for a kidney infection. A nurse arrived to give him an injection of furosemide, a diuretic used to flush out extra fluid. However, instead of furosemide, the nurse drew up 20 cc of concentrated potassium chloride, the same drug used to kill prisoners in Texas. Brown had had furosemide previously and instantly knew it was the wrong medicine. He screamed in pain and begged her to stop. He even pulled his arm away, but the nurse held it down and forced in all of the medication. Within seconds, Brown was unconscious, and within minutes he was dead.[9]

A similar problem killed eleven-year-old Claire Lewis. Claire entered Hamilton General Hospital in October 2001 for elective surgery to remove a non-malignant brain tumour.[10] The operation was a success, but the patient died. The eight-and-a-half-hour surgery went smoothly, but when Claire left the recovery room at the Hamilton General Hospital for the pediatric intensive care unit at McMaster University Hospital, her medical records didn't go with her and the misadventures began. The ICU staff were not aware of the volume and type of fluids the staff at the General had administered. In a situation eerily reminiscent of Esther Winckler's trials, over the next two days a series of errors led to massive fluid overload, brain seizures, and death. Her father, John Lewis, is a nurse, but his cries for help appear to have been ignored, as were the Winckler's family's. At one point, with his daughter "as flat as a pancake," Lewis raised his concerns with a nurse at the nursing station. According to Lewis, she looked up at a monitor and claimed Claire was fine.[11]

Although misuse is the first type of problem that most people visualize when they think of poor quality, it may not be as significant as the others: overuse and underuse. Overuse is the provision of health care in the absence of evidence that it will do more good than harm. Underuse is the failure to provide care that evidence indicates would likely be effective.

The pulmonary artery catheter was developed in the 1970s to provide real-time information on pressures in the left and right sides of the heart. At first the catheters were used just for very sick cardiac patients, but gradually they began to be used for patients with other serious illnesses. According to Dr. Dean Sandham, an intensive care physician in Calgary, "it became such a standard of care that if you questioned the use of the catheter, people wouldn't take you seriously."[12] However, Sandham was right to be skeptical. In January 2003, he and his colleagues shook the medical world when the *New England Journal of Medicine* published their study of these devices.[13] Sandham and his group of Canadian investigators showed that pulmonary artery catheters provided no benefit to sick patients undergoing non-cardiac surgery. The study patients were high risk with an overall mortality rate approaching 8 per cent, but there were no differences in outcome between those patients who had the pulmonary artery catheter and those who didn't—no difference except that eight catheter patients developed a blood clot in their lungs compared with none in the control group.

The history of medicine features many promising innovations that were quickly adopted into practice and then shown later, sometimes much later, to be deadly.

Quality problems relating to underuse are also far too frequent. Pain is badly undertreated in hospitals, nursing homes, and community settings. Fewer than half of patients with chronic illness are taking the correct medications, and most are not receiving appropriate physical, psychological, or dietary therapy. Delay is another kind of underuse, and waiting times and perceived personnel shortages are the health system's top complaints.[14]

New Rules for Fixing the Health System's Quality

Crossing the Quality Chasm identified six key values to guide quality improvement initiatives:

1. *Safety*. Patients should feel as safe in a health care facility as they do at home or at work.
2. *Effectiveness*. The health care system should use the best science to continually reduce ineffective care and maximize the delivery of effective care.
3. *Patient-centredness*. The health care system should respect the individuality, values, ethnicity, social endowments, and information needs of each patient. The primary idea is to put patients in control of their own care. The system should be transparent and provide a high level of accountability to patients.
4. *Timeliness*. The health care system should continually attempt to reduce waits and delays for providers and patients.
5. *Efficiency*. The health care system should continually strive to reduce waste, including waste of supplies, equipment, time, and ideas.
6. *Equity*. The health care system should continually endeavour to reduce disparities in health between different groups characterized (for example) by socio-economic status, gender, ethnicity, or race.

Crossing the Quality Chasm identified four levels of change: the patient level, the level of the clinical team (such as the operating room, ICU, or outpatient psychiatry team), the level of the organization (such as the hospital, primary health care centre, or regional health authority), and, finally, the level where policies are developed to govern the health care system's payment, regulation, accreditation, and so on. The authors of the report appreciated that complex systems such as a health care system are very resistant to change. They suggest focusing on frameworks and "simple rules" to drive reform instead of relying upon so-called big-bang legislative and regulatory solutions.[15] The institute then suggested ten simple rules that should guide health care re-engineering.

Crossing the Quality Chasm:
Ten Rules to Heal the Health Care System

1. Care should be based upon continuous healing relationships instead of mainly in-person visits.
2. Care should be customized for individual patients' needs and values instead of being dictated by professionals.
3. Care should be under the control of patients not professionals.
4. Knowledge about care should be shared freely between patients and providers and between different providers. This transfer should take maximal advantage of leading-edge information technology. Patients should have unrestricted access to their records.
5. Clinicians should make decisions on the basis of the best scientific evidence. Care should not vary illogically from clinician to clinician or from place to place.
6. Safety is the responsibility of the whole system not individual providers.
7. The content of care is made transparent instead of being held in secret. The health system should give as much information as is required to patients and families to enable them to fully participate in clinical decisions, including where to seek care.
8. Patients' needs should be, as much as possible, anticipated and not treated in a reactive fashion.
9. The health care system should continually decrease waste (goods, services, and time) instead of focusing on cost reduction.

10. Providers should cooperate and work in high-functioning teams instead of attempting to work in isolation. Concern for patients should drive cooperation among providers and drive out competition based upon professional and organizational rivalries.

Crossing the Quality Chasm stressed that the task of quality improvement is so immense that it is beyond the capabilities of individual providers and organizations to effect the changes necessary: "In its current form, habits, and environment, American health care is incapable of providing the public with the quality health care it expects and deserves." This led the institute to call for system redesign rather than tinkering. The same case for reform applies to Canada. Christie Blatchford is right about that.

Improving Quality Leads to Sustainability

We tend to think that sustainability is a synonym for cost control. But focusing on cost control is shortsighted. That's because we can see the savings up front but we don't see the impact until much later. Using cheaper building materials might save on construction but might cost more in repairs later (and possibly lawsuits!). As Ken Fyke pointed out in his health care commission for the Saskatchewan government, good-quality health care usually costs less.

We will examine innovation through the lens of average Canadians. Canadians think that the health care system could do a better job of managing its resources, but there is also strong political pressure to throw money at the system to do more of what it is already doing. Many Canadians are concerned that they will end up like Joshua Fleuelling—very sick without a hospital to go to. Many Canadians don't have a family doctor and others are concerned that they won't be able to see a specialist in a timely fashion. Prescription drugs have been the fastest-rising component of health care spending for nearly thirty years. Some Canadians don't have drug insurance and face drug bills that are larger than their incomes. Even Canadians with insurance (public or private) have to pay an increasing share of the bills themselves. We will probe each of these problems for its true diagnosis. Then we will find that someone somewhere in Canada has found a solution.

Overcrowded Hospitals

In January 2003, Ontario hospitals were under pressure as they were three years earlier when Joshua Fleuelling died.[16] This time the trigger was the Norwalk virus,* not influenza, but the results were similar. Many nursing homes were closed to admissions.[17] They weren't even taking their own patients back from hospitals. In the meantime, many hospitals had to close wards because they were contaminated by the pesky virus. As three years earlier, on the first Monday after the holidays, elective surgery resumed. Within days, Toronto ERs were stuffed to the gills. But what patients were using the beds that other patients desperately needed?

- At least one-third of hospital patients needed some care (such as palliative care, home care, or long-term care) but not acute hospital care.[18]
- Many patients who did need hospital care could have had their acute episode of illness prevented with better management of pre-existing chronic conditions (such as diabetes or asthma).[19]
- Many illnesses, including the majority of heart attacks, strokes, and lung cancers, could have been prevented entirely.[20]

In chapter 4, we will discuss how good-quality palliative care can improve the quality of end-of-life care. In chapter 5, we will examine

---

* Norwalk causes a usually mild gastroenteritis with nausea, vomiting, and diarrhea being the cardinal symptoms. However, the elderly and debilitated can get very sick and require hospital care.

enhanced chronic disease management, which promises to improve the duration and quality of life of the millions of Canadians living with chronic illness. In chapter 6, we will review home care's immense role in the re-engineering of our health care system. In chapter 7, we will consider long-term care and demonstrate how innovations in care for severe chronic illness, frailty, and disability can enhance the quality of life for some of our most vulnerable citizens. In chapter 8, we will explore the possibilities of health promotion and disease prevention. This is the best way to free up hospital beds—to keep people too healthy to need them.

Too Many Drugs, Not Enough Doctors, Waiting Too Long?

In chapter 9, we will review Canada's alleged shortage of doctors. Replacing visit-based health care with continuous healing relationships and a focus on individual providers with an accent on teamwork can dramatically improve access. In chapter 10, we will review Canada's exploding drug bill and demonstrate that improving the quality of therapeutics and prescribing is the best method to keep patients healthy and control costs. In chapter 11, we will consider our long waits for care. Occasionally new resources are needed to reduce delays, but, most of the time, re-engineering of services is required to ensure timely care. In the last three chapters, we will discuss in more detail how to re-engineer our system for better quality.

Anesthesia: Pointing the Way?

Doctors first administered general anesthesia in the 1840s. Sometimes patients never woke up. New techniques made anesthesia safer, but after one hundred years, there was still 1 anesthetic death for every 2,500 general anesthetics. Over the next thirty years, the rate gradually fell to 1 in 10,000, but that still amounted to 3,500 avoidable deaths every year in the United States. In 1972, a young engineer, Jeffrey Cooper, started work at the Massachusetts General Hospital developing machines for anesthesia researchers. But he was soon fascinated by the dysfunctional design of operating rooms. For example, the doctors had to turn some dials clockwise. Others they had to turn counterclockwise. Vials of some medications looked exactly like others that had the opposite effect.

In 1978, Cooper published a landmark paper in which he analyzed 359 anesthetic mishaps and looked for causes.[21] His technique was the same as that used by safety engineers who investigate aircraft mishaps: critical incident analysis. This method, like good police work, is built upon structured conversations conducted to acquire all the important facts and to identify plausible causal factors. Critical incident analysis requires honesty and transparency to accomplish its goals and, therefore, requires the lifting of possible sanctions against those who come forward to disclose. The US Federal Aviation Administration absolves pilots of any punishment if they reveal an incident within ten days. Airline safety could not have made its major advances without its culture of blamelessness to individuals and its focus on measurement and continuous quality improvement.

Over the next decade, the American Society of Anesthesiologists led a revolution. All dials now turn the same way. Drugs are colour-coded. It's impossible to turn off the oxygen. Before surgery and after surgery patient hand-offs are accomplished with aircraft-type checklists to remove human error. All this re-engineering had a big impact. In the next ten years, anesthetic deaths fell by 95 per cent, to 1 in 200,000.[22] The anesthesia revolution quickly spread to Canada, Europe, and the rest of the world.

Just think if Esther Winckler's or Jeffrey Brown's or Claire Lewis's hospital care could have been as safe as modern anesthesia. They would all have survived their hospital stay. The safety revolution in anesthesia demonstrates that we can dramatically improve health care quality.

Conclusion: Quality and Innovation Point the Way

The Canadian health policy debate is stuck in a rut. We endlessly debate the roles of the federal government vs. the provinces, and the public sector vs. the private sector. We talk forever about money— too much vs. too little. These are important questions, but by focusing on them we miss the forest for the trees. There would be no point in endlessly debating the merits of public vs. private ownership and federal vs. provincial jurisdiction for air travel if 10 per cent of planes crashed upon takeoff. But we continue to ignore quality in health care even though thousands of patients die every year from poor-quality care.

Chapter 4

Dying in Canada: Sweet Chariot or the Grim Reaper's Tale

Last year early in the morning, a code was called on the third floor. By the time I arrived with the crash cart, CPR [cardio-pulmonary resuscitation] was in progress and a nurse was starting an IV. On the bed was a thin little old lady, and I heard a couple of cracking ribs as someone pushed down for cardiac compressions. Our routine is well rehearsed . . . Cardiac monitor shows ventricular fibrillation. No pulse. Defibrillate. No change. Give IV medication, continue CPR. Since she was so little, I used a small adult dose of electricity for defibrillation. Still no response. I felt sick. I asked, "How old is this lady?" She was ninety-four. "What are we doing?" Everyone looked sick. "We have no choice Peggy, she is not a 'no code.' She's not sick. She's here for respite care while her family is out of town." A doctor arrived, learned the age of the patient and asked again, "What are you doing?" I felt as though I had committed a profound, unforgivable sin.

A nurse named Peggy told this story to the BC Royal Commission on Health Care in 1991.[1] We have taken some small steps to improve care for the dying since, but far too many Canadians die like Peggy's patient.

There are too many cancer patients who are in their terminal phase who suffer while they die in hospital beds. There are too many people in the final phases of other terminal illnesses such as heart disease who die in a similar undignified fashion. There are too many people in the late stages of Alzheimer's disease who are whisked from their nursing homes to hospital to die with cracked ribs.

All told, thousands of hospital beds are devoted to providing active, aggressive hospital care to patients who are ready to die. It's a double loss. Patients and their families usually don't get the symptom control and spiritual care to help make their last days comfortable and meaningful. The health care system also wastes resources that could be used to provide the end-of-life care that patients and families really want.

This chapter discusses the core human question of death and dying and then outlines a series of exciting programs that demonstrate that Canada is poised to ensure that everyone has adequate access to high-quality end-of-life care.

Death and Denial

We all die. But we spend most of our days living in denial that death will ever occur. A hundred years ago, most families lost a child and many lost a young mother in childbirth. Most people died at home. While growing up, it was nearly impossible to live without being aware of death. But today, thank goodness, deaths in childhood are very rare and modern health care has nearly eliminated childbirth deaths. Now few people have first-hand experience with death until a grandparent passes away.

At the same time, the health care system tends to regard death as a failure it doesn't want to be reminded of. Hamilton family doctor Elizabeth Latimer is one of a few Canadian physicians who have chosen care of the dying as their specialty. She notes that the Middle Ages' *ars moriendi*—literally, the art of dying—is a good model for current end-of-life care.[2] Death was so common in the Middle Ages that it was a visible part of communal life. People died at home. As death approached, they got their affairs in order—forgave long-standing conflicts, wrapped up legal and financial issues, and spoke final words to loved ones.

However, death today has become more high-tech than high art. While movies portray deaths from yesteryear as spiritual and sombre family reunions, the current reality is often very different.

Harry von Brommel, a Toronto advocate for better end-of-life care, remembers with discomfort assisting his mother while she was dying twenty years ago. "The pain was overwhelming . . . Overwhelming pain means you can't eat, you can't talk, you can't breathe." In May 2000, he commissioned a survey of 2,400 Canadians and found that one-third had a friend or relative die of a terminal illness in the past two years. Of these, 29 per cent said that pain was unsuccessfully treated most of the time, and 28 per cent said that pain was unsuccessfully treated some of the time. Von Brommel estimates that 30,000 Canadians die with almost unrelenting pain.[3]

It doesn't have to be this way. Almost all dying patients can be made comfortable to the end.

What's Wrong with End-of-Life Care

The unelected Canadian senate has been the butt of jokes and jibes since 1867. However, the Red Chamber occasionally does display that it is the home of "sober second thought." The Senate has published two reports on palliative care—one in 1995 and a follow-up five years later. The 2000 report, chaired by Manitoba's Sharon Carstairs, documented a litany of concerns:[4]

- Fewer than 10 per cent of dying patients get good-quality care in their final days.
- Many patients do not get adequate pain relief or emotional or spiritual comfort.
- Doctors do not get adequate training in end-of-life care.

- A minority of cancer patients receive palliative care services, but even fewer other terminal patients receive good-quality end-of-life care.

Overall, about 70 per cent of the 222,000 deaths every year in Canada occur in hospital, down slightly from over 75 per cent in the early 1990s.[5] One in six deaths now occurs in an intensive care unit. But being in a health care facility is no guarantee by any means of good end-of-life care. Most dying people do not receive adequate symptom control, especially amelioration of their pain.

In fact, the health care system deals very poorly with pain of all sorts. The Canadian Pain Society estimates that over half of all hospital patients suffer from moderate to severe pain and that most of this unhappiness could be remedied with better care.[6] The Canadian Pain Society hopes that health care providers will soon measure pain as the fifth vital sign (in addition to temperature, respiration, pulse, and blood pressure), just as they do in the US Veterans Administration health system.

Dying Patients Know What They Want

Dr. Peter Singer, the director of the University of Toronto's Joint Centre for Bioethics, has ascertained five key domains for good-quality end-of-life care that sick patients identify for themselves:[7]

- Adequate controlling pain and symptoms
- Avoiding inappropriate prolongation of dying
- Achieving a sense of control
- Relieving burden from loved ones
- Strengthening personal relationships

It is not possible to cure everyone. We will all die even if some of us won't pay taxes. But a properly organized health system would assist dying patients and their families to attain these five goals.

Dr. Michael Gordon is the vice-president of medicine for the Baycrest Centre for Geriatric Care in Toronto and one of Canada's best-known geriatricians. However, even he and his health-provider sister couldn't guarantee proper care for his mother as she was dying in a US hospital. Dr. Gordon relates how his elderly mother was struck with a massive stroke when she was eighty-three, leaving her half paralyzed and unable to eat or even breathe on her own. Eventually her immobility led to a blood clot, which turned her non-paralyzed leg gangrenous. Her doctors suggested amputation to save her life, but Dr. Gordon and his family decided to eschew the surgery, remove her feeding tube, and provide her with comfort care to let her die with dignity. However, Gordon relates, "We got zero support. In fact, a nursing supervisor demanded to know why we had chosen 'to starve her to death.'"

Gordon's personal and professional experiences led him to membership on an Ontario College of Physicians and Surgeons committee on end-of-life care. The college notes that for over twenty years, report after report has recommended that physicians engage their patients and families in discussions about end-of-life care. Unfortunately, this is still not happening.[8]

Dignity is the key issue for most people as they face death. Dr. Harvey Chochinov, a Winnipeg psychiatrist, realized during his training at Winnipeg's Health Sciences Centre that dying patients and their families were afterthoughts in a world where death occurs routinely and is frequently an expected event. Chochinov, who is internationally known for his work on end-of-life issues, claims that we should build end-of-life care on an overarching framework of conservation of dignity.[9]

A recent US study of seriously ill patients in five teaching hospitals concluded that physicians engaged their patients in a discussion of their end-of-life preferences only 40 per cent of the time.[10] Even so, in 80 per cent of these cases, physicians misunderstood their patients' preferences, leaving fewer than 10 per cent of patients whose wishes were actively pursued by their physicians. In 50 per cent of the cases, doctors even failed to respect their patients' preferences for no resuscitation.

Elizabeth Tayti of Welland, Ontario, tells a sad story about her husband's death in August 2001.[11] Tayti brought her husband's do-not-resuscitate order (DNR) and living-will documents to hospital when he was admitted for terminal care. However, once in hospital, he was given a drug to prolong his life and was placed on dialysis, a procedure he had specifically prohibited. According to Tayti, hospital staff even prevented her from joining her husband in the intensive care unit, where she could have more effectively advocated for him.

Many Canadian communities have developed effective end-of-life programs, but too few physicians are referring their patients to such programs. One issue is that doctors routinely overestimate the time remaining before death and consequently do not make appropriate arrangements for end-of-life care.[12] A US study showed that at the time of referral to palliative care, doctors estimated that their patients would live an average of four months. In fact, they lived an average of twenty-four days. Perhaps doctors are simply trying to offer more hope. Perhaps they have had bad experiences underestimating a patient's chances. Sometimes miracles do happen.

A second problem is that doctors are concerned that a referral to palliative care is a "death sentence," when it may in fact be essential to make a patient's remaining life worth living. According to Dr. Larry Librach, director of the palliative medicine program at Toronto's Mt. Sinai Hospital, "There are patients in agony whose physicians won't refer them to palliative care."[13] Librach criticizes his colleagues for routinely telling their patients "there is nothing we can do for you," when modern medicine has the tools to abolish most pain and suffering.

Toronto medical writer Felicity Stone remembers feeling that her mother's family doctor abandoned her when she was diagnosed with cancer—"never once visited, never called, made no referrals."[14]

When Stone and her family asked hospital staff about palliative care, they were told it was premature. After a failed chemotherapy trial, the cancer specialists told her that there was nothing more to be done and they discharged her. Stone's family then, in her words, "staggered along" on their own for four months until severe symptoms finally led them to Mt. Sinai's palliative care unit.

Typically, most cancer experiences are like that of Mr. B., a Winnipeg patient with kidney cancer. He continued to see his oncologist for follow-up until his cancer was found to have spread to his liver and other vital organs. At that point, it was his wife who suggested palliative care services, not the cancer specialist.

One of the striking points about Canada's palliative care story is that the health care system has done little until recently to foster its development. Montreal palliative care pioneer Dr. Balfour Mount suggests that health care professionals are so afraid of death themselves that it interferes with their ability to administer to the needs of terminally ill patients.[15] Dr. Mount offers this as one reason for the slow progress of palliative care in Canada. But the picture might finally be brightening.

Light at the End of the Tunnel

There are now rays of hope for better end-of-life care. We have an effective national advocate in Senator Carstairs, who is tirelessly crossing the country to support enhanced palliative care services. Roy Romanow recommended adopting a palliative care benefit, and there was funding for end-of-life care included in the subsequent federal/provincial/territorial accord.

The Canadian Palliative Care Association defines palliative care as follows:

> A philosophy of care and combination of therapies intended to support persons living with life-threatening illness. Palliative

care strives to meet physical, psychological, social, and spiritual needs, while remaining sensitive to personal, cultural, and religious values. Palliative care may be needed at any time in the disease trajectory, and bereavement. It may be combined with therapies aimed at reducing or curing the illness, or it may be the total focus of care. Care is delivered through the collaborative efforts of an interdisciplinary team including the individual, family, and others involved in the provision of care. Where possible, palliative care should be available in the setting of personal choice.[16]

Canada has many examples of effective end-of-life programs. In fact, Canada has been in the forefront of these developments since Winnipeg's St. Boniface Hospital established North America's first palliative care unit in 1973. The following year, Dr. Mount helped establish the unit at the Royal Victoria Hospital in Montreal, which has trained hundreds of doctors, nurses, and others.

However, it took until the 1990s before palliative care really appeared on the health care system's radar screen. In 1994, one year after a similar move in Saskatchewan, Alberta established regional health authorities that took over the budgets for all hospitals, long-term care, home care, and public health. This manoeuvre led to more integrated planning for influenza care, which kept hospitals running in those provinces while hospitals in Toronto were gridlocked. This policy has also been instrumental in improving the situation for palliative care in these provinces.

In Ontario, the provincial government still sets the budgets for each hospital, nursing home, and home care unit. As Dr. Russell Goldman, assistant medical director of Toronto's Mt. Sinai Hospital's palliative care program, notes, "There is no incentive for any one party to look after people properly." Hospitals have an incentive to get people out as quickly as possible but little incentive beyond professionalism and malpractice suits to ensure that patients get the community care they really need. Most Ontario family doctors, as in other provinces, are paid on a fee-for-service basis. Provincial medicare plans typically pay for palliative care services at one-third the rate that the doctor could bill for seeing a series of patients with colds. Even so, with some provincial assistance and wealthy local sponsors, Ontario has developed innovative palliative programs in certain communities.

In 1994/95, the Alberta government cut the budget of the newly established Edmonton regional health authority by 20 per cent. It is said that there are only two conditions in which innovation is eagerly sought: when there isn't enough money, and when there's too much. With necessity the mother and Edmonton CEO Sheila Wetherill and her staff the midwives, the region delivered a number of innovative projects. One of them was palliative care.

The Edmonton regional palliative care program began in 1995.[17] The goals of the program were to increase access to palliative care services, decrease the number of cancer-related deaths in acute care facilities, and increase the participation of family physicians in the care of terminally ill patients.

The program started with the existing fourteen-bed tertiary palliative care unit and a weekly tertiary multidisciplinary palliative care clinic based in a cancer centre. There were four new components created:

- Three palliative units with a total of fifty-six beds were established in three long-term care hospitals.
- Four consultation teams (consisting of a salaried physician and nurse) were established to provide consultations in the three long-term care hospitals, the three community hospitals, and other long-term care facilities in the Edmonton region. Another team was added to the existing team, serving tertiary care facilities.
- Increased funding was given to the regional home care program to permit twenty-four-hour palliative care at home.
- The region established a registry of family physicians willing to take on new palliative care patients. The region offered an

increased fee out of its own budget for family doctors to care for these patients.*

By the second year of the program, 84 per cent of cancer patients had a palliative care consultation, compared with 22 per cent prior to the program. There was a reduction in the proportion of cancer deaths in acute care facilities from 86 per cent to 49 per cent. Thirty per cent of deaths occurred within hospices, and 18 per cent at home. Seventy-seven per cent of the region's family doctors had been involved in some way with joint care for palliative care patients, and 18 per cent of the family doctors agreed to take on new palliative care patients from other doctors. The program saved at least 17,600 hospital days. If we implemented a similar program nationwide, we would free up approximately 1,500 hospital beds—almost as many as in the whole city of Winnipeg.†

Shortly after Edmonton implemented its palliative care program, the Calgary Regional Health Authority's Pam Brown began to design one there. The Calgary program includes

- A community consultation team, and one for each of the city's three hospitals
- The eighteen-bed Agapé Hospice (run by the Salvation Army)
- A twelve-bed unit at the Glenmore Park care centre
- A ten-bed tertiary care unit located at the Foothills Hospital
- A home palliative care program that supports nearly five hundred deaths per year
- A seven-bed hospice not formally affiliated with the regional authority

---

* The budget for physicians' services largely remains with the province, even in Alberta with a regionalized system.

† Those 17,600 bed days translate into 48 beds. Edmonton is approximately ½₂ of Canada's population. This equals roughly 1,500 beds.

The Calgary program is increasingly focusing on patients who don't have cancer. Nearly all terminal AIDS patients and amyotrophic lateral sclerosis patients (ALS, or Lou Gehrig's disease) now receive palliative care services. The region's collaboration with the University of Calgary's medical school led to all family medicine trainees being educated in palliative care. And cancer specialists (oncologists) now spend at least one month on the palliative care service during their training.

The establishment of the palliative care unit at Foothills facilitated co-operation between palliative care staff and those from the Tom Baker Regional Cancer Centre. Dr. Neil Hagen, the medical director of the Foothills palliative care unit, notes that oncologists increasingly see palliative care doctors as having special expertise in symptom control that can be applied to patients even during attempted curative treatment. Dr. José Perreira, who used to be in Edmonton but who now practises with Dr. Hagen, thinks that the closer proximity has also resulted in earlier referrals—a crucial issue for improving symptom control.

The results of the Calgary program mimic Edmonton's. From 1996 to 2002, booming Calgary's population increased by 18 per cent but the number of cancer deaths in hospital decreased by 31 per cent. By 2000, fewer than 40 per cent of cancer patients died in hospital.

Hospice for the Homeless

Ottawa developed a series of innovative programs for the homeless in the late 1990s. One of those projects is a hospice based at the Union Mission, a short walk from Parliament Hill. Heading toward death is hard enough for anyone, but this burden is magnified by the hazards of homelessness and the desperation of mental illness and addiction. Wendy Muckle, director of the Ottawa Inner City Health Project, insists that her clients are citizens who deserve basic human dignity. She claims that how we care for the dying destitute is a measure of our own humanity. If we are a civilized society, we provide everyone with a "gentle walk into the night."

Muckle relates a story of John M., a middle-aged man with liver cancer, who arrived at the hospice from the Ottawa Hospital at 5 p.m. The doctors expected him to die within hours. Muckle recalls placing a fentanyl patch for pain on John while he cursed her. Then she went home expecting she would be called back later for his death. To her surprise, he was up and about in the morning. Over the next few months, John slid slowly toward his eventual demise. Muckle gently prodded, and finally John agreed to let her contact his mother, whom he hadn't seen in twelve years. Within hours, John's mother, brother, and sister showed up at the hospice and continued to visit him until he passed away. John and his family were extremely grateful to have had the opportunity to reconnect and make their peace with each other before his death.

Muckle and her staff go to great lengths to reconnect people with their long-estranged families. Muckle remembers one attempt to reconnect a dying man with a son whom he had abused. The son was understandably reticent to reopen this unhappy chapter of his life. But, with Muckle's encouragement, they did get back together and managed to make peace before his death. The Union Mission Hospice exemplifies the art of dying brought up to date for the twenty-first century. Muckle also notes that providing better care for her clients makes things easier for the system as well. An evaluation of the program estimates that the hospice saves the rest of the health care system approximately $570,000 per year.[18]

Warm Home Care in a Cold Country

Marie Ball is a nurse who works for Winnipeg's home care program. Ball grew up in Ontario, but when hospitals laid off nurses in the 1990s, she found a haven in Texas working in Bryan College Station, home of Texas A&M University. She started in home care and then worked in a hospice for six years. In 2000, she was lured back to Canada by an energetic Manitoba advertising campaign that promised good benefits and compensation for her moving expenses.*

Ball's first visit one crisp November morning is to seventy-year-old Jeanie C.† Jeanie has suffered from ovarian cancer for two years and she is becoming increasingly frail. However, she beams when Ball walks through the doorway of her suburban apartment. Ball goes through her checklist of questions while engaging in pleasant banter. She skilfully puts a stethoscope to Jeanie's chest and then gently palpates her abdomen looking for tumour progression. Finding no problems, she goes through Jeanie's other services. Jeanie still gets help with meal preparation three days a week, light housekeeping every two weeks, and assistance with bathing twice a week. Jeanie has some unpleasant memories about feeling helpless lying on a gurney in the emergency department waiting for a doctor, but she is very pleased with the care she is receiving through home care and with how she has been able to retain her independence despite her growing disabilities.

Dr. Russell Goldman checks his personal digital assistant (PDA) at Mt. Sinai's Temmy Latner Centre for Palliative Care office before he starts his rounds in midtown Toronto. The PDA stores information on nearly five hundred patients, and each of the centre's six doctors carries one. Goldman has been working here since he completed his family medicine training in 1995. Despite working in Canada's largest city, the thirty-five-year-old Goldman sees himself as an old-time country doctor doing his rounds. He is adamant that patients should have a choice about where death occurs. He and his colleagues are strong advocates for their patients, who are often pushed by well-meaning family and professionals to institutions.

First stop on this chilly January afternoon is Florence D., a

---

* Of note, she turned down Ontario because home care nurses no longer received benefits from their new private employers.

† Many names have been changed and/or abbreviated to protect privacy.

seventy-eight-year-old living in a Victorian house near the University of Toronto. Doctors diagnosed Florence with lung cancer two years ago, and she has lived longer than her original prognosis. Now the cancer is showing signs of recurrence. She is frail but doesn't use her walker enough to suit Dr. Goldman, who gently chides her. Pride surely goeth before a fall, and Florence took a tumble a few days ago. She found herself unable to get up for several hours. This leads to another admonition from Dr. Goldman that she should have been wearing her portable alarm bell, which would have alerted caregivers that she was in distress. Goldman checks her heart, lungs, and abdomen and then reviews her medication. Seeing that snow remains on the sidewalk from yesterday's flurries, Goldman does the shovelling and then it's off to the next patient.

Ruth B. is an eighty-year-old with ovarian cancer who lives alone in an upscale apartment in the well-to-do Forest Hill neighbourhood. Ruth's concern today is her expanding abdomen, indicative of fluid build up, a symptom characteristic of advanced ovarian tumours. Ruth is also concerned about her increasing shortness of breath. Dr. Goldman uses a portable oximeter to measure the oxygen saturation of Ruth's blood, listens to her chest, and then examines her stomach. He tells her that the breathlessness is probably a result of her swollen abdomen. Dr. Goldman will make arrangements for the fluid to be drained at the hospital or, if it is Ruth's preference, he will perform the procedure in her apartment.

It is clear that Ruth appreciates the option. She is getting very frail and it would use up her strength for the day to have to take an ambulance to hospital. Also, most people who are as sick as Ruth prefer not to share their condition with the rest of the world.

For the last couple of years, Dr. Goldman has been working in a team with two nurses who have been seconded by the Toronto home care agency. He says the teams have really helped with communication between doctors and nurses, who often used to chase each other on the telephone all day. He notes that he now cares for roughly one hundred patients—nearly double what he was able to manage before teaming up with the nurses. He hopes the pilot project will be continued.

Nurse Lois Ozkaynak came to New Brunswick's Extra-Mural Hospital program in 1990 after several years of work at the Toronto General Hospital.* The Extra-Mural, as it's called, is New Brunswick's home care program. Dr. Gordon Ferguson, a surgeon, and now-senator Brenda Robertson developed it in the early 1980s. Palliative care has always been a priority for the program, which has assisted thousands of persons to die comfortably in their own homes.

This morning, Ozkaynak is driving a large circuit outside of Saint John. The second visit is to Graham F., an eighty-eight-year-old with advanced prostate cancer. She chats with Graham and his daughter-in-law Nancy while she examines an area of inflammation on his abdomen. He has been pretty comfortable since her last visit. Graham has a pump connected to his intravenous line, which provides a constant supply of morphine. She checks how much medication is left and then, seeing all is well, it's off to the next patient. Ozkaynak loves her work and it shows.

Ozkaynak has a big area to cover, but not as large as that served by Dr. Rob Wedel. Dr. Wedel lives in Taber, a town of 7,500 about 50 kilometres east of Lethbridge in southern Alberta. He acts as the palliative care consultant to the Chinook Health Region, and he regularly travels from the Rockies to the Badlands helping other family doctors and nurses manage their dying patients.

Quebec Experiments
Montreal's Royal Victoria Hospital may have started one of the first palliative care units in North America, but Quebec has been slower than the western provinces in implementing community-based palliative care. Over the past two years, a consortium of five Montreal-area

---

* Now part of the University Health Network, which includes the General, the Toronto Western, and Princess Margaret.

centres locaux services communautaire (CLSCs)* has co-operated with the Montreal General Hospital and the Royal Victoria Hospital in piloting community-based palliative care. Quebec's CLSCs are the only true network of primary health care services centres in Canada. Since 1972, federal and provincial commissions have recommended having doctors work in groups along with nurse practitioners, social workers, and other professionals. There are some community health centres in other provinces, but only in Quebec is there a full network of centres—147 of them—that combine physicians, home care, public health, mental health, and social services.

The pilot palliative care project began in the late 1990s and integrated the regular CLSC home care with twenty-four-hour palliative care through a dedicated telephone line and on-call physicians, nurses, and pharmacists. The project also provided in-home respite care, psychological support (including for bereavement), the loan of equipment and technical aids, a day hospital for more intensive evaluation, and specialist backup services in medicine, occupational therapy, and social work.

Ginette Villecourt is an occupational therapist with a CLSC in the Montreal neighbourhood of Notre Dame de Grace/Montreal West. Occupational therapists integrate the psychosocial and physical approach into their work more directly than most other professions. Villecourt saw this a perfect fit for palliative care, which requires an integration of all dimensions, including physical, mental, social, and spiritual health. Villecourt feels that the most important skill she brings to her patients is the ability to actively listen. To her, it is a privilege when her patients let her into their lives. She uses art and music to help her patients unlock their inner feelings, which can facilitate the resolution of long-standing inner and outer conflicts.

---

* Quebec was the only province to implement a network of multidisciplinary, prevention-oriented community health centres as recommended by Dr. John Hastings in 1972. The CLSCs involved with the pilot project were NDG/Montreal-West, Côtes-des-Neiges, Métro, René-Cassin, and Saint-Louis-du-Parc.

The palliative care pilots were spectacularly successful. Sixty-four per cent of the project's patients died at home, compared with 19 per cent of patients treated before the project. The Province of Quebec plans to extend these pilots throughout the CLSC network in the next few years.

Saskatchewan Integrates Palliative Care with Regional Planning

Saskatchewan, the home of medicare, has developed many innovative community programs. As in several other provinces, Saskatchewan's strategic plan makes palliative care a priority for regional authorities and primary health care projects. Saskatoon's palliative care services resemble those in Calgary, Edmonton, and a number of other western cities:

- A twelve-bed acute care unit at St. Paul's Hospital
- Consultation teams at Royal University Hospital, Saskatoon City Hospital, and St. Paul's Hospital
- A consultation team for all long-term care facilities
- A pain and symptom management clinic at the Saskatoon Cancer Centre
- A volunteer program and grief and bereavement groups
- Palliative care at hospitals in Humboldt, Lanigan, Rosthern, Wadena, Wakaw, Watrous, Wynyard, and the Nokomis Health Centre

Integrated Palliative Care in Rural PEI and Nova Scotia

The West Prince and Kings health regions of PEI and the Northern Health Region in Nova Scotia developed an integrated palliative care project. The project in West Prince used telehealth technology to facilitate care in rural areas in the late 1990s. In May 2002, it expanded to include telehome care, and it is currently functioning in Kings Health Region as well.

The program aims to reduce the need for patients to go to ERs by connecting patients and their families to health professionals twenty-four hours per day with a live visual and audio feed. A machine in the patient's home measures blood pressure, pulse, blood oxygen level, and blood sugar, as well as listening the patient's chest and monitoring wounds. The equipment supplements but does not replace regular nursing visits—it simply allows a more sophisticated version of the telephone call that health professionals have been using for over a hundred years to improve the efficiency of their work. Results from the one-year pilot project showed a 20 per cent drop in the number of patient visits to doctors' offices and 15 per cent fewer outpatient visits.

Advance Directives: Maintaining Control

Paralleling the growth and interest in palliative care for advanced cancer has been increasing attention paid to other end-of-life issues. Like Dr. Michael Gordon's elderly mother, many older people and their families do not wish for aggressive medical treatment as they get close to death.[19] Advance health care directives offer older people and their families an opportunity to choose their preferred level of intervention *before* they develop a life-threatening illness.

Dr. Willie Molloy was born in Waterford, Ireland, and qualified in medicine at University College, Cork. He came to Canada in 1981 and trained in geriatrics at the University of Manitoba and the University of Western Ontario before coming to Hamilton. He now holds the St. Peter's/McMaster Chair in Aging in the Faculty of Health Sciences at McMaster University. Molloy and his group first introduced advance directives into a home for the aged in Hamilton in 1989. The "Let me decide" directive allows people to document their wishes in the event of non-reversible (Alzheimer's, certain strokes) or reversible (pneumonia, bleeding ulcer) life-threatening illness. Individuals can state what conditions they consider reversible or irreversible in their directive's personal statement. The four treatment options are palliative, limited, surgical, and intensive care.

Treatment Options
for Advance Clinical Directives

1. *Palliative care*. Care is designed to promote comfort. No treatment is given to prolong life.
2. *Limited care*. May include the use of antibiotics with non-invasive investigations and treatments short of elective surgery.
3. *Surgical care*. Patients may receive surgery but are not sent to an intensive care unit and would not be ventilated except during and after surgery.
4. *Intensive care*. Patients would receive all treatments available in a modern hospital.

By the second year after the introduction of the directive, 80 per cent of residents had completed the form. Approximately one-third of patients made changes from the first to the second year, with most changes tending toward less intensive care. In the year before the directive had been implemented, nine residents had died, eight of them in acute care hospitals. In the second year after the introduction of the directive, there were eight deaths, only one of which was in an acute care setting.

Molloy and his research team recently completed an experimental investigation of their advance directive.[20] Three Ontario nursing homes were randomly allocated to an experimental group that used the "Let me decide" directive, and three were used as controls. After eighteen months of follow-up, there were similar numbers of deaths in both groups but the "Let me decide" nursing home participants used 61 per cent fewer acute hospital days. The investigators estimated that overall health care costs were 33 per cent lower for the participants in the "Let me decide" homes than for the controls. A similar program implemented nationwide would free up roughly 1,500 hospital beds.

One of the participants in Dr. Molloy's study was Lenore Craig.

Craig was a resident of Victoria Manor in Lindsay, about 150 kilometres northeast of Toronto. She had watched her husband slowly die over six months in hospital, and she had seen her sister expire while hooked up to a respirator in an intensive care unit. Craig decided that she didn't want any modern medical miracles. When completing her directive, she eschewed all acute care. She didn't want the home even to call 911. She decided to chose a peaceful end at the Manor.

Dr. Molloy is quick to clarify that advance directives are not part of a plot to sacrifice our elders when their health care becomes expensive. Rather, completing an advance directive should be part of patient-centred care. Either directly or with the assistance of designated proxies, patients should be in charge of their own care. Advance directives promote this control.

In the evaluation of the "Let me decide" directive, the average cost for the staff time to complete a directive was $110. This reflected the counselling and facilitation to help patients and families identify their preferences. "You can't just slip forms to people and expect them to be completed. Counselling sessions, videos, and education are necessary to back up the form," claims Dr. Molloy.

However, there are no requirements for advance directives, no standards for how they are completed. As a result, so far they have had little impact on practice. But legislation might not be the answer. In 1990 in the United States, the Patient Self-Determination Act (PSDA) was passed. It requires that health care facilities complete advance clinical directives on all patients. Many lawmakers were personally touched by the issue and wanted to ensure that patients were informed of their right to accept or refuse medical care. Each state can establish and define its own legislation concerning advance directives. The PSDA has increased the implementation of advance directives, but progress has been slow.[21]

In Canada, a 1995 Alberta study showed that 84 per cent of dialysis patients thought that it was important to have an advance directive but only 18 per cent had one.[22] A more recent Canadian study looked at whether ICU staff established do-not-resuscitate (DNR) orders on their patients within twenty-four hours of admission. ICU patients are the sickest of hospital patients and are most likely to die. The study of fifteen ICUs in four countries included eleven from Canada. The ICU staff established DNR orders on only 11 per cent of nearly three thousand patients.

Conclusion

Dying patients who are seeking only symptomatic relief too often die in hospital intensive care units. Despite thirty years of recommendations, most patients who could benefit from palliative care services still don't get them. Denial of death, concern for privacy, and a bizarre series of perverse financial incentives have conspired to keep end-of-life issues at the end of health policy-makers' agendas.

Your Community and End-of-Life Care

- Does your community track the number of deaths in hospitals, hospices, and homes? If your community has more than 50 per cent of cancer deaths occurring in hospital, there aren't adequate palliative care services.
- Do your community's hospitals and nursing homes measure pain as the fifth vital sign (on a scale of 1 to 10, in addition to temperature, respiration, pulse, and blood pressure)?
- Do your community's palliative programs provide care to non-cancer patients (for example, HIV/AIDS, congestive heart failure, chronic kidney disease, and chronic neuromuscular diseases)? These patients should make up more than 25 per cent of the total caseload.
- Are palliative care programs available for the homeless?
- Do your community's long-term care facilities and home care

services complete advance clinical directives on all their clients? Does this process involve professional counselling and appropriate written and audiovisual decision aids?

- What proportion of long-term care facility patients' deaths occur in hospital? More than 70 per cent of deaths should occur within the facility.
- Do intensive care units have dedicated staff to counsel patients and families about preferences for care?
- Do ambulance dispatches and paramedics respect advance directives?

But this chapter shows that the tide is beginning to turn. From Dr. Goldman's travels through Toronto's tony Forest Hill neighbourhood to the mean streets of Ottawa, palliative care is poised to finally make a breakthrough, promising all Canadians compassionate care as we live our last days. And better-quality end-of-life care is a tonic to the health system as well—leaving hospitals for folks who really need acute care.

Chapter 5

A Tonic for Chronic Illness

Tim McCaskell grew up in Beaverton, a small town 100 kilometres north of Toronto on Lake Simcoe. There wasn't much discussion of homosexuality in Beaverton—or in Toronto, for that matter—in the 1950s and 1960s. But when McCaskell moved to Toronto in 1974, gay liberation was in full swing and Toronto was one of its capitals. Ten years before, Toronto had been overwhelmingly white, but now it was on its way to having a majority "visible minority" population. Ten years before, Toronto had been known for its churches, but now it was starting to be known for its theatre and restaurants. And ten years before, homosexuality had been against the law. But now Pierre Trudeau was prime minister. As justice minister, he had led passage of the long-overdue legislation that had taken "the state out of the nation's bedrooms."

The *Body Politic* was the original organ of gay liberation. McCaskell recalls reading the *Body Politic* in a large field in Riverdale Park in east Toronto. That way, he could see if anyone was approaching him and then hide it before it was identified. McCaskell was already a political activist, a veteran of demonstrations against the Vietnam War, but he approached his first gay liberation demonstration with trepidation. He was soon swept up into this new cause and became a member of the Body Politic collective and one of its most articulate spokespersons. It was also at this time that he began his life-long relationship with Toronto video artist Richard Fung.

In 1981, McCaskell found himself feeling unwell. He had enlarged lymph nodes, intermittent diarrhea, weight loss, and other symptoms. His doctors were mystified. The only abnormal test was a decreased level of platelets—a blood constituent that aids clotting. But McCaskell was ahead of his doctors, because he had been following intently the international gay press reports of the so-called gay plague that would soon be called acquired immunodeficiency syndrome, or AIDS. He knew that he likely had AIDS, but it took until 1984 before HIV was recognized as the cause, and until 1986 before a definitive blood test became available.

Throughout this time, he acquired a black belt in karate and developed internationally known anti-racism materials for the Toronto Board of Education. Impatient with government's lack of attention to the growing AIDS epidemic, in 1987 and 1988 McCaskell was one of the activists who created the Toronto-based AIDS ACTION NOW! AAN was not a traditional disease group like the Cancer Society or the Heart and Stroke Foundation. AAN's main mission wasn't raising funds for research. It was political action.

McCaskell recalls that one of the hottest issues AAN dealt with in the late 1980s was access to aerosolized pentamidine (AP). At that time, many AIDS patients were dying of pneumonia caused by a previously obscure micro-organism, *Pneumocystis carinii*. Pneumocystis pneumonia (PCP) had a high death rate, but McCaskell and other Toronto activists knew that inhalation of AP once a month would effectively prevent it. Health Canada had not formally approved AP and was insisting on a double-blind study before it was licensed in this country. McCaskell and other AAN members were incensed that people on a placebo would be dying when there was already enough evidence for them that AP worked. Eventually Health Canada made AP available to anyone. AAN had made its point that if patients with a potentially fatal condition had to risk taking a placebo to get active treatment, their consent to participation in research was meaningless.

While battling for better treatment for people with AIDS, McCaskell was fighting another battle—for his own life. In the late 1980s, researchers found the first effective drug against the human immunodeficiency virus (HIV): azidothymidine, or AZT. Marketed as Zidovudine or Retrovir, AZT was the first of a new generation of anti-viral drugs that would change the face of AIDS. One of McCaskell's doctors strongly suggested that he take AZT, but he saw friends who seemed to be sickened more by the drug than by their illness. Eventually, research showed that McCaskell was correct: it was better to start AZT later in the course of the infection and at lower doses. Later, when he did start AZT, he wanted to take it in combination with another antiviral. This was different from accepted medical opinion at the time, but his physician, Dr. Philip Berger, saw no harm in McCaskell's approach and believed that patients are ultimately in charge.

Now McCaskell takes four different drugs. He had to leave his job in 2001, but he is still well enough to work on a number of human rights causes. He continues to be an involved patient, and he continues to work with his health care team, which over time has included physicians, nurses, pharmacists, and others.

When AIDS first appeared, it was a disease that usually killed people within one to two years. The fervent goal of activists in the 1980s was to turn AIDS into a chronic disease, like arthritis, that people would live with until they died of something else. Tim has lived for over twenty years after being infected with HIV and hopefully has many more years to enjoy life and contribute to our civil society. People with AIDS, like Tim McCaskell, have a lot to teach the health system about the management of chronic illness.

This chapter outlines the burden of chronic illness and the problems our health care system has in managing it. Then it describes a model for chronic disease management and offers examples of a number of exciting, innovative programs. In the end, informed, active patients like Tim McCaskell, working with a prepared, proactive practice team, are the best hope for the treatment of chronic illness and the renovation of the health care system.

Chronic Diseases:
Big Problems for the Canadian Health Care System

The Canadian health care system was originally built to treat acute problems such as injuries, tuberculosis, diphtheria, measles, and scarlet fever. Now there are many fewer serious acute illnesses, especially in young people. Chronic illnesses such as cancer, heart disease, diabetes, and AIDS have become a much greater burden. And they also occur in an older population who are often frail and who sometimes suffer cognitive problems. Hospitals are overcrowded with patients who have suffered a complication or an acute exacerbation of a pre-existing chronic illness.

Chronic illnesses place a big burden on the health care system:[1]

- Chronic diseases account for 70 per cent of all deaths.
- Chronic diseases account for more than 60 per cent of health care costs.
- Chronic diseases account for one-third of the years of potential life lost before age sixty-five.
- People with five chronic illnesses (mood disorders, diabetes, heart disease, asthma, and hypertension) account for one-half of all US health expenditures.[2]

It is often said that systems are perfectly designed to get the outcomes they produce. As we discussed in chapter 2, the Canadian health care system is perfectly designed to do a poor job of managing chronic illness. The system was designed for hospital treatment of acute illness and injury. It was not designed for primary health care management of chronic illness. Depending upon the disease studied, 40 to 80 per cent of patients with chronic illness are *inadequately* treated.

- Fewer than 30 per cent of Canadians with high blood pressure have their blood pressure properly controlled.[3]

- Sixty per cent of diabetics have not had an eye examination, and 70 per cent have not had their urine checked for protein, in the past year.[4] Nearly one-half of all new cases of kidney failure in Canada are related to diabetic kidney disease.[5]
- A BC study of asthma showed that only 20 per cent of patients met the criteria for appropriate medication management.[6] A national survey showed that 60 per cent of Canadian asthmatics did not have their disease properly controlled.[7]
- A McMaster University study found that Ontario family physicians offered only 40 per cent of the preventive manoeuvres recommended by the Canadian Task Force on the Periodic Health Examination.[8]
- Over 20 per cent of patients discharged from hospital with congestive heart failure are readmitted within sixty days.[9]

But these problems also present a wonderful opportunity. Better management of chronic illnesses can save lives, relieve suffering, and save resources for the system. In many cases, savings accumulate within months or years. Better primary health care for diabetes could cut the rate of new cases of diabetes-related kidney failure by over 50 per cent.[10] Better care for patients with congestive heart failure can decrease hospital admissions by over 60 per cent.[11]

Yankee Know-how Shows How

Seattle: Home of Microsoft, Jimi Hendrix, and the Group Health Cooperative

It's a busy Monday morning at the Northgate Medical Center in suburban Seattle. Northgate is one of fourteen Seattle health centres run by the Group Health Cooperative. One of Dr. Elizabeth Lin's first patients this morning is Amanda P., a fifty-two-year-old marketing manager who hurt her shoulder gardening over the weekend. After Dr. Lin examines her shoulder, she tells Amanda to get dressed and then enters her name into the office computer. Up comes Amanda's file in a friendly Windows format. It includes a list of chronic illnesses and the medication she is taking. Amanda has diabetes, and Group Health's information system automatically knows that she is behind in her follow-ups. The computer screen says in big red letters that Amanda needs her long-term blood-sugar control measured with an HgA1C test and that she is six months past due for her eye examination (to check for diabetic retinopathy).

The record also reminds Dr. Lin that she treated Amanda for depression in 1998. Amanda is presently taking no medication for depression. Dr. Lin returns to the examination room and reassures Amanda about her shoulder, recommending some exercises and a new posture for her gardening. Then she signs a lab requisition for a blood test and asks her to book a return appointment for an eye examination and follow-up discussion of her diabetes with her practice nurse. Finally, Dr. Lin asks Amanda a short battery of questions about her mood and social function. Finding no evidence of recurrence of depression, she wishes her well with her roses and is off to the next patient.

Although the American system overall has more problems than ours, the US also has many interesting programs that can provide us with valuable lessons. In the United States, there are prepaid health plans that not only insure care but also provide it. Some own hospitals and employ doctors. Most establish a network by contracting with hospitals, doctors, nursing, homes, and other components.

Up until the 1970s, these health plans were almost exclusively nonprofit. Many, like Group Health, were co-operatives. They were known for innovative practice organization and were seen as utopian and somewhat un-American. But after President Nixon's health advisers (who included present secretary of defence Donald Rumsfeld) got through with them, these organizations were rebranded as health maintenance organizations, or HMOs.[12] Now most are for-profit and are often owned by multinational corporations. They are known for denying people care and are seen as a nightmare excess of American devotion to free markets for everything. The 2001 hit film *John Q* featured Denzel Washington as a father who took hospital staff hostage because his HMO denied his son a needed transplant. However, the early HMOs such as the Kaiser Permanente system and Group Health Cooperative are still innovators in patient care. There's a lot for Canadians to learn from these organizations.

The Kaiser system got its start in the late 1930s when industrialist Henry Kaiser persuaded surgeon Sidney Garfield to set up a group-practice prepayment plan for the construction of the Grand Coulee Dam on the Columbia River. The plan grew rapidly during the Second World War when Dr. Garfield organized health care for thousands of Kaiser shipbuilding workers in California. Now Kaiser Permanente is the largest not-for-profit health maintenance organization in the US, serving 8.1 million members in nine states and the District of Columbia.

A group of idealistic Seattle residents established Group Health Cooperative in 1947. It provides care to about 600,000 people in Washington and Idaho, most in the Seattle metropolitan area.

The Chronic Care Model

Dr. Ed Wagner is the director of Group Health's MacColl Institute for Healthcare Innovation. Group Health and Dr. Wagner have pioneered new approaches to chronic illnesses. The McColl Institute also serves as the national office for the Robert Wood Johnson Foundation's program Improving Chronic Illness Care (ICIC).*

ICIC has three underlying rationales:

1. There are highly effective clinical and behavioural interventions for most chronic illnesses.
2. There is good evidence on how to change the delivery system to improve care.
3. There is a need to develop action-oriented improvement strategies to accomplish the changes.

---

* See the Improving Chronic Illness Care Web site at http://www.improvingchronic care.org.

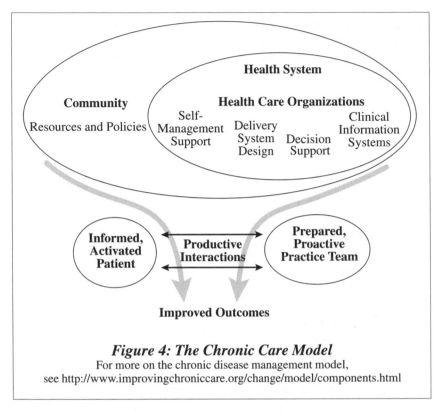

Figure 4: The Chronic Care Model
For more on the chronic disease management model,
see http://www.improvingchroniccare.org/change/model/components.html

Dr. Wagner's group developed the chronic care model (CCM) to guide the development of an organized approach for chronic disease management. The model identifies the essential elements of a system that encourages high-quality chronic disease management: the community, the health system, self-management support, delivery-system design, decision support, and clinical information systems. Appropriate action at these levels should lead to more productive interactions between patients who are actively involved in their care and providers who have the resources and skills needed for the attainment of improved functional and clinical outcomes.

We can see this exemplified in Tim McCaskell's care. He is clearly actively involved in his care with a proactive, prepared team of Dr. Berger and other providers. He has the support of the general community. Canadian AIDS Treatment Information and Exchange (CATIE) offers scientific updates to McCaskell and other AIDS patients. CATIE provides information to patients, as well as to families, providers, and AIDS service organizations. It operates a Web site (http://www.catie.ca) and two electronic mailing lists, publishes print publications, and manages a toll-free, bilingual telephone service. CATIE and other resources enable Tim McCaskell and other AIDS patients to maintain their own health and be effective partners in their own care.

The modern methods of chronic disease management can be applied to a variety of chronic illnesses, health care settings, and target populations. But they are easier to implement at Group Health Cooperative for a number of reasons. Group Health strongly believes in patient self-management, to the extent that it is run as a co-operative with consumers on the board of directors. Its Web site includes education for patients with a variety of illnesses and links with disease support groups. It has had a diabetes registry linked to its electronic medical record since 1996. The records are fully interactive and are linked to targeted scientific literature as well as to search engines. Group Health has organized its Seattle services into fourteen family medicine centres, typically with thirty-five to forty doctors, one hundred nurses, a laboratory, medical imaging equipment, and a pharmacy. Most of the staff within the centres have been further organized into clinical teams with two family doctors, one nurse practitioner, two registered nurses, and four medical assistants.* Each team manages between 4,000 and 4,500 patients. Nurses have the responsibility for maintaining chronic disease registries.

---

* The medical assistants have less than six months of training and do mainly clerical and administrative work.

Get a Road Map or Be Roadkill

Group Health used the CCM to develop its own groundbreaking programs for the management of chronic illness. It convened a group representing different parts of the organization (doctors, nurses, administrators, researchers) to design a "road map" for diabetes. Other organizations use phrases like "clinical pathways," "service frameworks," or "guidelines" to describe their organized approach to care. Dr. Bruce Perry, currently medical director for the Kaiser Permanente Medical Group in Georgia, coined the term "road map" when he was director of total quality management for Group Health in the early 1990s. Group Health chose "road map" because it conveys the concept that there are many ways to get to the destination of better patient care but that some are better than others.

Dr. Wagner says that they started with diabetes because it is a very common condition, it causes considerable death and disability, and there are interventions available that have been proven to improve patient outcomes. The diabetes road map consists of four key elements:

- Group Health implemented an electronic diabetes registry in 1995. This allowed Dr. Lin to immediately know that Amanda was behind in her follow-ups. The needed services are highlighted in red. Staff joke that their task is like the tag line for Visine eyedrops: "Get the red out." They also have registries for another ten conditions, including depression. As a result, Dr. Lin knew to quickly screen Amanda for a recurrence.
- Group Health created an expert team of diabetologist Dr. David McCulloch and diabetes nurse consultant Dr. Martha Price. Drs. McCulloch and Price visit Group Health's fourteen family medicine centres to talk with doctors and nurses about better control of diabetes.
- The road-map teams developed their own clinical practice guidelines, based on a rigorous review of the scientific literature.
- Group Health supports patient self-management through Right

Track, a patient notebook distributed through Group Health pharmacies free of charge by physician prescription.

Now over 80 per cent of patients have documented adherence to clinical practice guidelines—a level almost unheard of anywhere else in the world.

There were some start-up costs associated with the development and implementation of the diabetes road map. But Dr. Wagner reports that these costs were quickly recouped because, as predicted, diabetics were less likely to develop complications and need specialist and hospital care.[13]

Group Health North: Sault Ste. Marie, Ontario

It's a perfect clear early summer morning when Cathy McCullough pulls up to Maria P.'s house just off Queen Street overlooking the rushing water of the St. Marys River. This historic part of Canada lies along the ancient trade route connecting Lake Superior to Lake Huron and is close by the site of the first battle of the War of 1812, at the Straits of Mackinac. Maria is nearly eighty years old and suffers from a variety of ailments, including diabetes and heart disease. She was in and out of hospital during the late 1990s with congestive heart failure. McCullough is a family health nurse with the Group Health Centre in Sault Ste. Marie.

Congestive heart failure, or CHF, is the end stage of any heart disease, when the heart no longer functions effectively as a pump and begins to back up fluid, especially in the lungs and legs. As modern medicine has developed more effective treatments for heart attacks, more and more Canadians are living to suffer from CHF. Now CHF is the number-one cause of adult non-reproductive admissions to hospital—almost 60,000 every year.[14] Twenty years ago, CHF patients used to stay in hospital for three weeks. Now they stay ten days on average, and many are discharged before they feel 100 per cent and before they are on their final doses of medication. Unfortunately, the care for most is so inadequate that 20 per cent of CHF patients are readmitted to hospital within one month of their discharge.

Maria hasn't been readmitted to hospital for her CHF since McCullough has been working with her, nearly four years. McCullough saw Maria while she was in hospital with her last CHF admission and then continued to work with her to keep her well. She educated Maria about CHF. She taught her when her condition was Green, Orange, or Red. Green means that she feels well with no weight gain. Orange means that she has some mild symptoms including weight gain of 1 kilogram. She should then take an extra diuretic (water pill) every day for three to four days. She is also supposed to check in by phone with McCullough. Red means more serious symptoms: she should immediately contact McCullough or her doctor. Maria has a card in her kitchen with these guidelines displayed like a traffic light. McCullough keeps up to date with Maria's doctor through e-mail and checking the electronic record, which is maintained for each Group Health patient.

McCullough remembers another patient, whom she visited thirty-one days after hospital discharge. The doctor had given her a one-month prescription for spironolactone, a diuretic, but the patient didn't know that she was to continue taking it. Fortunately, McCullough saw her before she slipped back into heart failure, and restarted her medication.

The CHF project has been a major success for patients and the health system in the Sault. After nine months, the rate of thirty-day readmissions decreased by 57 per cent compared with patients of other Sault doctors and 68 per cent compared with previous Group Health CHF patients.[15]

The Jewel in the Crown of Medicare

In the late 1950s, former Algoma Steel pipefitter John Barker led the battle for the development of what Royal Commissioner Roy Romanow later termed the "jewel in the crown of Medicare"—the

Sault Ste. Marie Group Health Centre. Barker was staff representative for the United Steelworkers of America and an acknowledged community leader.* Isadore Falk, a consultant to the Steelworkers US head office saw an opportunity to promote prepaid group practice.[16]

The Group Health Centre opened in 1963 and there have been several bumps over the years. Many of the other Sault doctors refused to have anything to do with the clinic's doctors or patients.† Even though evaluations demonstrated that the clinic's patients had health costs one-third lower than other city residents, the Ontario Ministry of Health seemed to do its best to obstruct its development.[17] In fact, the centre recently went ten years without an increase in its budget.

Group Health now has over fifty-six thousand enrolled patients, sixty-four doctors, eight nurse practitioners, ninety-six registered nurses, and fifty-two other professionals. Like its larger American cousins, the Sault Group Health Clinic has been an innovator in the use of teams and of preventive services. The Ministry of Health has always paid the centre on a non-fee-for-service basis, although the details have changed over time. This flexible funding allowed the centre to explore the better use of nurses and other staff. Originally, the ministry rewarded the centre financially if it reduced patients' hospitalization rate below the regional average. This permitted Group Health to develop better home care programs, such as the one for congestive heart failure, well before most other jurisdictions.

Like its cousin in Seattle, the Sault's Group Health Centre also has an electronic health record (EHR) system with registries for diabetes and some other conditions. In fact, Group Health has Canada's largest ambulatory clinic electronic charting system. Group Health frugally used savings from a number of other areas to put it in place. It's Unix-based, so it's not as user-friendly as Group Health Seattle's

---

* Many other organizations and hundreds of individuals were actively involved in the founding of Group Health, but it is safe to say that it wouldn't have happened without the Steelworkers and John Barker.

† Fortunately, this has since been remedied.

record, but it was a lot less expensive. Perhaps best signifying the way the Ministry of Health has treated Group Health over the years, at one point Her Majesty's representatives told the clinic that the EHR was an unauthorized expenditure and demanded that they scrap it. Fortunately, the execution was stayed.

One of the driving forces behind Group Health's foray into chronic disease management is internist Dr. Hui Lee. Dr. Lee, a Queen's grad, says malaria drove him up north. In the early 1990s, he and his physician wife planned to go to Africa. But she was pregnant, and the infectious disease consultants couldn't agree on the safest malaria prevention medication. There was no danger of malaria in Sault Ste. Marie, so they took jobs at Group Health instead. Dr. Lee heads up the centre's Health Promotion Initiative (HPI), which includes the programs for CHF and diabetes.

Group Health has a diabetes registry that includes over 2,400 patients, the largest such registry in the country. The registry keeps track of long-term diabetic control (with the HgA1C test), as well as eye examinations, kidney tests, and other measures of diabetic follow-up. All of these measures have improved since the implementation of the HPI.[18] The proportion of patients with a documented acceptable blood pressure increased from 28 per cent to 50 per cent, the proportion with foot examinations doubled from 26 per cent to 52 per cent, and the overall index of diabetes control improved from 40 per cent to 65 per cent.

In 2002, Dr. Lee started feeding performance data back to the family physicians. The doctors get the scores for their patients and the anonymous scores for the other doctors, so they know where they stand. Dr. David Fera decided he could do better. Group Health in Seattle and some other organizations found that seeing chronic disease patients in mini-clinics can make a big difference in diabetes control,[19] and Dr. Fera decided to give it a try.

The mini-clinic started with groups of four patients and a diabetes educator to review their education and clarify the goals of follow-up. After the first group visits, Dr. Fera set aside one day per month as his diabetic day, when he sees a quarter of his diabetics (about forty patients). He says that he really looks forward to that day and he feels his patients get better care because he is focused on their diabetes. He claims that the mini-clinics force him not to "cheat" on their diabetes care the way he might if he were seeing them for another complaint and was already behind in his schedule. For example, each patient takes off his or her shoes and socks while waiting to see him, ensuring that he examines their feet (to check for ulcers and infections and to prevent amputations). Dr. Fera's patients have been getting better care since he started these clinics[20]—he is now examining nearly 75 per cent of his patients' feet compared with fewer than 25 per cent before the mini-clinics. Now two other Group Health doctors are conducting such mini-clinics, and others are watching.

Take a Deep Breath:
Vancouver Program Opens Airways

In chapter 1, we told the sad story of Joshua Fleuelling's death from asthma. For reasons that are not fully understood, asthma is becoming much more common. There are more and more effective treatments for asthma available, but at least five hundred people die every year in Canada because of asthma. And, like Joshua Fleuelling's, almost all these deaths are preventable.

Jo-Anna Gillespie took her nursing training at Victoria's Royal Jubilee Hospital. After eighteen years of working in hospitals on psychiatry and maternity services, Gillespie decided to work in the community. She has asthma herself and had endured poor control because she didn't have enough information to manage the condition herself. When she met Dr. Michael Mandl, a Vancouver allergist with a special interest in asthma, in the early 1990s, the two found they were both interested in enhancing patient self-management of asthma. They established the Asthma Allergy and Teaching Unit.

The unit, located in a medical building in Vancouver's East End, became the heart of a groundbreaking study of patient education and self-management.

Mandl and Gillespie had been seeing patients for several years when they were offered an opportunity by the BC government and the federal government's Health Transition Fund to study their model in the "real world." There was already substantial evidence that experimental studies of asthma patients' self-management could improve asthma control and patient quality of life and even reduce health care costs.[21] They wanted to show that this improvement could happen in the real world.

Starting in 1999, Mandl and Gillespie visited fourteen rural communities throughout British Columbia. They convened a two-hour town hall meeting in the evening where Dr. Mandl provided education on asthma and its management. Then, the following day, the asthmatics met with Gillespie or another asthma educator to develop a self-management plan, which they then discussed with their physicians. The patients gave their consent for the investigators to track their medication consumption and use of the health care system prior to and subsequent to the asthma education.

The pre-education results were similar to what had been found in other studies. Just like Joshua Fleuelling, too many of the patients were using short-acting "rescue" medications and too few were using "preventer" medications. Because the education sessions took place at different times in different parts of the province, the researchers were able to track the changes in outcomes and medication use in the patients, depending upon when they received their education.

The researchers found that initially, the subjects visited their family doctors more, but that was because they were getting preventer medications, mainly variants of inhaled cortisone. In fact, all the subjects who hadn't been on these life-saving drugs got them during the trial. The final results showed that there were decreased family physician visits, increased use of preventer medications, reduced use of rescue medications, improvements in asthma control, and increased quality of life.[22]

Dr. Mandl is adamant that asthma education programs train their patients in guided self-management. Programs that use only written materials and videotapes about asthma enhance knowledge, but programs that focus on self-management actually improve asthma outcomes.[23] Dr. Mandl estimates that fewer than ten full-time asthma educators could service all of British Columbia. That means we would need only roughly one hundred for the whole country. And we could likely pay for them within the first year with fewer hospitalizations, doctors' visits, and deaths.

Let Guided Self-Management Take You the Healthy Way

When people live with a chronic illness, they can't rely upon a health care professional to tell them what to do every day for their whole lives. Diabetics have to learn to adjust their insulin or other diabetic medication according to their diet, exercise, and blood-sugar readings. If we waited for asthmatics to contact a doctor every time they needed to change their medication, doctors would have no time for anything else.

All of this seems to be common sense. Unfortunately, the health care system has both encouraged and disparaged patient dependency. Just think how often we are told to check with our family doctor when we could take some action ourselves, be taught what to observe, and then contact a doctor—or a nurse—only if we didn't seem to be responding appropriately. It's simply better-quality care. And with the growth of chronic illness, we cannot afford to miss opportunities to enhance patients' ability to manage their own care.

Dr. Tom Creer, a psychologist from Ohio University, first coined the term "self-management" when working with asthmatic children in the 1960s. Since then, Dr. Kate Lorig, a professor of nursing at

Stanford University, has researched and popularized the concept. Dr. Lorig identifies five core self-management skills:

- *Problem-solving.* Structured problem-solving is being used in fields from computer systems to treatment for depression to organizational development. Problem-solving methodologies encompass problem definition, generation of possible solutions, implementation of solutions, and evaluation of results.
- *Decision-making.* This involves both information and the development of decision algorithms.
- *Resource utilization.* This includes not just educating people about where to find resources, but helping them with the tasks necessary to access them. For example, patients may need assistance with basic literacy or how to use the Internet. Tim McCaskell is quick to add that without assistance in these areas, only middle-class, educated patients will be able to effectively participate in their own care.
- *Forming a partnership with the health care system.* Self-care has tended to focus on the patient side of the equation. The new approach focuses on forming effective partnerships. This aspect is at the core of the chronic disease model.
- *Taking action.* This involves assisting people to take small steps immediately. Typical action plans deal with the next seven to fourteen days and focus on a specific behaviour.

Dr. Lorig concludes that there is evidence that self-management can improve outcomes and reduce costs for arthritis, asthma, and possibly other conditions.[24]

And self-management is more effective if it really focuses on improving patients' capacity for self-care as opposed to simply educating people about their illness. In other words, Mandl and Gillespie's model is the right one. We need to unlock the ability of patients to manage their own care and then ensure that the health care team is ready to support them.

Chronic Disease Management Care
Spreads across the Country

There are new developments in diabetes care all over the country, but none is more exciting than in the Northwest Territories. Dr. John Morse, a Yellowknife internist, developed the NWT program with a public health nurse and a dietitian in 1995. In Yellowknife (home to 18,000 of the 42,000 residents of the Territories), some patients are followed by family doctors. However, in smaller communities, diabetic patients are identified in a registry and followed by the public health nurses, who hold regular diabetes clinics. Because the communities are small, the nurses know pretty much everyone who has diabetes.

The public health nurse acts as an entry to the care team, which includes (depending upon the community) family doctors, dietitians, and social workers. Dr. Morse acts as medical director. The program uses paper records, but according to program staff, over 90 per cent of diabetics are registered and over 90 per cent have had requisite monitoring.

At least partly because of their diabetes program, there has never been a diabetic in the Northwest Territory who has developed renal failure because of diabetes. In the meantime, diabetes ravages kidneys in other parts of Canada. The number of dialysis cases is currently growing at over ten per cent per year. In Manitoba, nearly sixty per cent of patients starting dialysis suffer from diabetes. Across the country forty-four per cent of new dialysis patients have diabetes, and their proportion is growing every year.[25]

The Mid-Main Community Health Centre, located in Vancouver's East Side, recently took the concept of group appointments further. The clinic identified its diabetic patients and then started two pilot groups. The first meeting covered remedial diabetes education and involved a physician, a nurse, and a pharmacist. Now the patients are taking charge. Some patients have developed tricks for dealing with exercise. Others have recipes to share. And they take tremendous strength from their shared experiences. Susan Troesch, the pharmacist, says that their goal is to make the patients better self-managers. She notes that one group recently tackled depression with their own facilitator. Susan hopes that eventually these groups will be self-sufficient.

A few kilometres to the east, the REACH community health centre is located in a densely populated immigrant community. Since 2001, REACH has been running a program funded through the federal government's diabetes strategy for the local Vietnamese, African, and Latin American communities. Pat Dabiri, the director of the centre's multicultural programs, notes that all disease has meaning and that diabetes has special meaning because of its relation to food. Each cultural group has taken its own approach to the topic, but all have focused on diet and exercise within their cultural context.

Dr. Hertzel Gerstein is an internationally known researcher at McMaster University. He has led large clinical trials in diabetes, but in the late 1990s he was looking to do something locally. His leadership led to Diabetes Hamilton, which has held community meetings for up to 500 people as well as providing continuing education for physicians, pharmacists, and other professionals. Diabetes Hamilton also maintains a Web site where patients and providers can register.*

So far, 1,500 diabetics have done so, and Dr. Gerstein feels it is an excellent resource for self-management.

In Taber, Alberta, nurse practitioner Mary Nugent works with asthmatic patients, along with nine doctors and six other staff. She organizes services for chronic disease management. Nugent uses a plan similar to that of Mandl and Gillespie: she educates the patients, teaches them to manage their own medications, and then sends them back to their doctors with an action plan to sign.

Nugent also runs an annual town hall meeting for patients with diabetes and hyperlipidemia. In January 2003, Taber began the

---

* The Web site can be found at http://www.larkimageworks.com/dh-main.htm.

Building Healthy Lifestyles program. Providers can refer their patients, but many patients are self-referred. Healthy Lifestyles offers a series of classes on topics such as nutrition, exercise, and stress management. All patients have their charts assessed when they are referred. High-risk or unstable patients first see a nurse-educator and then move into the groups. As Eileen Patterson, the Taber Project co-ordinator, says, they are trying to build their patients' capacity to self-manage. They have adopted a model within which they will be coaching their patients into better health.

Victoria has been working on improving diabetes care since the mid-1990s. They are working with provincial officials to establish a complete community registry.[26]

Dr. Jean Bourbeau and his team at the Université de Laval in Quebec City recently completed an experiment, in which patients with chronic obstructive pulmonary disease* were trained in self-management techniques. Bourbeau's team found that self-management reduced hospital admissions by 50 per cent while improving patients' quality of life.[27]

Another research team at Laval has demonstrated that training asthmatics in self-management techniques improved lung function and reduced use of doctors compared with a program that simply provided education.[28]

The Calgary Regional Health Authority is developing a comprehensive approach to chronic disease management. Dr. Peter Sargious, who co-chairs the process, says that after Calgary managed to get its acute care services under control, the senior managers felt that they needed to better manage chronic disease. Dr. Sargious claims that better management of chronic illness is imperative for maintaining the sustainability of the acute care system. We'll read more about Calgary's approach in chapter 14.

---

* Emphysema and chronic bronchitis are two of the most common diseases that cause chronic obstructive pulmonary disease.

Conclusion

The Canadian health care system does quite well at treating acute conditions. Canadians have much better access to primary health care than do Americans. Fifty per cent of Canadian doctors are family doctors compared with about 13 per cent in the US, and there are no user fees to see one. And Canadians get better care for some conditions, such as depression.[29] However, management of hypertension seems to be poorer in Canada.[30] There is substantial room in Canada to improve care of chronic illness. Better primary health care for chronic illness would improve Canadians' health and would be an excellent strategy to improve the sustainability of the institutional system.

Your Community and Chronic Disease Management

- Do family physicians and other primary health care practices have registries of patients with chronic diseases? Registries are a prerequisite for providing effective population-based care for chronic illness.
- Can these registries provide reports indicating what percentage of patients with chronic illness are receiving care according to clinical practice guidelines?
- Does your community have an organized program for outpatient management of congestive heart failure and other serious chronic illnesses? What is the thirty-day readmission rate for patients discharged with these conditions that have a high likelihood of re-admission?
- Does your community have programs to teach guided self-management for patients with diabetes, asthma, HIV/AIDS, and other chronic diseases?
- Does your community offer the means for patients to update their knowledge on their illnesses?

This chapter demonstrates that there are beacons of best practices in Canada that demonstrate the potential for improvement. And there are internationally proven methods to enhance system performance.

It is also clear that the financial incentives and organization of the health care system mitigate against effective chronic disease management programs. The Sault Ste. Marie Group Health Centre clinic has made big strides in this area because its doctors are not paid on a fee-for-service basis and the clinic's funding includes nurses and other professionals. Canada's health care system will have to make these and other structural changes to really advance the marker on chronic disease management.

Chapter 6

There's No Place Like Home: Home and Continuing Care

It's mid-June in Fort Smith, just north of the Alberta–Northwest Territories border. The sun will barely set tonight, and Darlene Dimsmore seems to hardly sleep either. She is a home care nurse with the Fort Smith regional health services. This morning she starts her day at Mary M.'s house. Mary is a sixty-eight-year-old Native grandmother. She suffers from arthritis and chronic obstructive pulmonary disease, or COPD.* Mary isn't one to complain, but as she sits drinking tea in her simple but well-tended living room, it is obvious that she is unwell. She is coughing a lot and finds it a struggle to pour Dimsmore's tea while describing her symptoms. Dimsmore recognizes that Mary is suffering an acute exacerbation of her lung disease. She makes a phone call to Mary's doctor, who agrees that antibiotics are necessary. He will phone a prescription to the drug store, and one of Mary's grandsons will pick it up for her.

Dimsmore's next patient is Ken G., another First Nations elder. He suffers from congestive heart failure. Dimsmore brings her bathroom scale because Ken doesn't have one himself. Ken feels well and has gained no weight since her last visit one week earlier. She reviews his symptoms and diet and then takes his blood pressure and

---

* Chronic bronchitis and emphysema are the most common manifestations of COPD, and smoking is, by far, the most common underlying cause.

listens to his chest. She has been encouraging Ken to exercise. She notes that the pelicans are back on the river, a timeless reminder of spring renewal. She encourages Ken to go out to see them. Ken wants to but complains that there is no place to sit on the way downtown and he needs to take frequent breaks. Dimsmore says that she will look into how to raise the issue of a bench on the path with the town council, and then it's off to her next appointment.

Dimsmore's job is both new and old. Home care has caught the public's fancy as more and more hospitals discharge their patients "sicker and quicker." However, Darlene's job is reminiscent of the "district nurses" of old. When the Victorian Order of Nurses began its work in Canada in 1897, the nurses spent much of their days just like Darlene Dimsmore, visiting the frail and chronically ill in their homes. Dimsmore and the other home care nurse in Fort Smith visit over one hundred patients on a regular basis, roughly 4 to 5 per cent of the town's population. And this doesn't include the twenty or so residents of the long-term care facility. The nurses facilitate the discharge of patients from hospital early. They also prevent the need for hospital care by picking up problems in a timely fashion, like Mary's acute bronchitis, and nipping them in the bud.

Will Godot Arrive before a National Home Care Program?

Home care is touted as the newest flower for Canada's health care system, but its roots run deep. Before there were any hospitals, there was care at home. Although Roy Romanow's royal commission raised hopes with his recommendation for limited coverage for home care services, Justice Emmett Hall's royal commission had recommended full public coverage forty years earlier. It looks like the permanently governing Liberals in Ottawa are likely to mandate only limited amounts of post–acute care home care coverage.

We have known for years that many acute care patients really need home care. But the knee-jerk policy response has usually been to recommend building more long-term care beds. There is no question that some people do need the comprehensive care of a long-term care facility. However, most continuing-care patients simply need more care in their own homes. If their own homes are not suitable, they can often get the care they need in a non-institutional supportive living arrangement.

This chapter outlines examples of programs that demonstrate the capacity of home care to reduce pressure on acute care and long-term care facilities. We examine these programs from three perspectives:

1. Diverting patients who would otherwise need to be admitted to hospital
2. Facilitating the early discharge of patients from acute care
3. Providing ongoing management of complex patients with chronic illness

Almost all of these patient groups tend to have chronic illnesses. But not all patients in the first two categories have such complicated problems that they need continuing-care services beyond a few weeks. Patients in the third category do have significant chronic illnesses and associated disabilities that prevent them from performing normal activities of daily living, or ADLs. This means that in addition to management of chronic illnesses such as heart disease and diabetes, they also need hands-on assistance with tasks such as dressing, eating, and toileting. The chronic care model, which we introduced in chapter 5, will be especially useful in developing service frameworks for these people.

Diverting Patients from Hospital

John P.'s parents were going out of their minds in paradise. They live in White Rock, one hour south of bustling Vancouver. It has some of

Canada's nicest weather and most beautiful scenery. Like other parents, they had heard the old saw "small kids, small problems; big kids, big problems," but they were totally unprepared for their son's bizarre behaviour. He spent most of his time in his room listening to music but could occasionally be heard screaming obscenities. He was prone to getting into arguments over the dinner table and then sulking for days. He had been sent home from school three times that term for being verbally abusive to his teachers; the last incident had resulted in a suspension.

Fortunately, John's school guidance counsellor had attended a presentation from the Fraser Health Region's Early Psychiatric Intervention program. She got in touch with Dr. Karen Tee, a psychologist who is the program co-ordinator with the EPI program. Within twenty-four hours, John met with the social worker. Soon after, he saw a psychiatrist, who diagnosed John with early schizophrenia and prescribed anti-psychotic medication. The team worked with John's school to get him back into the classroom. They were able to decrease his workload and extend some deadlines to permit him to decrease his stress. For clients who cannot continue in their own school, EPI runs a day program that includes education at Surrey Memorial Hospital. All the while, EPI educates the family about their child's problems. It also connects them with support groups made up of other parents who have experienced the trauma of a child with a serious mental illness. Not all stories are as bright as John's, but only one-quarter of EPI's community-referred patients ever need hospital care. Dr. Tee hopes that this proportion will continue to shrink if their education efforts in the community are successful and they can get referrals sooner.

Canada has considerable experience with innovation in psychiatric services. In 1992, Toronto's Centre for Addiction and Mental Health launched one of the world's original First Episode Psychosis programs. There are early psychosis programs in Halifax, London, Thunder Bay, Calgary, and other Canadian cities.

Home Care When You Need It: The Quick Response Team

In 1987, inspired leadership at the provincial and local level led to the Victoria Health Project, which developed a number of innovative hospital and community partnerships. One of the successful programs launched during this time was the Quick Response Team (QRT). The principle is simple: if sick people can get the care they need outside of a hospital setting, there is usually a win-win situation. It's better for the system to focus its acute care resources on people who really need them, and it's better for a person not to be in hospital if he or she doesn't strictly need to be there. Hospitals are full of nasty antibiotic-resistant bacteria. About 15 per cent of patients over seventy-five years of age develop delirium after admission. Although the symptoms usually abate, some people are left with permanent brain damage. Of course, there are other potential dangers in hospital to which we referred in chapter 3, such as getting the wrong medication.

If the patient meets the criteria for the QRT, extra home care staff can be placed in the home for up to a week or, in special circumstances, even longer. In April 2002, Anne Weicker, a home care nurse with the Vancouver Island Health Authority, had an elderly woman patient, Sarah S., who suffered a fall in her home. Sarah's daughter called Weicker the next morning and Weicker came to see her. After a discussion with Sarah's family doctor, she sent the patient to the emergency department, where she had an X-ray that showed a broken pelvis. Most patients with pelvic fractures do not need hospital care, but they may not be able to perform their own activities of daily living for several days. After the radiologist gave the diagnosis to the family doctor over the telephone, Weicker spoke with the doctor and then mobilized extra home care resources for four days. With assistance from Sarah's daughter, this extra home care allowed Sarah to stay home and avoid a hospital admission.

The QRT concept seemed to work in Victoria, and also when it was tested in Windsor.[1] It has spread across the country to Calgary, Saskatoon, and a number of cities in Ontario.

In London, the local home care agency has been implementing a pilot project, Integrating Physician Services in the Home, or IPSITH, for the past three years.[2] The IPSITH program better links family doctors and the home care system. The program hired a nurse practitioner, Joan Mitchell, who can see patients quickly and assist family doctors in their management.

One patient, a seventy-two-year-old woman, was referred by her family doctor for a flare-up of her congestive heart failure. Within hours, she was receiving oxygen therapy, and intravenous diuretics were helping to mobilize excess fluid out of her body. Over the course of six days, she had three physician visits and eleven nursing visits (including six visits from Mitchell). She also had a personal support worker for two hours a day. Her daughter stayed in the house the first night. By the second day, the patient was feeling well enough that she was able to sit up and play Nintendo. Her favourite game? Dr. Mario, of course!

Across Canada, thousands of patients are hospitalized every year simply to receive intravenous antibiotics for skin infections, pneumonias, and other conditions that otherwise could be treated outside of hospital. Other patients return to emergency rooms several times a day to get their intravenous medication. However, these patients can safely receive their therapy in their own homes or in community settings. An Israeli study showed that home intravenous antibiotic treatment saved over $3,000 (US) per patient compared with hospital therapy.[3] One study from Vancouver showed that the Ministry of Health saved $7,000 for each patient who received outpatient intravenous antibiotic therapy compared with similar patients who were hospitalized.[4]

Sixty-eight-year-old Selma B. scraped her left forearm when she fell on a rug in her east-end Toronto apartment. After a couple of days, the area became swollen, tender, and warm. By the time she went to see her family physician, Dr. Stephen Tulk, at the South Riverdale Community Health Centre, her left arm was twice the size of her right. At this stage, oral antibiotics wouldn't be enough—she needed intravenous medication to stem the infection. Dr. Tulk fortunately had another option besides referral to hospital. He referred Selma to the wound care and intravenous care clinic in the East End Community Health Centre.

Since 2002, Calea, a home care products company, has run the clinic for Toronto's home care agency, the Community Care Access Centre. Laurie Dryburgh, a nurse in the clinic, administers Selma's medication, and after fifteen minutes she's ready to go home. She will have to come back twice a day for at least three days, but she can continue to stay at home, help her disabled husband, and enjoy her grandchildren, who live nearby. It's a lot easier to come here than to the closest ER, and a lot less stressful.

Dryburgh's next patient is Georgio T., an eighty-two-year-old retired construction worker. He has had a festering wound (venous stasis ulcer) on his right leg for ten years. It has been treated with a variety of therapies over the years, but none has successfully healed the area. However, in the two months that he has been attending the clinic at the health centre, the wound has nearly healed.

In 2000, there were over 23,000 hospital admissions in Canada for skin infections and wounds.[5] These conditions require nearly 600 hospital beds, as many as would be found in a medium-sized city. However, many of these patients could get care at home, and others could have had their hospitalization averted if they had received better care earlier.

Dr. Gary Sibbald, a professor of dermatology at the University of Toronto, is an international leader in wound care education and the director of the International Interdisciplinary Wound Care Course at the University of Toronto. Hundreds of health care professionals have been through Dr. Sibbald's course, including staff with the Calgary and Winnipeg regional health authorities. Increasingly, health care organizations are realizing that having wound care specialists can greatly speed patients' discharge from hospital and can often preclude the need for hospitalization.

Facilitating the Early Discharge of Patients from Acute Care

In the late 1980s, the Ontario Ministry of Health started providing small monetary rewards to hospitals that had higher severity of illness. Savvy administrators scrutinized their data and identified newborn infants and their mothers as having the lowest "resource intensity weighting" (RIW). Soon, it was women and children first. That is, hospitals were sending new mothers and their children out of hospital first. However, there was initially little co-ordination with home care services. Several other provinces followed suit. The result in Ontario was a dramatic increase in the number of newborns who needed to be readmitted to hospital.[6]

However, not all early maternal discharge programs had problems. A review of early discharge programs in the US shows that while some early discharge programs are associated with an increased risk of readmission, others are not.[7] A study of over 100,000 births in Ohio showed that readmissions had actually fallen, while maternal lengths of stay were reduced by 27 per cent.[8]

Gradually, researchers have concluded that early maternal discharge is safe for mothers and newborns when there are community services available to provide care. What a bolt of common sense! If someone is technically an alternate-level-of-care, or ALC, patient, then by definition he or she does not require hospital care but does need some care.

By 1999 in Alberta, 99 per cent of new mothers were being telephoned by home care staff and 93 per cent had at least one home visit. The result—no increase in readmissions.[9] Dr. Patrick Pierse, an Edmonton pediatrician and former president of the Canadian Pediatric Society, notes that the early discharge program appeared to work in his city because of the provision of telephone advice and public health nurse home visits.

Moving Ahead with Early Discharge Programs

Gradually, researchers have concluded that early discharge can provide better care and reduce overall health care costs in certain situations.[10] An early discharge program for stroke patients at Montreal's Royal Victoria Hospital not only saved six days of hospital care per patient, but also improved patients' ability to perform their activities of daily living. The program also better reintegrated these patients into their family and community roles.[11]

We met Saint John, New Brunswick, nurse Lois Ozkaynak in chapter 4. She works with the province's innovative Extra-Mural Hospital program. Today she pulls up to the house of Aidan R. The seventeen-year-old fell off his all-terrain vehicle and sustained several serious fractures in his left leg. He had surgery for the implantation of six steel rods and, in the old days, he would have been in hospital for weeks. But he was home within days. Ozkaynak checks his wounds and then, satisfied with the healing, gives him new bandages. Aidan is happy to be at home instead of in hospital. His father is especially pleased to have his son at home and notes that it is a lot easier to deal with Ozkaynak than with dozens of different staff in the hospital.

The Northwest Territories employs three nurses and a part-time medical director to monitor the care of its residents in Edmonton hospitals. As soon as they can be treated back in the Territories, either in hospital or at home, they are airlifted back. The Ministry of Health concludes that the rapid repatriation of its residents saves money and permits people to better recover closer to home.

Providing Ongoing Management of
Complex Patients with Chronic Illness

From San Francisco to Edmonton:
Comprehensive Care for the Frail Elderly

Sam Wong came to San Francisco nearly eighty years ago as a young boy. He worked in his uncle's laundry and then toiled in Oakland's shipyards until he retired. Now he lives in a small room in the city's historic North Beach neighbourhood. He suffers from diabetes, congestive heart failure, and arthritis in both hips. Starting two years ago, he began to have trouble with his short-term memory. Fortunately, a sister-in-law was already part of the On Lok program for all-inclusive care of the elderly, so his niece contacted an intake worker and soon he was attending the Jade Centre on Bush Street.

Four days a week, an On Lok van picks Wong up from his small apartment and takes him to the Jade Centre. At the centre, one of seven that On Lok runs, health promotion is the centrepiece of programming. The staff make sure that each participant engages in graded exercise, eats a nutritious diet, and is intellectually and socially stimulated to his or her full potential. The staff also rigorously monitor their clients' chronic conditions to catch acute flare-ups before they have become serious. Instead of only bringing services to people's houses, On Lok brings people to its services. Program participants must come to one of these centres at least once a week. Most come at least three times.

The Cantonese words *on lok geui* mean "abode of peace and happiness" and were chosen to reflect the philosophy of this program. On Lok SeniorHealth opened its non-profit operation for the frail elderly in 1973 with a day health centre located in a renovated nightclub in downtown San Francisco. Today On Lok serves nine hundred high-risk seniors, whose average age is eighty-three. Clients of this program are very frail. Three-quarters of On Lok's participants are incontinent, and over 60 per cent have some type of cognitive problem, mostly Alzheimer's disease. In addition, many are at special risk because of poverty and isolation. Sixty per cent of participants live alone, and 40 per cent are poor enough to qualify for SSI (Supplemental Security Income). Located as the centre is in San Francisco's Chinatown, most of On Lok's enrollees are Chinese, although Filipinos, Italians, other Caucasians, and blacks also use its services.

One of On Lok's distinguishing characteristics is its multidisciplinary team, consisting of doctors, nurse practitioners, nurses, social workers, audiologists, podiatrists, physiotherapists, speech therapists, and non-professional staff. On Lok works very closely with its clients and families to develop advance care directives. Its founder, Mary Louise Ansak, notes that it is frequently the program's drivers who have the opportunity to talk to the participants about their wishes for care should they fall acutely ill. Just as a stranger will often confide his innermost thoughts to a taxi driver, so On Lok's clients sometimes choose one of their drivers to engage in such weighty discussions. The drivers have become key team members in discussions of participants' desires for acute care.

On Lok became the prototype for PACE programs (Programs of All-Inclusive Care for the Elderly). Now there are over eighty.* The model appears to work. PACE participants' care typically costs 5 per cent less than traditional care[12] and they use a dramatically different array of services. On Lok spends only 22 per cent of its dollars on hospitals, long-term care facilities (LTCFs), lab tests, X-rays, medications, and medical specialists. This leaves almost four-fifths of the program's dollars to be spent on day programs, home care, and family doctors. The program's participants use less hospital care than the average for the entire US over-65 population, even though participants are very old and very frail.[13]

In 1996, the Edmonton Capital Regional Health Authority opened a PACE replicate program—the Comprehensive Home Option of

---

* For more information on PACE in the US, see http://www.natlpaceassn.org. For On Lok, see http://www.onlok.org.

Integrated Care for the Elderly (CHOICE). Now there are five day centres, including one specifically for people with mental health problems, and approximately four hundred participants. CHOICE appears to manage patients at a slightly lower level of personal care dependency than On Lok. The average age of participants is seventy-nine, with almost half of the participants eventually being discharged to LTCFs while approximately half die in the program. On Lok focuses on patients who would otherwise require an LTCF, but CHOICE also targets those elderly who are medically unstable.

The Good Samaritans, an Edmonton-based non-profit society, started the first CHOICE centre and runs two in total, while the Capital Care Group, a branch of the Capital Health Authority, runs the other two. Most of the staff originally worked in institutions, so they are given an approximately one-month reorientation to community care. The home care workers attached to the program work both in patients' homes and in the day centres. The first shift spends the morning in the community and the afternoon in a day centre, while the second shift starts the afternoon in the day centre (where they receive the hand-off from the first shift) and then finishes in the evening in patients' homes.

Each centre has a nurse practitioner, as well as physicians, and up to six beds for subacute care where patients' minor episodic problems can be managed. If a participant needs intravenous care for a couple of days, it can be had in the CHOICE facility. After hours, a nurse is on call with a physician backup. CHOICE hasn't been as rigorously evaluated as the PACE model in the US, but patients are much less likely to end up in hospital after they join the program.[14]

A few years after Edmonton, Calgary developed its version of PACE—the Comprehensive Community Care, or C3, program. It operates out of an LTCF in southwest Calgary and provides care to approximately one hundred frail seniors. Like CHOICE and On Lok, the day centre is the focus, but C3 also provides home care and is available to participants twenty-four hours per day.

Home Care for the Homeless

Paul H. was known as the "mammoth man." As he roamed the streets of downtown Toronto, he wore all the clothes he had, including several coats, giving him the appearance of a woolly mammoth. Paul was very uncommunicative, and often intoxicated. Over time, a worker at a downtown community centre discovered that Paul was almost blind. He convinced Paul to come to the Annex at Seaton House.

Seaton House is Canada's largest men's hostel and has been housing the homeless for over seventy years in downtown Toronto. Since 1996, the staff at the Annex Harm Reduction Program has been dealing with people like Paul who are chronically homeless and who also suffer from alcoholism.

Up until about ten years ago, the mantra for staff working with people with alcoholism or other substance abuse problems was "sobriety forever." But the AIDS epidemic in the intravenous drug community finally forced providers and governments to think outside of the box. At Seaton House's Annex, they started providing alcohol, in a controlled fashion, to their alcoholic clients. As a result, Paul didn't have to agree to quit drinking to start getting the care he needed. Every hour, he lined up with some of the 140 other residents of the Annex to get 5 ounces of wine.

Now that he had a roof over his head, Paul began to trust the Annex staff. As they peeled off layers and layers of clothing, they discovered that the "woolly mammoth" was in fact emaciated and suffering from a variety of skin problems. Dr. Tomislav Svoboda, Seaton House's medical director, and the other health care staff helped clear up his skin. Dr. Svoboda then worked with Paul to try to get him to do something about his eyes. After eight months at Seaton House, Paul finally agreed to surgery and was admitted to St. Michael's Hospital, where one of his cataracts was removed. Back at Seaton House, when the patch was removed from his eye, Paul was able to see for the first time in years. He no longer required a wheelchair and he started to hope again. "Hope changes everything," says Art Manuel, the burly former longshoreman who runs the Annex program.

Manuel says that the shelter system's old abstinence policy didn't work. Hardcore alcoholics knew they couldn't drink in the shelter so they usually stayed out on the street, where they would get into more trouble. Men would guzzle down their last alcohol just before entering the centre, presenting a severely intoxicated problem for staff. Expressing the philosophy of harm reduction, Manuel asks rhetorically, "Could it be any worse to let them drink inside the shelter in a controlled fashion?"

Manuel notes that the alternative to a warm bed at Seaton House isn't cheap. It's usually a $900 ham sandwich. Manuel explains that people like Paul used to run around in circles between the police, courts, ambulances, emergency departments, and hospitals. For example, they would fall on the street and an ambulance would be called. At the emergency room, they would get X-rays, maybe a CAT scan, blood tests, and lots of time with doctors and nurses. After $900 had been spent on their care, Art says, they would be given a ham sandwich and dropped off at Seaton House. They would eat the sandwich then leave the shelter because they couldn't drink there.

Now, someone like Paul can receive shelter but still drink as well. Not surprisingly, Manuel reports that almost every man cuts back his drinking when he enters the shelter. He claims that these men use alcohol as a coping mechanism for their unhappy lives. Stable housing reduces their stress and they don't need to drink as much.

Manuel says that it is important to differentiate this group from other homeless people. Two-thirds of the people who come to Seaton House are in and out of the shelter system very quickly, usually within six weeks. Their homelessness is due to temporary events like house fires or job loss. About one-quarter of the people who come through Seaton House have had frequent shelter use in the previous twelve months but have also found other temporary options for themselves, such as "couch surfing." Finally, 10 per cent of the people who come through Seaton House have been only on the street or in shelters for years. Most of these people have both mental health and substance abuse problems. And because of their lifestyles, they usually have significant medical problems. Dr. Svoboda reports that before coming to Seaton House, the average Annex resident has forty times more ER visits per year than the average Toronto resident.

A Capital Idea!

Wendy Muckle, whom we met earlier, is the director of the Ottawa Inner City Health Project, which includes all of the downtown Ottawa shelters. She notes that their first goal is usually to get their clients to stop using non-beverage alcohol. She notes that some are drinking up to twelve bottles of cooking sherry a day with a chaser of mouthwash. They often need 10 ounces of wine or more per hour just to prevent seizures from alcohol withdrawal.

If the clients want to get off alcohol entirely, they are given 50 mg of chlordiazepoxide to start and then choose their own dose over the next few days. The clients have to accept medical care, because that is the purpose of the program. However, the staff do not force them to have treatment for their mental health and addiction problems. Eighty per cent of these people do have severe and persistent mental illness.

Muckle remembers one client who was dubbed the "million-dollar man." In the month prior to his entering the program, he was in a constant drunken stupor. He made thirty ER visits along with multiple visits to community health centres. He was also at each shelter every day. He had a problem with his shoulder that had lasted for years, but he had had five shoulder X-rays that month alone. Muckle estimates that he was using hundreds of dollars of services every day, perhaps a million dollars over the previous five years. Once he was allowed to drink in the shelter, he stopped using other services. Another patient had forty ambulance trips to hospital because of seizures in an eight-month period. Since entering the program, he has been seizure free.

An evaluation of the project is glowingly positive.[15] All the clients report decreasing their drinking when they join the program. And overall the project saves roughly $1,000 for each person it enrols. The clients dramatically reduce their use of hospitals, ERs, and ambulances. They also have far fewer interactions with the criminal justice system. If clients do need to be hospitalized, the project takes them back as soon as they don't need acute care. As Wendy Muckle states with pride, "Our clients don't have ALC days!"

ACTing Up in Ottawa

Some cynics see the deinstitutionalization of psychiatric patients, which started in the 1960s, as the first failure of health reform. The concept seemed to make scientific and economic sense. At that time there were tens of thousands of Canadians who had spent years, sometimes decades, living in large psychiatric hospitals. The new anti-psychotic drugs developed in the 1950s usually relieved patients of their hallucinations, delusions, and subsequent bizarre and occasionally dangerous behaviour. Advocates for community care claimed that with the appropriate housing and community resources, these patients could move into the community and live productive lives. However, deinstitutionalization went only halfway in most communities. Patients were discharged. The psychiatric hospitals did have outpatient programs available to treat their former residents. But we didn't develop the housing and the community programs to stabilize people in their communities. As a result, researchers soon documented the so-called revolving-door syndrome, where patients were treated and then discharged without proper follow-up. Soon they would be back in hospital again, only to be discharged back into a community without adequate resources.

Starting in the 1980s, several communities began to develop intensive home care programs for the severely mentally ill. These have come to be called assertive community treatment, or ACT, programs. Ten years ago, Dr. Chantal Whelan helped to start the ACT program that runs out of Ottawa's Carlington Community Health Centre, and she couldn't be happier. She realizes that hospitals are necessary for some people at some times, but she says the ACT program permits the flexibility needed to ensure that patients can get the care they need outside of hospital.

Dr. Whelan and Jean Michels, the project co-ordinator, claim there are many advantages to the ACT model. They relate the story of a businessman, Peter S., who developed a severe depression in his early forties that required hospital care. The ACT team worked with Peter and his family to get him out of hospital and since then have worked closely with them to keep him in the community. It hasn't been easy. Peter has a variety of physical problems, including heart disease and diabetes, as well as his depression and chronic brain damage secondary to alcoholism. Dr. Whelan says their approach to insurmountable problems is to "whittle" away at them. The process is remarkably similar to the structured problem-solving described in chapter 5.

They whittled away at Peter's psychiatric problems. They have kept him on medication. He took neuropsychiatric training and got his driver's licence back. They helped him with his disability pension. Then they whittled away at his family problems. They helped Peter's wife with her alcohol problems. The family took some group therapy. Michels has also been helping Peter's teenage daughter and son with their psychiatric and school problems. The result isn't a perfect *Leave It to Beaver* family, but the family is functioning better than it has in years. And Peter has been in hospital only once, for three days, in the nearly four years he has been part of the ACT program.

The ACT teams are real teams. Carlington's includes, besides Dr. Whelan (who is half-time) and Jean Michels, three other nurses, one addictions counsellor, a part-time psychologist, a vocational rehabilitation worker, a social worker, and a consumer representative who does peer support. The team start their day with a one-hour meeting, and one of the team is always on call.

ACT teams have proven their utility. Dr. Leonard Stein, a Wisconsin psychiatrist, pioneered the original ACT team in the 1970s and elegantly demonstrated their effectiveness.[16] A study of one of the original Canadian ACT programs showed that ACT clients were more likely to stay out of hospital and enjoyed a better quality of life.[17] Dr. Donald Wasylenki, chair of the Department of Psychiatry at the University of Toronto, has helped establish ACT teams and evaluated them. He claims that there is more good evidence to support ACT teams than almost any other psychiatric intervention.

"Preventive" Home Care: Frill or Fundamental?

Over the years, there has been much controversy about the cost-effectiveness of home care services. And there has been a specific controversy about whether small amounts of home care services such as bathing and light housekeeping twice a week are a frill or whether they fulfill a preventive function.

Dr. Marcus Hollander, a researcher in Victoria, found a natural experiment that provided some compelling evidence. In 1994, the province of British Columbia instituted a policy to cut from coverage those home care patients who had low levels of service. But the regional health authorities implemented the policies differently. This allowed Hollander to study what happened to clients living in areas with cuts and without cuts to their service. It turned out there was little difference in the first year, but by the second year, home care patients had greatly reduced their use of hospitals and long-term care facilities.[18]

Interviews with people who had had their services cut revealed that while some coped (through family, paid care, or simply improving function), 27 per cent specifically reported suffering hardship as a result of the cuts. One sadly reported, "I just don't clean as often, just a little at a time. I don't have any company visiting because of the effort. Many things are left undone." Not surprisingly, 60 per cent of this group reported that their health was worse in the year after their service cuts.

Hollander pled with decision-makers to make policies about home care by "meaningfully embracing evidence-based decision making." Apparently, Ontario health minister Tony Clement didn't read the report, because within the month, he instructed the province's home care agencies to cut funding to preventive home care and focus resources on post–hospital discharge patients.

There is another BC example showing the importance of prevention. Dr. Nancy Hall of Vancouver found that adding six to eight public health nurse visits to the first few months of home care service translated into 40 per cent less likelihood of death or admission to an LTCF by the end of three years.[19] If you are sick enough to require ongoing home care services, you are very likely to benefit from a review of your diet, physical activity, and other factors that underlie your health.

Disabilities and Directed Services, *Schnell*!

This chapter has primarily discussed elderly people with progressive disabilities associated with serious chronic illness. But there are significant differences between the needs of this group and of younger people with fairly fixed long-term disabilities. For example, a twenty-five-year-old with paralysis secondary to a lower spinal-cord injury today looks forward to forty or fifty years of future life. Such a person has needs different from those of an eighty-seven-year-old with Alzheimer's disease and congestive heart failure.

In 1994, Germany introduced a policy of offering the disabled of all ages the choice of money or services. People's needs are assessed and then they are offered home care services, long-term care (LTC), or they can take a cash payout, which varies according to three levels of disability.[20] The cash payments are about one-half to two-thirds of the value of the home care services that a person could choose instead. The cash can be used for any purpose, but recipients who choose to purchase home care services have to do so from an approved list of providers or from family members. In practice, most of the money is used to compensate family caregivers.

The German policy is politically very popular and has been retained and expanded by the Social Democrats even though it was introduced by the Christian Democrats. The costs have actually been slightly less than originally forecast, partly because more recipients than expected have chosen the self-directed option. Now more resources are being used for community care instead of for long-term care facilities. Forecasts of the number of disabled and of the uptake for the program have been quite accurate. Similar estimates are available on the numbers of disabled in Canada.

The US has had a fair bit of experience with so-called consumer-directed programs.[21] Some provinces here have small pilot programs that provide resources to younger disabled persons, but this model has not become mainstream for the elderly.* This model deserves more consideration, and Germany's example shows that it can be very successful.

Putting It All Together

Home care is not a frill by any means. It is an essential component of the system. Without home care, hospitals and long-term care institutions could not possibly cope with the numbers of clients who would fall through the cracks into their beds. It's about time that the federal and provincial governments ensured that home care services are available to all Canadians who need them.

Your Community and Home Care

- Can your community prevent people from being hospitalized unnecessarily for conditions that do not require hospital care?
- Does your community have a quick response team that can mobilize home care resources immediately to avert inappropriate admissions?

---

* For example, see the Individualized Funding Project Web site, British Columbia Coalition of People with Disabilities, http://www.bccpd.bc.ca/if/index.html.

- Does your community have community intravenous and wound care?
- Does your community offer preventive home care services (such as housekeeping, meal preparation) to frail people who do not need ongoing professional attention?
- Can your hospitals organize home care services quickly so they can discharge patients as soon as they no longer require acute care?
- Does your community offer PACE-type programs so the frail elderly who are dependent for their personal care have an alternative to long-term care?
- Does your community have "wet shelters" that provide emergency and rehabilitative housing to people suffering from alcoholism?
- Does your community offer early psychosis intervention to prevent psychiatric hospitalizations?
- Does your community offer assertive community treatment programs to provide ongoing maintenance for persons with serious persistent psychiatric illness?
- Does your province offer consumer-directed care that allows home care recipients to hire and direct their own care providers?

Chapter 7

Long-term Care

Jane D. had always considered herself independent, but she was losing confidence rapidly. She was born in northern Ontario just after the First World War. Although her father survived the trenches of France, he didn't make it through the epidemic of Spanish flu in 1919. Jane helped her mother run a boarding home during the Depression and then married a local boy just before he went overseas to fly a Spitfire in the Battle of Britain. He didn't make it back. Jane moved to Toronto, went to teachers' college, and taught grades 3 and 4 in a north-end primary school for nearly forty years. She lived in a small house not far from the school and never remarried. She always said her pupils were her children.

Jane prided herself on her good health. She didn't smoke, didn't drink, and always took a thirty-minute walk after breakfast—for her constitution. However, at her eightieth birthday, she seemed to have trouble remembering the names of her favourite ex-students. Within a couple of months there were other troubling episodes where she left a stove burner turned on. Her family doctor assessed Jane and then referred her to a neurologist. The diagnosis: early Alzheimer's disease.

Jane's niece helped as much as she could, but she had her own family and lived an hour away. She couldn't keep up her aunt's house anymore—then there was the garden. Jane's house wasn't suitable for someone developing cognitive problems. Her bedroom and bathroom were on the second floor. The laundry was down a dangerous flight of stairs in the basement. After fifty years at the same address, Jane had to move. Eventually, Jane and her niece began to think about her moving into a nursing home.

As described in the previous chapter, home care has a large capacity to meet the health needs of people who don't need hospital care but cannot perform their own activities of daily living. However, as people deteriorate further, housing becomes an important issue for many seniors. In the past, the only place where people could get assistance with personal care was in a long-term care institution. But there are an increasing number of housing options for people who can no longer stay in their homes.

This chapter discusses residential care for the elderly. There are new options available, variously called "retirement homes" or "assisted living centres." They offer the potential to increase the independence of frail seniors, but the devil is in the details. And there are a lot of details for this policy option. Finally, the chapter discusses long-term care institutions and highlights some new models that show tremendous promise to revitalize the lives of the seriously disabled elderly.

Supporting Assisted Living: How the Prince of Denmark Became the Pauper of Des Moines

In the 1980s, Denmark faced a situation similar to the one Canada faces today. The numbers of elderly people were increasing rapidly. There were already many elderly people living in long-term care facilities but there were incessant demands to build more. However, Denmark bucked the trends and became an international beacon for care of the elderly.[1] In 1988, Denmark passed legislation limiting the construction of new long-term care facilities. In 1997, the parliament passed legislation that directed that all new seniors' accommodation must have at least a sitting room, a kitchen, and a bathroom in addition to a bedroom.

Skaevinge, a small community north of Copenhagen, was the inspiration for the Danish policy. Starting in 1984, Skaevinge renovated its nursing home and changed the home's function. The building's rooms were changed into full apartments for assisted living, and it became the heart of an expanded system of community care, including twenty-four-hour home care, elderly day care, and rehabilitation. The nursing home guaranteed staff job security and retrained them to provide home care.

The Danish government removed perverse incentives that promoted institutionalization. The elderly would no longer have to be admitted to a nursing home to get coverage for personal care, medications, and supplies. Now home care clients got these goods and services as well. Health and social services are now provided according to need wherever people reside.

The Danish policy seems to have been very successful. From 1987 to 1997, the number of nursing home beds decreased by 30 per cent despite an increase in the number of elderly people. Over that period there was a 250 per cent increase in the number of supportive housing units. Now almost one-quarter of Denmark's seniors get some home care. The health of the Danish elderly improved and people were more satisfied with their health and health care. In addition, overall Danish health care costs (as a percentage of GDP) plateaued, as have the costs for home care and long-term care. The Danes demonstrated that it is possible to provide good care for a frail elderly population without relying upon traditional long-term care institutions. They also proved that a universal home care program can be affordable.

The Danish notion of combining supportive housing with enhanced home care spread to North America. Oregon was one of the first jurisdictions to jump, and soon "assisted living" became the darling of corporate America as well as of policy-makers. Assisted living grew rapidly in the US during the 1990s. The idea was seductive. Assisted living centres weren't nursing homes, so they didn't have to meet often onerous regulations. Plus residents could just pick the services they needed from an à la carte menu. Choice! Didn't it sound wonderful?

If someone needed help with meals, they could just pay for food. If they needed help with bathing, they could just pay for that. Of course, over time, more and more tenants become frail and the assisted living facilities become unregulated long-term care facilities. And the bill soon adds up to thousands of dollars of extra charges per month. The opportunity to make big bucks drew large corporations, especially real estate companies, into the market. However, in the late 1990s, a spate of investigative reports highlighting horror stories in assisted living led to a crash of the market and the bankruptcy of many assisted living companies.[2]

An Illusion of Safety

One of the major problems with assisted living facilities is that people believe that they are living in a safe place that can offer them assistance if they need it. But that isn't necessarily the case. Assisted living facilities are supposed to offer twenty-four-hour supervision, but this doesn't have to be a nurse. Sometimes it's a janitor who can't speak English.

In the early morning of January 5, 2003, eighty-three-year-old Arthur Dowling suffered a paralyzing stroke at the Quest Assisted Living Centre in downtown Winnipeg.[3] His daughter Donna phoned his room repeatedly that day from her British Columbia home, but there was no answer. Finally, unable to contact her father at 8:30 in the evening, Donna phoned the Quest front desk and demanded that they call an ambulance for her father. A few days later he was dead from a stroke. His daughter thinks her father might well have died in any event. But she is greatly troubled that her father wasn't checked at all that day—she understood that there was a mechanism in place to check up on residents who missed a meal. Arthur missed all three that day. She also can't believe that there is no specific regulation of such facilities in Manitoba. As in other provinces, Manitoba does not regulate independent living centres as they do long-term care facilities.

Housing the Frail or Fleecing the Helpless

The concept of assisted or supportive living is basically a good one. It seems to work in Denmark, and some places in Canada, as we will soon discover. But the solid notion that we should separate housing from health care has become a business opportunity to charge residents for uncovered services. In some facilities, a resident could pay as much as $1,800 a year for housekeeping as well as $12,000 for meals, bathing, medication management, bathing, foot care, blood pressure monitoring, incontinence management, and other services. If a resident needs a companion or nursing care, this could increase the total by $20,000 or more. Of course, all of this is on top of monthly rents, which start at around $1,200 but run past $3,000.[4] Clearly, this particular model of supportive care is not a general solution to the housing problems of the frail elderly.

In some provinces, residents of assisted living centres are supposed to be able to get their nursing and other personal care from home care. But the provinces have passed decisions about these policies to regional health authorities. And, as revealed by Marcus Hollander's study of preventive home care in BC, there is almost as much patchwork within as between provinces these days. Didn't somebody say something about a *Canadian* system?

There is much talk in this policy area of the moral need to "level the playing field" for coverage. Denmark levelled coverage up. In that country, the elderly in other accommodations have the same generous coverage for medication, supplies, and personal and support care as those living in long-term care facilities. However, in Canada, we have tended to level the playing field down. If a person is not resident within a long-term care facility, he or she is considered home care client and may have to pay privately.

Denmark, like other northern European countries, also has a commitment to social solidarity through economic equity that is, shall we say, not matched by many governments in North America. The Danish government constructed a lot of supportive housing, while Canada's national housing program was canned in 1993. In Canada there is a shortage of affordable housing for seniors and other low-income groups.[5] Without suitable housing and with significant extra-billing levied by facility operators, assisted living has morphed from a dream into a financial nightmare.

There are many places in Canada like the Quest. Some cater to a high-end clientele, while others seem almost Dickensian. These facilities do have to meet general public health standards for cleanliness. But there is often no supervision of the care that might be provided because people are supposed to direct their own care.

However, people in these facilities seem to be pretty frail after all. Professor Gina Bravo at the University of Sherbrooke concludes that while healthier than their counterparts in licensed facilities, assisted living residents still need a lot of care. However, the facilities have little capability of attending to them.[6] In particular, the staff–patient ratio is eight times higher in licensed than in non-licensed facilities. People are supposed to be *independent*, remember? The basic notion of supportive or assisted living is still sound—if we could make it look more like Denmark.

The Good Samaritans Rescue Supportive Living

Jesus' parable in Luke provided the inspiration for the Edmonton-based Good Samaritan Society. Good Samaritan started with a 1949 donation from Leduc farmer Gottlieb Wedman to be used to help provide care for the elderly. The Good Sam, as it is often called, opened its first chronic care hospital in 1955, and it opened a community living facility for the developmentally delayed in the 1970s. But the renewal of the organization began in the late 1980s when the organization was discussing the renovation of a two-hundred-bed nursing home. The Good Samaritans have been involved with a number of very innovative projects for the elderly, including two of the sites for Edmonton's CHOICE program described in the last chapter, and the Oregon model of assisted living inspired several within the organization.

The Good Sams opened Wedman House in Edmonton in 1994, one of the first examples of supportive housing in Canada. On the property there are smaller units, each with five bedrooms for people with dementia who are relatively well physically. The Good Sams provide home care nursing as well as the attendants in the units. The staff are cross-trained in personal care, housekeeping, and maintenance to make it easier to establish relationships with the residents. There is partial coverage for medication, supplies, and equipment, which are provided free of charge in long-term care facilities.

The society presently has facilities in Edmonton, Stony Plain, Spruce Grove, Pincher Creek, Hinton, and Medicine Hat. And facilities are being planned or built in Evansburg, Lethbridge, Rocky Mountain House, and Lacombe, Alberta, as well as in Kelowna, Penticton, and Gibsons, British Columbia.

Victoria and Toronto

Since 2001, Anne Weicker, whom we met in chapter 6, has been the home care nurse attached to St. Francis Manor by the Sea. St. Francis is an old mansion on Dallas Road in Victoria overlooking the Strait of Juan de Fuca and the Olympic Mountains. Anne provides nursing services to all eleven residents. The Vancouver Island Health Authority also provides home support workers from 8:00 a.m. until noon and from 6:00 p.m. until 10:00 p.m. These workers assist residents with bathing and personal hygiene. They help the residents get out of bed and get dressed in the morning and help them get to bed at night. The health authority also contracts with the operators, Carol-Anne and Gerard Sullivan, to provide three meals a day and twenty-four-hour monitoring of the residents. The health authority subsidizes the rents for residents to make St. Francis affordable for all.* The

---

* Residents pay up to 70 per cent of after-tax income, leaving the most destitute with a minimum of $300 per month for incidental expenses.

residents do have to pay for their own medications and supplies, although BC has much better coverage for these items than most other provinces.

By the way, Jane D. was also able to get the assistance she needed in Toronto. She now lives at the Ewart Angus Home, which is run by Senior Peoples' Resources in North Toronto (SPRINT). SPRINT is a twenty-year-old non-profit agency that provides a wide range of community and home support services in North Toronto to seniors and people with cognitive and physical disabilities. The Ewart Angus Home is for seniors with early to mid-stage Alzheimer's or other dementias. There are four units, each with five bedrooms. Every bedroom has its own three-piece bathroom, and there is a large communal living room and family-style kitchen.

The Ontario Ministry of Health supportive housing program bases accommodation costs on market rent for similar apartments. They usually cost $600 to $1,200 per month, and seniors with low incomes are eligible for a subsidy that limits rents to 30 per cent of income. The Ontario Ministry of Health provides funding (approximately $25,000 per year per resident) to SPRINT for the personal care and housekeeping required by the residents. The local home care agency, the Toronto Community Care Access Centre, provides the professional nursing services. Unfortunately, there are long waiting lists for subsidized units.[7]

Restrained Mercy

Frances Lankin was Ontario minister of health from 1991 to 1993. She was well regarded by all parties in the legislature and is now the president of the United Way of Greater Toronto. Confident in her bearing, Lankin is the last person one would expect to have problems negotiating the health care system. However, in the fall of 2000, when she was the NDP health critic in the provincial legislature, she met her match.

At that time, her eighty-seven-year-old mother, Frances Ollman, was admitted to hospital with a gastrointestinal bleed. Ollman also suffered from dementia and several other health problems. She had a long-standing back problem and preferred to lie on her side. Lankin told the nurses about how to best position her mother before she left the hospital at 11 p.m. However, the following morning Lankin discovered that her mother had been tied to her bed during the night and given medication to sedate her. Evidently, Ollman had used the bathroom, and when she returned to her bed she was laid on her back. When she tried to protest the painful position, she was tied to the bed on her back and given Demerol, a painkiller. She remained "agitated" and then was given Ativan, a sedative. This, not surprisingly, produced delirium, so she was finally given Haldol, an antipsychotic medication.

After Lankin recovered from her shock at what had happened to her mother, she spoke with nursing staff and thought it wouldn't happen again. Imagine her surprise when she arrived the very next morning and found her mother tied down again.

After the hospital admission, Frances Lankin introduced a private member's bill to regulate the use of restraints in hospitals. Ontario had fairly specific legislation concerning the restraint of psychiatric patients and much milder legislation for restraints in long-term care institutions, but nothing for hospitals. Originally, the Ontario Hospital Association opposed the legislation and it died at the end of the legislative session. However, Lankin subsequently negotiated its re-emergence in June 2001 with the other parties and the Ministry of Health. The legislature unanimously passed Bill 135, the Patient Restraints Minimization Act, on June 28, 2001. This was quite a feat because almost no private members' bills ever become law. Ollman eventually died of a stroke in August 2002, at home, surrounded by her family and friends.

Frances Lankin and her family did the best they could to keep their mother out of a long-term care facility partly because they were concerned that the intermittent problems they had with hospitals would become daily events if their mother entered a nursing home. Physical restraints, like the smell of urine, seem to be part of the wallpaper of long-term care. In fact, it doesn't have to be this way. Canada, and specifically Ontario, seems to have among the highest rates of physical restraint of the elderly of any jurisdiction.[8] Ontario chronic care hospitals physically restrain one-third of all their patients daily.[9]

As with Frances Ollman, restraints are both a symptom and a cause of poor-quality health care. If the staff had properly listened to the family about the correct positioning of their mother and if they had passed on the communication properly to the next shift, then Ollman would have been laid on her side, would not have been in pain, and, therefore, would not have required either restraints or medication.

The way we physically restrain the elderly is a damning metaphor for the treatment of elderly people in this country. It's bad for them. It's bad for the staff. And it's bad for the health care system. But it doesn't have to be this way. This section will outline how to provide better long-term care.

From Restraints to Learned Helplessness to Depression: The One-Way Street of Long-term Care

Frances Lankin says she was shocked to learn that health care facilities restrain thousands of Ontario's elderly daily, "not because it's part of their medical treatment, not because they are necessarily a danger to themselves or to anyone else, but because they're old, because they're confused and because the system doesn't know how to respond to the growing challenge of aging."[10]

Most people assume that restraints are good things, like seat belts. However, physical restraints are often applied and then not monitored. This leaves confused and agitated elderly people even more confused and agitated. As they try to escape their bonds, they often injure themselves more severely than if they weren't restrained.[11] A study in the United States found sixty-three cases of strangulation due to restraints, and most had been applied properly.[12]

Among the worst effects is that restraints teach the elderly that they can do nothing for themselves. Like Frances Ollman, they might simply be seeking relief for pain, but they are ignored. Nearly half of all Canadian long-term care residents have pain, and almost one-quarter have daily pain.[13] They find themselves unable to get up to use the bathroom and, as a result, they just wet and soil their beds. It also doesn't take long for the frail elderly to lose muscle tone and mass. Within a few days of being restrained, they may never be able to get themselves out of bed again.

Partly as a result of being restrained, elderly people in long-term care facilities learn to be helpless, and this leads to high rates of depression.[14] Frances Lankin refers to restraints as "an attack on the heart and soul" of the elderly. A bad mood is often contagious, and long-term care staff also tend to burn out and become depressed.[15] This leads to high rates of annual turnover among long-term care staff, which typically run at 20 per cent for nurses and 40 per cent and more for aides.[16] This is devastating for quality of care. Residents value staff continuity because staff assist in the performance of intimate personal tasks. It's no fun continually training different people to help you go to the bathroom. Continuity has also been found to improve health outcomes.[17]

These dysfunctional circles of resident and staff unhappiness knit a fabric of despair that literally chokes the atmosphere of too many long-term care facilities.

Dr. Bill Thomas Wakes Up in Eden

Bill Thomas thought he would be an ER doctor upon graduation from Harvard Medical School. But after finishing his training in family medicine, he started a practice at Chase Memorial Nursing Home in New Berlin, New York. He found that he liked working with the elderly. He also found that there was much work to do. Even though the facility was modern and the staff were well trained and motivated, the residents were miserable. Thomas notes now, "It was painfully obvious to me that they were dying in front of my eyes."

He eventually concluded that nursing home residents suffer from three "plagues"—loneliness, helplessness, and boredom—for which modern medicine has no cure. The elderly are lonely because they usually leave all that has been familiar in their lives, including their pets. They're helpless because they can no longer control their own lives. They have to live their lives according to the institution's timetable. They're bored because they have little meaning in their lives. Thomas was struck by the lack of attention to the nursing home environment considering that most residents spent twenty-four hours within the four walls of the building. Modern zoos painstakingly provide exactly the right setting for their animals.

Thomas thought it was time to create a Garden of Eden, a truly human habitat, for the frail elderly. He and his wife, Judy Meyers-Thomas, a nurse, got a $200,000 grant to improve life for the facility's residents. This project gave rise to Eden Alternative.[18]

Thomas and Meyers, and others at the Chase home, developed the antidotes to the three plagues. Companionship is the antidote to loneliness. Helping others is the antidote to helplessness. And spontaneity is the antidote to boredom. They brought dogs, cats, and birds into the home. Although animals in nursing homes weren't new, they usually didn't live in. The animals became companions—even the most cognitively impaired residents formed relationships with them. They put plants all over the place. They brought in children—not once a year at Christmas, but all year round, through on-site staff day care and permanent liaisons with schools. Staff were retrained. The old management structure, with four levels, was scrapped.

The results were striking. Bill Thomas built evaluation into Eden. Chase residents' medication costs were 38 per cent less than those of another home in the same area, primarily through the decreased use of psychotropic medications. Thomas recounts the tale of a woman who had previously taken Haldol for agitation but who didn't need it after she started to help with the care of birds.

Residents and staff are encouraged to form meaningful relationships at Eden facilities. The staff of a nursing home have a unique workplace—it's someone else's home. Just as the residents thrive with more autonomy, so the staff also flourish when they can control more of their environment, such as their scheduling. "What you find is that as the managers do to the staff, the staff do to the elders," says Thomas. "So if you treat the staff well, the elders will benefit."

Eden North

Walking into the Sherbrooke Community Centre in Saskatoon in winter is like entering an oasis. Outside it's –30 degrees, but inside there are birds, tropical foliage, and smiling faces. Providing the tour is the irrepressible executive director, Suellen Beatty. Beatty came to Sherbrooke in 1987 as the director of nursing. Sherbrooke always considered itself at the leading edge of long-term care and was one of the first homes to call itself resident centred. Now Beatty says it's resident directed.

Sherbrooke was one of the first nursing homes with a residents' council and with residents on the board of directors. Beatty says she was given the best advice from former CEO Ed Marleau, who always said that the staff had to make the mission—"Sherbrooke Community Centre strives to provide an environment that enables residents to live full and abundant lives"—come alive.

In 1994, Beatty took over as CEO at a time of considerable change. The centre had recently completed the construction of a rather traditional four-storey building, which housed 160 residents. Now they were negotiating with Veterans Affairs for a new project, which would house forty veterans. She hired a resident advocate to assist the staff with the transition. One day the advocate told Beatty that she had discovered Bill Thomas's book, *Life Worth Living*. She said that Beatty should just have given her the book to direct her task! Beatty thought they already had created a wonderful human habitat, but after she read Thomas's book, she realized that Sherbrooke had a long way to go.

Sherbrooke started building the Eden Alternative at the end of 1998 when they officially registered with the organization.* But it took until June 2000 to complete the training and, as Beatty claims, the journey never really ends. Now Sherbrooke's vision refers to creating "a rich and diverse habitat where children, plants and animals are a natural part of everyday life."

A middle-aged Native man wheels his chair up to Beatty's office. It's 9:00 a.m. and Bill has come for his daily hug. Beatty throws her arms around his neck and Bill beams. He wasn't always this happy. He suffered a head injury as a young man and had a terrible time living in the community. Home care was spending thousands of dollars per month on his care, but he was always getting into trouble of one sort or another. He was in and out of court and emergency rooms. Now that Bill has been at Sherbrooke for five years, he has completely changed. Beatty says he needed Eden. He needed to be loved and to make a contribution.

Walking through Sherbrooke is like strolling through an indoor city. The second stage of the renovations was finished in 1999 and includes eleven "houses" along the sides of the mall's main street. Off to the left is Poppy Lane, with four houses for veterans. On the right is Bill's house, Green Gables. In the front there is a full kitchen and then a large lounge area. Around the back are the bedrooms. Each house develops its own character and has its own staff. As at Wedman House in Edmonton, the staff are cross-trained as personal care aides, housekeepers, and food service workers. This permits staff to establish strong relationships with their clients. Traditional facilities tend to place boundaries between staff and residents, but Eden and Sherbrooke encourage such bonding.

Sherbrooke's results with Eden have been spectacular. There have been no physical restraints used at Sherbrooke for over two years. Sherbrooke's annual staff turnover rate is less than 5 per cent.

---

* For more on the Eden Alternative, see: http://www.edenalt.com.

Initially, workers were understandably leery of the suggestion to remake Sherbrooke. Most weren't unhappy working in a facility that was already providing enlightened care to its residents. They were concerned about being cross-trained and feeling like they were jacks of all trades but masters of none. There was some cynicism that this was just the latest management consulting strategy for paring down a workforce.

Linda Vanjoff and Andrea Briscoe are executives in the local of the Service Employees International Union (SEIU), which represents workers at Sherbrooke. They say that staff in the newer part of the facility are thrilled with their work. They claim that the cross-training has allowed them to be the "den mothers" in their houses. They now not only have the permission to engage in meaningful relationships with the residents, but are encouraged to do so.

Vanjoff and Briscoe work in the day program area, which is open to residents and outside participants. They always felt Sherbrooke provided good care before "Edenization," but being an Eden facility empowered the staff to take more direct responsibility for their work. Briscoe remembers one day when some staff began to chat about their own impending retirements. Many participants joined in the discussion, some emotionally remembering their own retirements. Soon it was 1:30 and time for the scheduled carpet bowling. However, the staff felt no particular reason to stop an activity in which the residents were so intimately engaged. So a meaningful moment lingered. In another place, at another time, there would be trouble because the scheduled activity did not occur. In Eden, life is in the moment and schedules are flexible.

Home base for the Eden Alternative is an actual garden. Bill Thomas and Judy Meyers-Thomas are reclaiming 90 hectares of farmland from the rolling hills of upstate New York, 100 kilometres southeast of Syracuse. They bought the Summer Hill Farm and built a house, barn, retreat centre, and fourteen-room lodge. They have five children, including two with serious disabilities. They farm organically and preach the gospel of Eden.

Unfortunately, there has not yet been a rigorous evaluation of the model. A study in Texas showed that Edenization resulted in a 25 per cent reduction in patients who were bed-bound, a 60 per cent reduction in behavioural incidents, and a 48 per cent reduction in employee absenteeism.[19] On the other hand, a study from Kentucky found poorer patient outcomes and higher staff turnover, although interviews with staff and residents found that many were happier with the change.[20] The Kentucky authors concluded that one year of follow-up might not be enough. The Texas study took place over two years, and Suellen Beatty claims that it takes at least three years for an institution to plan and execute the change. A key point seems to be that if an organization is not ready to make some fundamental changes, the model is likely to fail.

Eden makes some experts on aging nervous because its advocates are such zealots. But people are voting with their feet. There are now over 250 Eden-registered homes in the United States and 11 in Canada, in BC, Saskatchewan, Manitoba, and Ontario. The Eden concept has influenced hundreds of others. It has also evolved so fast that it has partly grown beyond its founders. Last year, the Eden Alternative developed its first board, on which the Thomases both sit.

Gentle Diversion

Most residents of long-term care facilities are at least somewhat cognitively impaired. Behavioural problems are common. As described earlier, these inappropriate behaviours lead to physical and pharmacological restraint. Often these restraints will make the behaviour even worse. However, it has been obvious to those who work with people with dementia that they are very easily distracted. After all, if someone has short-term memory problems, then if one can distract them for a few minutes, the person often forgets what made him or her upset.

At Riverview Health Centre's Personal Care Home in Winnipeg, they are taking full advantage of this observation to provide more humane care for their dementia residents. Walking into a special care (dementia) unit at the bright, modern facility feels a bit like Disneyland for the elderly. An elderly women is playing with a Sunburst Spray, a fuzzy ball of optical fibres that glow in different colours as it is touched. Another is turning over a plastic pillow filled with water and colourful objects. A small fountain gently runs water over rocks, making a soothing sound. No one is shouting. No one is displaying disturbing behaviour. And it doesn't smell like urine.

Two Dutch therapists, Jan Hulsegge and Ad Verheul, developed the concept of Snoezelen in the late 1970s while working at a centre for people with intellectual disabilities. They heard that a colleague was having positive results by exposing his clients to a special sensory environment he had assembled. Hulsegge and Verheul set up an experimental sensory tent at their annual summer fair to further test the idea, and a new concept was born.

Hulsegge and Verheul called their concept Snoezelen, a contraction of the Dutch verbs *snuffelen* (to seek out or explore) and *doezelen* (to relax). The first Snoezelen room consisted of a roof on poles with plastic sheeting dividers. Inside, there were a fan blowing shards of paper, ink mixed with water and projected onto a screen, musical instruments, tactile objects, scent bottles, soaps, and flavourful foods. The tent was a smash hit, especially with low-functioning clients, who responded with positive verbal and non-verbal feedback. Snoezelen has generated interest across Europe and in North America. Research shows that Snoezelen rooms and props reduce chronic pain,[21] as well as apathetic, repetitive, and disruptive behaviours.[22]

Manufacturers are now using state-of-the art technology to provide wonderful, intriguing spaces with lights, sound, aromas, tactile surfaces, moving images, and other sensory experiences. Snoezelen is also becoming popular with mainstream consumers as an antidote to stress.

Patricia Johnston, a director of patient care at Riverview, says they have had great success using the Snoezelen approach and plan more. She shows off Josephine F.'s room, which features glow-in-the-dark stars and many touchable textured articles. Pat notes that residents really like bubblepack material. Some will hold and touch it for long periods of time, obviously deriving considerable comfort. Riverview also tries to maximize other sensory experiences, such as hot blankets after a bath.

While maximizing gentle sensory stimulation, Riverview has decreased disruptive stimuli. There is no paging overhead—all staff carry vibrating pagers. Movement is secure and quiet through the facility, with fingerprint-recognition touchscreens.

Diet: An Apple a Day . . .

Another group in Saskatoon has shown an innovative way of improving the health of the elderly. Wendy Dahl is a dietitian now taking her doctorate at the University of Saskatchewan in Saskatoon. She became interested in diet and the elderly when she was a new graduate providing services to the Kyle long-term care facility 150 kilometres to the southwest. The cook at the facility asked Dahl why everyone in long-term care was constipated and had to take laxatives. As Dahl looked closer at nutrition in long-term care, it became clear that most long-term care residents hardly consume enough dietary fibre to keep a three-year-old's bowels moving regularly. After a few phone calls, including one to the Saskatchewan Pulse Crop Development Board, Dahl supplemented the residents' diets with pea fibre. Eventually, many of the residents came off their laxatives. Back doing graduate work in Saskatoon, she did a formal study of pea fibre in a Saskatoon home, which showed an improvement in bowel habit.[23]

In fact, nutrition is a big subject for the frail elderly. A recent study in Saskatoon showed that over half of the long-term care residents assessed were at least moderately malnourished,[24] similar to international studies.[25] If you're frail to begin with, it's crucial to eat very, very well.

Because they tend to be malnourished, the institutionalized elderly are 85 per cent less likely to develop immunity after an influenza vaccination than their community counterparts.[26] And if they arrive in the nursing home with a good appetite after recovering from an acute illness, they can be in serious trouble. Many are chronically malnourished after a hospital stay and can fall prone to "refeeding" syndrome. This is the same problem that befell some concentration-camp survivors at the end of the Second World War. When they were able to eat their fill, overconsumption of protein in particular led to serious chemical imbalances within the body, even to death.[27]

A relatively sedentary 50-kilogram eighty-five-year-old woman needs less than half the calories of an active 80-kilogram man, but she has to get enough vitamins and other nutrients, and enough fibre. It's not easy. Dahl notes that a typical day in a facility includes a fairly large breakfast but relatively little protein. Lunch is usually a starch, and a sweet snack is served at 3:30 or 4:00. After a resident eats the snack, there is usually not too much appetite for dinner. Dahl notes that a lot of pork chops are thrown out every evening across the country. She suggests giving more protein in the morning meal and giving afternoon snacks with real nutrition but not too many calories.

Better Medical Care for Health Problems in Nursing Homes

Patients in long-term care facilities are at high risk for being hospitalized. They are frail and chronically ill and susceptible to acute illness. Better management of chronic illness and frailty can reduce acute flare-ups and hospitalizations.

The work of long-term care is personnel-intensive. Residents need assistance with personal care, and this requires people and hands.

It's not surprising that studies have shown that quality of care in long-term care is strongly related to the number of nursing staff and their training.[28] But other workers are also important. An experimental study in Alberta demonstrated that increasing the number of occupational therapists and physiotherapists fourfold saved nearly $300 per resident in nursing care.[29] And an American study showed that nursing homes with more physician or nurse practitioner time had reduced rates of hospitalization.[30]

Physicians' services in long-term care facilities are a big problem. As we will discuss further in chapter 9, some physicians' services pay very well, while others, such as maintaining patients in long-term care facilities, pay much less. For reasons that are either obscure or obvious but not uttered in good company, few doctors are interested in older people. However, these are the people who most need medical care. After all, people over sixty-five use almost half of the hospital beds and most of the drug budget.

Some long-term care facilities have a small medical staff paid on a salary or an hourly basis. However, the normal arrangement is for any family doctor to be able to admit patients to the facility and be paid the regular fee-for-service medicare payments pertaining in that province. This not infrequently leads to inconsistent, poor-quality care, such as the overprescribing of drugs.[31] Over the past twenty years, family doctors have been opting out of nursing home work,[32] and the medical directors of facilities are now taking on increased numbers of patients.[33]

Canadians conducted much of the original research on nurse practitioners (NPs),[34] but the role took off faster in the United States. Nursing homes are one of the prime venues for NP practice, and considerable research indicates that NPs can improve the quality of care for residents.[35] For example, the Group Health Cooperative in Seattle has used family physician/nurse practitioner teams in long-term care for many years. The teams of a half-time family doctor and a full-time nurse practitioner provide care for residents of long-term care institutions as well as for subacute patients, who might be getting rehabilitation care after a stroke or a hip replacement.

In 2000, the Ontario Ministry of Health developed over one hundred pilot projects involving nurse practitioners, including seventeen projects with nurse practitioners based in (or associated with) long-term care facilities.

Dr. John Joanisse and nurse practitioner Manon Bouchard in Ottawa jumped to be one of the long-term care pilots. The 1990s was a busy decade for Dr. Joanisse. He was fully engaged with two medical practices in East Ottawa, and he was also the chief of the medical staff of the Montfort Hospital. The Montfort is a small hospital run by the Sisters of Charity. It became the eye of a storm when the Ontario Health Services Restructuring Commission ordered it to be closed as part of massive changes to the province's hospitals. While other hospitals, such as Toronto's venerable Wellesley, closed their doors, Montfort stayed the death sentence with a court injunction. Montfort's ace in the hole? It was the only hospital in Ottawa providing bilingual services and training. Eventually, after a long court battle, the Ontario Court of Appeal ruled that Ontario did have a constitutional responsibility to ensure the bilingual education of health care practitioners.

Aside from all his responsibilities at the hospital, Dr. Joanisse also had a very elderly practice. Increasingly, like many family doctors, he was discouraged about working by himself, didn't feel that he was providing as good-quality care as he could, and longed for some of the teamwork he enjoyed within the hospital and nursing home settings. An opportunity arose when Manon Bouchard, who was training in the nurse practitioner program, applied to do a practicum in his office. The team clicked from the start. Bouchard started seeing his older patients for longer appointments, co-ordinating their chronic illness care. Her background as a critical care nurse was of great assistance in her new work.

After Bouchard graduated, she was attracted by a job opening at the Residence St. Louis, a two-hundred-bed long-term care facility in Orleans, 20 kilometres east of downtown Ottawa. Dr. Joanisse was despondent. He had grown accustomed to having a teammate in his practice. So he moved his practice to St. Louis as well. He sold his two practices to former students and took on the new responsibility of vice-president of academic affairs at the rejuvenated Montfort.

Bouchard manages seventy-five residents with Dr. Joanisse, but she has also become a consultant throughout the facility. Under Ontario law, she is allowed to prescribe some medications, order certain investigations, and perform some procedures (such as debriding a wound). She has taken Dr. Gary Sibbald's course in wound management at the University of Toronto and now consults throughout the institution on this topic. Waving her arms and flashing her eyes, Bouchard gleefully describes how she healed a Stage 4 ulcer in just four months. She is developing an institution-wide approach to wound care and increasingly finds herself consulted by nurses about other patients in the institution. Bouchard says she is thrilled that she can practise up to her level of competency.

Dr. Joanisse says that he feels that his patients are getting much more complete care. For example, they have implemented a comprehensive fall-prevention program for their residents. Falls are devastating for the elderly, but they are also devastating for the health care system. Falls are the leading cause of injury-related admissions to Canada's acute care hospitals, accounting for almost 1.4 million days of care.[36] That's nearly 4,000 hospital beds—more beds than all New Brunswick's, Newfoundland and Labrador's, and Prince Edward Island's put together.

Dr. Joanisse has placed those of his patients at particularly high risk for hip fracture on so-called triple therapy, including calcium, vitamin D, and a bisphosphonate medication. He is also using plastic hip protectors, which have been shown to reduce hip fractures by 40 to 60 per cent.[37] It is often difficult to get patients and nurses to comply with the hip protectors, but with Dr. Joanisse intermittently making the case with evidence and Bouchard there every day, they feel they have achieved excellent compliance with the regime.

John Joanisse and Manon Bouchard are excited about their work and it shows. It's hard to believe from talking with them that care of the frail elderly is the least favourite area for most doctors and nurses. None of Bouchard's patients have had to be transferred to a chronic care hospital since she began work in 2000.

A Good Idea Spreads

The Niagara Health System has eight hospitals in Niagara Falls, St. Catharines, and five other communities in the Niagara Peninsula. In another Ontario nurse practitioner pilot project, three NPs (two part-time, one casual) are based in the Greater Niagara General Hospital ER and are available twenty-four hours per day. The LTCF physician or staff of the facility call the emergency department when they have a patient who requires assessment. The nurse conducts the assessment and then can order investigations and treatments (within her scope of practice), as well as discussing management with a physician.

Although there is no formal evaluation available yet from the pilots, the Niagara project has been very well received by patients, physicians, the LTCFs, and ER staff. In the first year, there were 705 visits, and staff claim they have averted many ER visits and admissions. As an example of the impact, a nursing home resident with a healed fracture needed his cast cut off. Normally, the patient would have been transported by ambulance to the ER, had the cast removed, and then been taken by ambulance back to the LTCF. Usually there would be long waits expected for each ambulance. However, the nurse practitioner heard about the patient and then simply went to the LTCF and cut the cast off.

Nancy Griffiths works out of three long-term care facilities in London and somehow manages to deal with 400 patients. Valerie Gosse in Thunder Bay also works in three facilities, with over 340 residents. She manages to go the hospital most days to see any of her patients who might be admitted. Then she spends one day a week at each home and fits in her emergency visits. Both Griffiths and Gosse deal with many different doctors in each setting. Gosse says she established herself with the physicians when she was allowed to access the doctors' lounge in the hospital. These two nurses are no doubt adding a lot to patient care, but it might be better if they didn't have quite so many patients to manage.

Dr. Garey Mazowita's major responsibility is as medical director of community and long-term care at the Winnipeg Regional Health Authority. But he also works with Alex Kowalski, a nurse practitioner at the Fred Douglas Lodge in the city's fabled North End. Kowalski is only at the home where he manages fifty patients one day per week. Dr. Mazowita goes to the home himself twice a month but is available by phone whenever the nurse practitioner is needed.

Conclusion: The Long Goodbye

Home care is not enough for some people. They must change their housing to get the care they need. There are many exciting examples of assisted and supportive housing that permit very disabled people to have care and choice. However, these models are in danger of being perverted into cash cows for real estate developers.

Your Community and Long-term Care

- Does your community offer supportive housing with on-site professional, personal, and supportive care? Is it affordable to all in your community?
- Are provincial benefits for drugs and equipment for residents of long-term care facilities also available to patients living in the community?
- Do the long-term care facilities in your community take part in the Eden Alternative, or do they have some other system for ensuring compassionate care for the institutionalized elderly and the severely disabled?
- Do the long-term care facilities in your community ensure adequate nutrition for their residents?

- Do the long-term care facilities in your community use Snoezelen or some other non-pharmacologic diversions for residents with dementia?
- Do the long-term care facilities in your community provide intravenous care or other acute care, to prevent unnecessary hospitalizations?
- Do the long-term care facilities have a core of physicians who spend at least ten hours per week working in these facilities? Do the long-term care facilities use nurse practitioners to enhance continuity of care?
- Is the turnover of staff in your community long-term care facilities higher than 20 per cent? If so, this is a sign of quality problems.
- Do the long-term care facilities in your community use physical restraints? If so, this is a sign of quality problems—usually reflecting poor behavioural management of dementia patients.

When even more care is required, particularly for those with dementia, the Eden Alternative offers a new model for re-engineering the long-term care experience. Some say it is only common sense, and many facilities claim they are already providing an enhanced experience for their residents. But Eden does offer a replicable model with a broad support network throughout North America.

Many of us will need long-term care before we meet our maker. As this chapter demonstrates, much could be done to enhance the dignity in independence of the frail elderly who use these services.

Chapter 8

Prevention

It's a mild late-winter evening, and Ann Livingston and Robert G. are walking the hard streets of Vancouver's Downtown East Side, or the DTES as the locals call it. They're from VANDU, the Vancouver Area Network of Drug Users. She's not a user herself, but Livingston seems to know everybody. She's pushing a stroller with her new baby boy, and people stop to admire him and chat. They also ask for safe injection kits. She and Robert will hand out dozens this evening.

Welcome to the messy world of public health and prevention. You'll remember from earlier chapters that many of the patients in our crowded hospitals are suffering from illnesses that are preventable. A healthy lifestyle (consisting of a nutritious diet, physical fitness, and meaningful work and family relationships) could prevent over 80 per cent of cases of coronary heart disease,[1] type 2 diabetes[2] (90 per cent of diabetes cases), and over 85 per cent of cases of lung cancer and chronic obstructive lung disease (such as emphysema). If the potential for prevention could be translated into reality for these four conditions alone, we could free up over six thousand hospital beds.* This is more

---

* According to the Canadian Institute for Health Information Hospital Morbidity Database, in 2000 there were roughly 1,820,000 bed days, or 5000 hospital beds, used for care of patients with coronary heart disease; roughly 300,000 bed days, or 870 hospital beds, used for care of patients with diabetes; and roughly 710,000 bed days, or 1,940

than the entire complement of beds in Atlantic Canada. Before you know it, we could really uncrowd those hospitals.

Although we are a long way from where we could be, we haven't done all that badly. Canadians are among the healthiest humans who have ever lived. Life expectancy at birth hit a new high in 2001 of 82.2 years for women and 77.1 years for men.[3] These stats place us seventh in the world for women and fifth for men—out of the medals, but a significant achievement nonetheless; especially considering that the US, which collects so many Olympic golds, comes up eighteenth for women and tied for seventeenth for men.[4] The top countries are Japan, Switzerland, and Sweden.

Some people think that our high levels of health are a result of our health care system. Clearly, health care has some role, but the greatest gains in life expectancy actually took place before medicare. The sanitary revolution of the late nineteenth and early twentieth centuries did more to improve health than all the ineffective therapies that were available at the time.

Due to both health care and improving social conditions, recent gains in health have been impressive. Our population is growing and aging, but we are healthier than ever.[5] Most cancer death rates are decreasing.[6] Breast cancer mortality has dropped by 20 per cent in the past thirty years. Colon cancer death rates have been cut by 30 per cent. Despite our expanding waistlines, heart disease continues its forty-year decline.[7]

Of course, we have a long way to go. Diabetes and other obesity-related illnesses are increasing.[8] In the last thirty years, female lung-cancer death rates have rocketed almost 400 per cent.[9] And while our physical health is improving, there are signs that the prevalence of some mental disorders is increasing, including addictions.[10]

Good health is not shared equally by all segments of society.

---

hospital beds, used for care of patients with lung and throat cancer and chronic obstructive lung disease. If 80 per cent of these cases could have been prevented, that would have freed up over 6,000 hospital beds.

Typically, those with lower incomes, fewer years of education, inadequate housing, and dangerous jobs face many fewer years of life than the rest of us.[11] A homeless injection-drug user in the DTES is dozens of times more likely to die this year than the average Canadian. We like to think we live in an egalitarian society where every child has the same chances in life. We are a more equal society than the US, where poor kids start off life with two strikes against them. But poor Canadian kids still start off with at least one strike against them before they step to the plate.

This chapter discusses prevention and public health. Prevention offers the greatest potential for improving health and controlling health care costs, but little of this promise is actually fulfilled. AIDS is now a chronic illness, not an immediate death sentence. But it is still not curable and kills nearly five hundred people a year in Canada.

It turns out that prevention is a lot more about hard-nosed politics than about exhorting us to get out of our La-Z-Boys. We know the causes of most of our health problems, but political barriers prevent us from implementing solutions.

Public Health on the Streets

Vancouver's DTES is the poor side of one of the world's wealthiest cities. Retired lumberjacks and fishers were the first residents. It was one of the original "skid rows," where they used to slide, or "skid," the logs down to the Pacific Ocean. In the last two decades, the DTES has become home to Canada's largest community of injection drug users, or IDUs. Three to five thousand of the area's twenty thousand residents are users, and tonight they seem everywhere.

The police recently chased the dealers from Main and Hastings, the neighbourhood's most famous corner, but the dealers haven't gone far. Dozens of sellers and buyers form a swarm moving up and down the block. Some are composed, but others show the effects of too much cocaine and not enough sleep.

This environment is not healthy for human beings, but it is the best breeding ground for the "3 H's": HIV and hepatitis B and C. Nothing more efficiently transmits these nasties than shooting up with a used needle.

For the last fifty years, North America has tended to treat IDUs as criminals. Our "war on drugs" has put millions of addicts in jail and interdicted thousands of shipments of drugs. The result: drugs are cheaper than ever.

On September 2, 2000, Canadian law enforcement officers intercepted a shipment of 100 kilograms of pure heroin in Vancouver Harbour. At the time, this was the largest-ever seizure of heroin in Canada. The US Customs Service confiscated only 113 kilograms of heroin along its Mexican border *in all of 2000*. If enforcement really worked, one would have anticipated that there would have been a major drop in the availability of heroin on the streets of Vancouver. Addicts should have been going into withdrawal all over the DTES. Far from it. UBC researchers documented that the price of heroin on the street decreased after the seizure. Heroin was actually more available *after* the apprehension.[12]

In the past ten years, health care workers, the public, and even many police officers have realized that we cannot rely upon enforcement as the main tactic because it cannot keep drugs out of the arms of addicts. The price keeps dropping.

The illegal drug trade has destabilized neighbourhoods. Many murders and violent crimes are related to gang turf battles. Dozens of deaths can be traced to Montreal's biker war alone.* Just as alcohol prohibition turned penny-ante hoods like Al Capone into the rich and powerful Mafia, so drug prohibition has promoted neighbourhood bullies into fabulously wealthy international criminals.

One of the ironies of drug prohibition is that it has also made the drugs more dangerous. Narcotics or opiates like heroin and morphine

---

* The gangs are also involved with prostitution, gambling, smuggling, and extortion.

are not that dangerous if you have a safe supply and a roof over your head and if you don't have to share needles. Opiates tend to make people somnolent, but some narcotics addicts have good jobs and good health. Some are doctors, lawyers, and business people.

Cocaine is a lot more dangerous than heroin, and injecting it is a one-way trip to hell. Cocaine addicts can go through twenty or more needles a day, dramatically increasing the risk of needle-sharing. Coke also tends to make people aggressive and violent. Both cocaine and heroin can cause death from overdose.

By the 1990s, injecting drugs in the uncontrolled conditions of the back lanes of the DTES had become a dangerous way of life for thousands of miserable people. More than two hundred people a year were dying of drug overdoses, most inadvertently. HIV infection rates among IDUs went to 25 per cent. This was one of the highest rates in the world outside of New York City.[13]

Harm Reduction

In the 1960s, health care workers began to suggest alternative strategies to abstinence for drug rehabilitation.[14] The approach is called harm reduction. Maybe in a perfect world people wouldn't use drugs. Maybe in a perfect world people wouldn't suffer the pain that drives some to take their first shot. Abstinence has been the hallmark of addiction treatment for decades. It is the keystone of Alcoholics Anonymous and many other popular treatment programs. However, abstinence doesn't work for everyone.

You'll remember our visits to Ottawa's Union Mission and Toronto's Seaton House from chapters 4 and 6. The harm reduction approach recognizes that we don't live in a perfect world, but in the real world, we can still do a lot to reduce the damage without forcing people to stop using before we help. Harm reduction promotes the development of productive relationships between health workers and people with addictions.

Methadone was one of the first tactics used for harm reduction for IDUs. Methadone is a long-acting opiate that relieves the cravings for heroin without delivering its high. It is usually drunk, mixed with fruit juice. Taking methadone in the morning permits addicts to get on with their lives without worrying about where they will find their next fix. Methadone works. It markedly increases compliance with treatment, decreases the use of illegal drugs, and reduces mortality.[15] Under epidemic conditions, methadone therapy can avert five to seven HIV infections for every hundred persons on therapy.[16] It allows people to get off the treadmill on the street and start dealing with their problems. However, it isn't all that easy to get methadone.

Robert G. is on methadone now. He was sixteen when he first tried heroin but wasn't a regular user for ten more years. For three years after that, he successfully coped with his addiction and had a career and a three-bedroom house. Then he broke up with his fiancée, and a few other personal problems pushed him over the line. He ran out of money. He knew where there was an unsecured computer at the university; the police caught him when he attempted to steal it. He served nine months in jail in Kamloops, but he was back on heroin within five minutes of returning to Vancouver. He didn't want to keep using, so he sought out methadone treatment. It took him three weeks to get his methadone because of the multitude of forms and of blood and urine tests. All this time he was injecting to prevent withdrawal, but he stopped when he started his methadone. He's been clean for nine months now. He credits a lot of this to his work with VANDU.

Ann Livingston and some others established VANDU after BC chief coroner Dr. Vincent Cain's 1994 report highlighted the severity of the problem. Ann saw the carnage every day as a resident of the DTES. VANDU registered as a non-profit society in 1997 and now counts over a thousand members. One of the key features of VANDU is a weekly meeting, which can draw two hundred people.

Robert's family doctor said that he needed to get out more and volunteer, so he went to a VANDU-organized meeting on hepatitis C. The more he saw of VANDU, the more he liked it. He is now facilitating a small user's group on Commercial Drive, a few kilometres east of the DTES. They meet every week for a few hours. Just like VANDU's main group, they set the agenda every meeting and go from there. They're drawing strength not only from VANDU, but from groups as far-flung as Australia and Germany.

Robert now spends much of his time helping with needle exchange and peer counselling. He notes with pride that he was recently able to help a young man get off the street into a shelter and then into a halfway house. The young man may start methadone and is thinking about going back to high school.

Building Relationships

This is the real essence of harm reduction—striking up relationships with users. Relationships are important for Heather Hay. She is the director of community health services for the Vancouver Coastal Health Authority, the regional health authority for Vancouver and the surrounding area.

The authority funds VANDU's needle exchange and others' while also running some of its own. In total, they distribute over 4 million needles a year. The health authority runs a basic life-saving program called "59 Minutes Can Save a Life," which has been given to thousands of users. It also conducts a three-day harm reduction course, which trains them as "Peer 2 Peer" counsellors. It has over five hundred graduates. Sheree Hudson, the nurse educator who organizes these programs, notes that many users find themselves in a classroom for the first time since they dropped out of school. She remembers one woman who wept when she received her three-day certificate.

The graduates take new pride in their work as peer counsellors and needle exchangers. For many, like Robert, it is the first step to their new future. But Hay cautions that success is defined differently for different people. For some, it's getting off drugs and out of the neighbourhood. For some, especially women, it's having enough confidence to refuse to take the second shot from a needle.

Hudson remembers Vern, a low-level dealer who used to sell

drugs on Carroll Street. Hudson said hello to him every day. Finally she asked his name, then some other personal details, including his birthday. On his birthday, she bought him a cake and invited him into the health centre to blow out the candles. (She first had to ask Vern's "overlord" for permission to take him off the street for five minutes.) After a few months, Vern asked about detox, and Hudson helped him get into a program. Now he's off heroin and off the street. He has a job with United We Can, an innovative agency whose goals include creating jobs for self-sustaining environmental businesses, such as recycling.

Hudson runs some of her courses out of the Lifeskills Centre across the street from Oppenheimer Park at Jackson and Powell. The health authority conducted foot care clinics in the park last summer, and that brought dozens of new people into their programs. It's all about building relationships.

There is a new downtown community health centre, which sees 150 patients a day. The health authority also runs the Health Contact Centre, where people can get off the street and hang out. A nurse does foot care and deals with other health problems. The Health Contact Centre had 76,000 visits the first six months it was open.

Another key actor in the crowded political stage of the DTES is the Portland Hotel Society. The society was established in the early 1990s when plans were announced to demolish the Portland Hotel, an old single-room-occupancy building. The society saved the Portland and now owns seven hotels with over three hundred rooms.

The Washington Hotel has seventy single-occupancy rooms. On the second floor, one room serves as the harm reduction office. Today, Unk and a couple of others are on shift. They have already exchanged over a hundred needles, and it's only 6 p.m. This year, they will distribute over 150,000 needles. They also pass out thousands of condoms.

Unk is an old hippie. Long grey-blond hair spills over his thick glasses, which can't hide the sparkle in his eyes. He sits on the DTES HIV/IDU Consumers' Board, which represents the many different communities within the DTES—HIV-positive, people with hepatitis, Native people, the disabled, and so on. The Consumers' Board has no paid staff. Like Unk, everyone is a volunteer. Unk managed to kick his own addiction seven years ago, but not before acquiring HIV and hepatitis. He proudly claims, "We're the lunatics who have taken over the asylum!" A resident strolls into the room and Unk exchanges conversation and needles with a cheerful smile. Afterward, Unk notes that it's hard to change an addict. But while we are helping them prepare for change, we can reduce the harm they do to themselves.

The Harm Reduction Mayor
In 1998, the problem in the DTES had become so severe that it even had its own TV show. *Da Vinci's Inquest*, the gritty, award-winning CBC drama, set many of its episodes in the DTES. When actor Nicholas Campbell stepped around a new corpse, he was following the choreography of a real coroner, Larry Campbell (no relation). A gruff, no-nonsense former RCMP drug officer, Larry Campbell has become a leader in the call to forge a new strategy to deal with illegal drugs. There are differences between Dominic Da Vinci and Larry Campbell, but there are enough similarities* that the resemblance helped Campbell become the real mayor of Vancouver.

Campbell became convinced that only politics would make a difference for the people of the DTES. The political process had already accomplished quite a bit. Dr. Cain's report had officially put harm reduction on the map. And on September 30, 2000, the city, the province, and the federal government signed the historic Vancouver Agreement, which commits the three governments to work together on comprehensive solutions to the problems.[17] The agreement proposed a "four pillars" approach to the DTES: prevention, treatment, harm reduction, and enforcement.

---

* For example, Larry Campbell's wife and Da Vinci's ex-wife are both pathologists.

There were two major rationales for federal involvement. First, there is a disproportionate number of Native people (constitutionally a federal responsibility) in the DTES, many reeling from unhappy lives on unhealthy reserves. Second, many if not most DTES residents in need of services originally came from other provinces.[18] Vancouver is the end of the road. If you're a Canadian who has to sleep rough in the winter, Vancouver is the place for you. The DTES is clearly a Canadian problem that happens to be located in Vancouver.

Philip Owen was mayor of Vancouver during this turbulent time. He hails from a patrician BC family and represented a conservative municipal party (the Vancouver Civic Non-Partisan Association, or NPA). His support for radical measures such as safe injection sites alienated him from his own party. Some businesses thought the problem should be legislated away, or at least away from them. NPA councillor Jennifer Clarke led a coup and prevented Owen from running in the 2002 election. Then she ran herself. However, Clarke was on the wrong side of this issue, and others.* On November 16, 2002, Campbell trounced her. His party, COPE, or the Coalition of Progressive Electors, won nine of eleven seats on council.

Campbell's victory inadvertently tripped up one the Portland Society's more controversial projects—a safe injection site. Quietly, they had renovated a storefront with six injecting areas, clean water, and a place for health care staff. But during much of 2002, everyone had thought Clarke would win the mayoralty in a walk. The Portland people knew she wouldn't support a safe injection site, so they planned to open it as an act of civil disobedience. When Campbell surprised everybody and won, they decided to wait.

Campbell supported safe injection sites, but he needed the go-ahead from Health Canada. As negotiations continued, VANDU became impatient and opened its own safe injection site on April 7,

---

* The NPA was also politically linked with the provincial government, which was going through a period of unpopularity. The mayor of Vancouver is often the real leader of the opposition in BC.

2003.[19] Finally, in June, Health Canada okayed a three-year pilot project,[20] and North America's first officially sanctioned safe injection site opened in September on East Hastings.[21] The Portland Hotel Society co-manages the site with the regional health authority. Despite the lack of publicity, twenty people used the site in its first two hours. By December, there were five hundred users a day.

Portland Society executive director Dan Small makes it clear that there is a lot more to do. Vancouver needs so-called low-threshold methadone therapy. Instead of making addicts fill out forms and wait for three weeks before they can get treatment, he wants them to get methadone right away. There is a pilot project in Toronto, which is showing promise. Early results indicate a significant drop in HIV risk behaviours and in the use of heroin, other opiates, and cocaine.[22]

Ann Livingston strongly agrees. She notes that she has seen women who tell her that they wouldn't be turning tricks that night if methadone were available. The reachable moment fades. A relationship is not formed.

How Is Vancouver Doing?

Unfortunately, by the time Vancouver started to get its act together, the HIV prevalence rate in drug users was already 25 per cent. However, as public health developed its response, new HIV infections in injection drug users fell from 10 per cent per year in 1997 to 1.5 per cent in 2000.[23] With three thousand to five thousand addicts in the DTES, this translates into nearly three hundred new HIV infections averted per year.

Vancouver also has one of the biggest methadone programs in North America. From 1996 to 1999, nearly 75 per cent of patients who started methadone therapy continued it for at least one year. This is one of the highest retention rates in the world.[24] Drug overdose deaths, which had reached over two hundred per year in 1993, were down to eighty-nine by 2001[25] and only 49 in the first ten months of 2003.

Not Everyone Completely Agrees

Dr. Stan de Vlaming graduated from the University of Manitoba medical school in 1985 and spent time in Kenora, Ontario, before coming to the DTES. In the early 1990s he opened an office on Blood Alley* between Abbott and Carroll. As he became involved with the neighbourhood and its problems, he took training in addictions medicine and started prescribing methadone. Up until a few years ago, he was the only doctor in the DTES prescribing methadone. But in 2000, the health authority contracted with Dr. de Vlaming and based two counsellors in his office. A year and a half later, de Vlaming moved his practice into the Pender Community Health Centre, joining six addictions counsellors, two other doctors, and a nurse. The facility deals with 250 methadone patients, 100 of whom are HIV-positive. Now de Vlaming splits his time between the Pender Health Centre and his position as head of the division of addictions within the department of family practice at St. Paul's Hospital, a couple of kilometres west.

Dr. de Vlaming believes that methadone can replace heroin but claims that his clients really need to leave the community to kick cocaine. He works with a series of non-traditional recovery houses in the suburbs, which take his patients. (The traditional ones will not allow methadone.) He usually has twenty-five to thirty patients in recovery houses.

While de Vlaming would not be normally labelled a conservative, he has concerns about safe injection facilities and even about needle exchanges. He accepts that the health authority runs a needle exchange out of the clinic, but he says the exchange will use the back door. He is afraid that seeing the needles in the front room might tempt some of his patients. He is concerned about safe injection sites for the same reason.

These views are stated in an extreme fashion by others, such as

---

* So called because one hundred years ago it was lined with butcher shops.

John Walters, the US drug czar. Walters, who received his MA from the University of Toronto, gave a speech to the Vancouver Board of Trade just days after the 2002 municipal election. He warned his audience, which included incoming mayor Campbell and outgoing mayor Owen, that harm reduction tactics just create new addicts. Campbell responded by saying that this was tantamount to claiming that flies cause garbage.

Walters also cautioned his BC audience that the province's marijuana industry was causing pain and suffering south of the border. He claimed that marijuana was more dangerous than heroin, cocaine, or amphetamines. Campbell softly noted that that wasn't the BC experience. Neither he nor Da Vinci ever put a marijuana overdose into a body bag. But he did zip up the lives of dozens of the real victims of our failing war on drugs. And now he's going to change things.

From Virchow to Lalonde

Many Canadians have changed their views about illegal drugs as the HIV epidemic has ravaged the injection drug community. Allowing communities like the DTES to fester creates infections that will spread throughout the country and the rest of the globe. Many DTES residents eventually return home and pass on their infections. Another HIV infection could be the one that starts a chain that eventually hits you, or your daughter, or your godson. Larry Campbell says it's just like a real war: there is little response until the body bags stack up.

Slowly, it is occurring to Canadians outside of Vancouver, Toronto, and Montreal that we need to radically change the way we think about psychoactive drugs. However, even though the solutions might seem clear to Campbell, Owen, and most public health authorities, implementation is slow. Many Canadians are opposed to the state's seeming to endorse, in any way, shape, or form, the use of certain drugs. We tolerate Chivas and cigarettes, but not marijuana or morphine. Some Canadians are concerned about repercussions from Washington if we liberalize our drug laws. Switzerland and Germany have had safe injection sites for years, as well as permitting the medical use of heroin, but they don't share a 6,000-kilometre border with the world's only superpower.

Most scientists think we will look back upon the war on drugs as a great embarrassment to the human race. However, there are a lot of voters who don't think that today. This isn't new. Illness, its causes, and its remedies have always been political issues.

Virchow Goes to Silesia

Rudolf Virchow was only twenty-six years of age in 1848, but he was already one of Europe's greatest physicians and scientists.[26] In that year, the city council of Berlin asked Virchow to investigate an epidemic of typhus that had broken out in Upper Silesia, now part of Poland. Virchow spent three weeks in Silesia and concluded that the cause of the epidemic was "mismanagement of the region by the Berlin government." He noted that the miners had inadequate housing, insufficient food, and lack of basic sanitation. Virchow's recommendations included full democracy, the separation of church and state, shifting the burden of taxation from the poor to the rich, a program of road construction, the elimination of the laws against union organizing, and the breakup of large estates owned by absentee landlords. The councillors in Berlin were pretty chafed with Virchow's report. They said that Virchow had written a political tract rather than a scientific paper. Virchow then made his famous statement, which resonates through the years: "Medicine is a social science and politics is nothing but medicine writ large!"

Virchow further claimed that if health care was to be successful, then it must enter political and social life, because diseases were caused by defects in society. He claimed that "if disease is an expression of individual life under unfavourable circumstances, then epidemics must be indicative of mass disturbances." A true Renaissance man, Virchow successfully combined his science with politics, becoming the designer of Berlin's sewer system and one of the main excavators of the city of Troy. He was also elected a member of the German Reichstag, where he was a thorn in the side of Chancellor Bismarck, opposing his military ambitions.

Health Is Politics

Our pattern of health and illness reflects who we are—our values, our culture, and our institutions. In other words, health is politics. North Americans have very high rates of coronary heart disease and lung cancer because we eat too much of the wrong food and because too many of us smoke cigarettes. We have low rates of water- and food-borne illness because of a relatively safe supply of food and drinking water. On the other hand, African peasants have low rates of coronary heart disease and lung cancer and high rates of water- and food-borne illness. A particular population's health status is as unique to that society as fingerprints are to an individual.

If we accept the principle that health is a political construct, then there are certain important rules that follow:

1. Major change in a society's pattern of health and illness requires change in that society's values, customs, and institutions.
2. Some powerful interests and communities will be threatened by this change and will oppose reform.
3. These threats to interests and values will inevitably cause political backlash. This backlash will modify policies so that they will be less offensive and, as a result, less effective.

We can use the epidemic of HIV among injection drug users in the DTES as an example of these rules. The epidemic developed because there was a large population of troubled people and easy availability of injectable drugs but poor access to clean needles, sanitary facilities, treatment, and housing. The authorities could control the epidemic only when they started to put housing and health services into the area. Typically, innovative non-governmental organizations such as the Portland Hotel Society and VANDU led the way. By the late 1990s, a majority of the city's citizens, including most of the economic and political elite, had concluded that focusing on enforcement would not work. The "four pillars" approach ratified the consensus that had emerged during the previous decade.

Some Vancouverites did not shift their values and continue to oppose the expansion of harm reduction. In other parts of the country, it is a struggle to begin to implement needle exchange and methadone treatment.[27]

The political backlash against harm reduction concentrates on individual treatment rather than systemic change. In the United States, the push is for more enforcement and for treatment with a religious flavour.[28] The backlash pushes the focus away from environmental solutions, such as needle exchange, methadone, and safe injection sites, toward education, law enforcement, and court-ordered rehabilitation.

It is particularly difficult to implement the broader policies needed to enhance health services. For example, stable housing greatly facilitates the effectiveness of harm reduction programs. However, Canada is the only wealthy country without a national housing program. Housing for addicts engenders opposition from those who oppose public housing and higher taxes, as well as from those who think drug addicts are lazy pleasure-seekers who have authored their own misfortunes.

In the end, public health and prevention are dependent upon a strong role for the public sector. In the nineteenth century, there were frequent cholera epidemics, which swept out of Asia and regularly devastated the rest of the world. Even though by mid-century it was clear that they were a result of improper sewage disposal and lack of safe drinking water, there was tremendous resistance to developing the necessary public works.[29] When the great Victorian reformer Edwin Chadwick proposed such projects, his upper-class friends asked, "Who will pay for all this sewering and watering?" When

London established the first Board of Health in the 1850s, it was dis-banded after a few years because of political opposition from private water companies, which opposed regulation of their businesses.

We see a replay of these debates today. Public health advocates such as Harvard's Nancy Krieger argue for a larger role for govern-ment, claiming that the foundation of public health is social justice.[30] Krieger asserts that public health "has a compelling desire to make the world a better place, free of misery, inequality, and preventable suffering, a world in which we all can live, love, work, play, ail, and die with our dignity intact and our humanity cherished."

Conservatives who think government should have a smaller role in our lives typically oppose this position. For example, in April 2003, *National Post* columnist Terence Corcoran reamed out Toronto med-ical officer of health Dr. Sheila Basrur for championing a by-law to restrict lawn pesticides.[31] He said she should "stick to her knitting" and deal with the severe acute respiratory syndrome (SARS) epi-demic. While others evinced concern that the SARS epidemic would drain needed resources from public health, Corcoran opposed more funding, claiming that Basrur's pursuit of the pesticide by-law was proof that the department already had too much. Although not a sci-entist himself, Corcoran wasn't shy about labelling Basrur's report as filled with "scientific exaggeration."

Governments Use Prevention as an Excuse to Cut Cure
There is an interesting sidebar to the prevention discussion. Some-times governments use the concept of prevention simply as an excuse to slash health care budgets as part of an overall strategy of government cutbacks. For example, in 1974, then minister of health and welfare Marc Lalonde released a landmark document, *A Report on the Health of Canadians*. It claimed that health care was not as important a determinant of health as other social factors, factors that should get more policy attention. Lalonde's report has been cited internationally by the World Health Organization and others as the government paper that changed international health policy dis-

course. However, the main impact in Canada was to soften up the policy community for the 1977 Established Programs Financing Act, which moved the federal government away from the 50:50 cost sharing that had brought the provinces into medicare. As discussed in chapter 2, there were other good reasons to change the federal financing arrangements at the time. But the policy shift to block funding meant that there were eager ears in the federal government for a document that claimed that there were scientific as well as financial reasons to give up the 50:50 deal.

In 1986, then minister of health and welfare Jake Epp released his *Charter for Health Promotion*. Like its predecessor, it has been favourably cited. Health promotion was seen as the new way forward. And like the Lalonde Report, the Epp Charter was an excellent document. But perhaps the real reason why the Mulroney government was so quick to put it out was that it supported the government's main health agenda: cuts to provincial transfer payments.

In 1994, the Federal/Provincial/Territorial Advisory Committee on Population Health released *Strategies for Population Health: Investing in the Health of Canadians*. It reiterated some of the same points as the first two reports, such as "There will be a more balanced emphasis on and investment in all of the determinants of health, with less of a preoccupation with health care." However, the 1995 federal budget further chopped health, education, and social transfers to the provinces.

Have We Pulled Our Goalie?
Public Health Is the System's Backstop

In May 2000, 7 people died and 2,300 became ill after the water supply in Walkerton, Ontario, became contaminated with manure that had been spread on a farm near the town. The epidemic went undetected for several days. The main problem was the incompetent and negligent management of the Walkerton Public Utilities Commission

(PUC). But Justice Dennis O'Connor's inquiry into the outbreak[32] concluded that provincial government budget cuts, especially to the Ministry of the Environment,* had caused hundreds of additional cases. Mike Harris's axe saved enough money to give wealthy taxpayers a tidy little stake in his "common sense revolution." But it also eliminated government laboratories without requiring private labs to notify the ministry and the public health authorities of abnormal results. This uncommon sense led to the delay in the warning that caused the additional cases.

The province has responded to many of Justice O'Connor's recommendations, but not, as of the fall of 2003, to the most important ones, which relate to watershed preservation. Dr. Murray McQuigge was the courageous public health physician who directed the response to the Walkerton disaster. His unflappable style and plain talk quickly calmed the panic, and he became a trusted voice on the issue. Justice O'Connor noted that the public health authorities had been diligent. If it had not been for the quick decision to post a boil-water order, even more illnesses would have occurred. When all the other safeguards failed, it was public health that acted as the backstop to the system.

McQuigge calls safe drinking water a common resource, and "the cornerstone of public health."[33] He also called for government to rebalance its support for business with defence of the public's health. We don't hear much about public health when there isn't an epidemic running rampant. How is public health doing, anyway?

Taking the Temperature of Public Health

Public health prevents illnesses, but it celebrates its successes silently. Prevention has none the of glory associated with triple

---

* The ministry's budget was cut by 65 per cent between 1995 and 1997.

transplants. When public health is working properly, the only visible sign is healthy people going about their daily lives. However, public health's veneer is peeling.

- Justice Horace Krever noted in his report on the blood system that "public health departments in many parts of Canada do not have the resources to carry out their duties."[34]
- A report on public health infrastructure was presented to the Federal-Provincial-Territorial Meeting of Deputy Ministers of Health in June 2001, but the deputies refused to allow the report to be tabled. The report noted that "There seems to be agreement that only one crisis can be handled at a time."[35]
- The *Canadian Medical Association Journal* referred to public health as "being on the ropes."[36]
- The federal SARS report chaired by Dr. David Naylor noted wryly, "There is much to learn from the outbreak of SARS in Canada—in large part because too many earlier lessons were ignored."[37]

Dr. John Frank, one of Canada's senior public health physicians and director of the Canadian Institute of Population and Public Health, has identified five major challenges to public health:[38]

1. One world, no boundaries
2. New epidemics of chronic disease
3. Environmental degradation and change
4. The perils of untested new technologies
5. Public health: an evaluative conscience for the clinical care system

Let us now look at each of these in turn.

One World, No Boundaries
While Canadians are smug about the elimination of epidemics of infectious diseases, the spring 2003 outbreak of severe acute respiratory

syndrome (SARS) reminded us that an infection thousands of kilometres beyond our borders can quickly wreak devastation here. A mutation in a coronavirus, perhaps by passage through the Asian civet cat, created the SARS epidemic.[39] Within a few months, air travel spread it to the other side of the globe.

HIV did not exist in North America prior to the 1970s, but it is now one of the leading causes of death for young men.

Tuberculosis is usually considered a disease of the past, but worldwide it is more common than ever. Unfortunately, Canada's public health system appears unable to mount the most basic tuberculosis control programs.[40] Canada is the only developed country without a national immunization schedule.[41] The provinces develop their own schedules, and there are many differences between them.

The West Nile virus did not exist in North America prior to 1999. That year, it arrived in New York City, probably with an infected bird, and caused sixty-two known human infections and seven deaths. The virus wasn't much more active in the next two years. However, in 2002, it took off.

Fifty-one-year-old Burlington, Ontario, truck driver John Stevens had a rash and a high fever when he arrived at Joseph Brant Memorial Hospital in July 2002.[42] The emergency room staff didn't know what he had. But Stevens had checked the Internet before going to the ER, and he thought he had West Nile virus. The ER staff poohpoohed the notion, but Stevens pushed them to test for West Nile anyway. Stevens became the first official human case of West Nile contracted in Canada. Months later, he was still complaining of exhaustion, poor memory, and lack of co-ordination.

Stevens was far from the last case in 2002. That year in North America there were 4,500 confirmed cases and 300 deaths.[43] Ontario reported nearly 400 confirmed or probable cases and 17 deaths. Given that for every confirmed case there were at least 100 that went undetected, Ontario probably had 50,000 cases. The Great Lakes region was hit the hardest, with nearly half of North America's cases. Oakville, Ontario, had the highest number of cases per capita on the continent.

As of October 2003, there were over a thousand Canadian cases of West Nile for that year, with seven deaths. In 2003, over 90 per cent of cases reported were from the Prairies. West Nile might be on its way to becoming a truly modern plague. Or it may peter out in the next few years. Or a vaccine might be developed. We will know only with time. However, it is noteworthy that this potential catastrophe is occupying considerably less political attention than the latest *crise du jour* in the health care system.

Finally, it appears that Canada's quarrelling governments cannot co-operate even with the public's health at stake. The auditor general criticized the Canadian Food Inspection Agency for not sharing information with public health services during an outbreak due to contaminated cheese.[44] And the Naylor Report felt compelled to point out that "Canadians expect to see their governments collaborate responsibly in the face of serious threat to the health of the population."

New Epidemics of Chronic Disease
The main health problems currently facing Canadians are chronic illnesses.

While many chronic illnesses such as heart disease are waning, the prevalence of childhood obesity is increasing rapidly. This is fuelling epidemics of diabetes and end-stage kidney disease and may portend a future resurgence in coronary heart disease.[45] Like other chronic illnesses, the burden of the childhood obesity epidemic falls more heavily on Canadians of lower socio-economic status.[46]

Mental health concerns are as common as or more common than physical problems.[47] Many Canadians, particularly children, are not able to get treatment for their mental health problems.

Environmental Degradation and Change
At the same time as there is a raging political debate about whether human activity is responsible for threats to the environment, there is major environmental change occurring that has grave implications for human health. Carbon dioxide concentrations and other "greenhouse

gases" are increasing at an exponential rate.[48] The earth is getting warmer. The sea level is rising.

There is widespread contamination of groundwater, from which many Canadians, especially in rural areas, draw their drinking water.[49] Yet there appears to be less public health capacity to protect us from outbreaks of water-borne illness like those in Walkerton, Ontario, and North Battleford, Saskatchewan.[50] The estimates of the costs to renovate Canada's water systems are in the tens of billions of dollars.[51]

There are also concerns about air quality, especially in the Greater Toronto Area and BC's lower mainland.[52] It has been estimated that in the city of Toronto alone there are approximately 1,000 premature deaths and 5,500 hospital admissions due to polluted air. Global warming may also change the distribution of a number of insect-borne diseases, including West Nile and malaria.

The Perils of Untested New Technologies
Canadians rely upon public health agencies to protect us from dangerous drugs, foods, and other products. There have been recent concerns that the fine balance between making effective drugs available in a timely fashion and protecting the public from dangerous products has tipped in favour of the drug industry.[53] Seven drugs approved since 1993 and later withdrawn from the market have contributed to at least one thousand deaths across North America.

There is also concern about dangers from untested new technologies, from agricultural practices to medical devices. When an Alberta cow was discovered with bovine spongiform encephalopathy (BSE), much of the rest of the world wanted to know why Canada still allows ruminant animals to eat feed containing other animals. Canada still permits routine administration of antibiotics to animals as growth promoters despite Denmark's demonstrating that this practice is unnecessary and causes increased antibiotic resistance.[54]

A recent investigative article in the *Toronto Star* showed that some children's jewellery imported into Canada is almost pure lead, contrary to regulation.[55] There are also concerns about the explosion of genetic tests and procedures, which are touted to a worried public. Closer evaluation often reveals that the benefits may have been overblown, especially for people at low risk.[56]

Societies have always had to balance risks with benefits. But our twenty-first-century high technology, mass marketing, and international air travel magnify risk, and sometimes the consequences are irremediable.

Public Health:
An Evaluative Conscience for the Clinical Care System

Health care systems have historically been based on treating those who come through the door and not on those who actually need care. As a result, family doctors spend approximately one in eight visits treating people for upper respiratory infections[57] while most chronic illnesses are underdiagnosed and undertreated.[58] Thousands of Canadians die every year and tens of thousands are hospitalized from heart attacks, strokes, kidney failure, and other complications of their chronic illnesses.[59]

While public health has responsibility for a geographical area, family doctors typically take responsibility only for one episode of care for their patients. Very few family doctors have lists or rosters of patients, and fewer still have lists of patients with certain conditions that require detailed follow-up, such as diabetes.

Most provinces have relocated public health services within regional health authorities. This has caused problems in some jurisdictions with public health's concerns being subordinated to those of the acute care system.[60] On the other hand, Ontario, the only province without regional authorities, downloaded much of the responsibility for public health onto municipalities.[61] Mergers of smaller municipalities into cities like Toronto and Ottawa further complicated this process.

What Can the Health System Do to Maximize Prevention?

If the major contribution to health comes from other sectors, then what is the health care system's role? Sometimes health workers can accomplish a lot themselves. Dr. Tony Hamilton, formerly of Beechy, Saskatchewan, was a tremendous influence on that community's health. For years, he warned his patients about the dangers of cigarette smoking. He worked tirelessly with local officials to make the curling rink and other public venues non-smoking. As a result, few people smoke in Beechy compared with other towns in southwest Saskatchewan. He also convinced a local Hutterite colony to use canola oil instead of lard in their cooking. This intervention would dramatically reduce cholesterol levels and the risks of heart attack.

Public health physician Trevor Hancock notes that there are a variety of reasons to explain why it is easier to implement preventive programs at the local level:[62]

1. The smaller, more human scale allows for closer ties among participants in local projects.
2. Policy-makers live where they work, so they are both more accountable for their decisions and more likely to be affected by their decisions.
3. Community and municipal bureaucratic structures are smaller and relatively more accessible.

It was easier for a well-respected local physician like Dr. Hamilton to make these interventions in a small town than it would be in Saskatoon or Toronto. However, while it is easier to take action at the local level, action at higher levels (federal, provincial) tends to have a greater impact on population health. Nationwide smoking bans and the elimination of lard and other heart-killing fats from deep fryers everywhere would save thousands of lives every year. But action at higher levels also engenders more political conflict. How do we escape this paradox?

The most effective preventive action combines activity at all levels and creates positive feedback loops to sustain itself. In the next section, we give examples of innovations in prevention. Some are making the leap from local action to global impact.

Innovation in Prevention

Kahnawake: Cultural Renewal for Health

Type 2 (formerly adult-onset) diabetes was very rare among First Nations people prior to contact with Europeans. At present, more than 25 per cent of adults over fifty years of age in some Aboriginal communities suffer from this condition.[63]

The Mohawk reserve of Kahnawake occupies 50 square kilometres on the south shore of the St. Lawrence River just across the Mercier Bridge from the Island of Montreal. The Mohawks are one of six nations of the Iroquois Confederacy, which dates back to the fourteenth century. Kahnawake was founded during the second half of the seventeenth century. The community has a long, proud history of physical accomplishment. Starting in the 1860s, Kahnawake men left the reserve to work on high steel projects, originally bridges and later skyscrapers. They are famous for this dangerous craft from Manhattan to Istanbul. Kahnawake is also known for its skilled canoeists; in 1884, fifty-six Kahnawake Mohawks paddled British cartographers through the cataracts of the Nile.

Traditionally, Kahnawake's residents also had a very nutritious diet. The river drew wildlife and provided fish. The Mohawk cultivated the three sisters of the Iroquois culture: beans, corn, and squash. Traditionally, these were planted together to support and thrive off one another. We know now that this diet and lifestyle makes diabetes a rare occurrence.[64]

Kahnawake and some other Aboriginal communities have developed diabetes prevention programs that approach the problem from a cultural perspective. In the 1980s, Dr. Ann Macaulay and the late Dr. Louis Montour, a Mohawk, worked as family physicians in Kahnawake. They noticed that a lot of patients had diabetes.[65] After seven years of hard work, Kahnawake finally won a grant from Health Canada to establish the Kahnawake School Diabetes Prevention Project in 1994. Two community leaders, school principal Alex McCumber and teacher Rhonda Kirby, formed the core of a small group who stimulate community-wide action. They started with children and schools, nutritious food and physical activity. There are monthly events such as broomball and sledding for parents and children. The project attempts to support the parents, who will then support their children's healthier lifestyles.

Other parts of the project include workplace and community interventions. One late fall day, dietitian Chantal Haddad and nurse educator Joyce Rice run a workshop for road and garage maintenance workers. The theme is bananas. The staff provide muffins, discuss recipes, and show how to make a smoothie. The community has fully integrated the project. To avoid becoming the lab animal in someone else's experiment, they have even developed an innovative code of research ethics.[66]

The 1994 grant enabled the project to get off the ground, and a 2000 partnership with the University of Montreal and McGill University led to more stable funding from the Canadian Institutes of Health Research in 2001. The results so far are encouraging. The project is now an intrinsic component of Kahnawake. It has been part of the resurgence of traditional Mohawk culture. The project has influenced policies in recreation and education.[67, 68] Kahnawake banned the sale of junk food in the community's schools.[69]

The Kahnawake program has had successes, but the diabetes epidemic still rages. It took several generations to develop the problem; it will take at least one to two generations to turn it around. There are other such programs in North America, and not all have been successful so far.[70] It is difficult for small communities to buck the North American trend to wide-screen TVs, supersized portions, and bigger waistlines.

While these programs show potential, they also highlight the health system's limited ability to engineer massive social change. It was a shift to fast food, TV, and a suburban, auto-dependent culture that brought us the epidemic of obesity and diabetes. Theoretically the epidemic could be alleviated with a return to slow food, live entertainment, urban densification, and public transportation. However, there are major interests that would fight these policies. Most policies implemented to control obesity and diabetes have so far focused on individual education rather than environmental redesign.

Kahnawake's ban on school junk food might not be a popular policy with fast food chains, which presently sell their products in 30 per cent of US high schools.[71] Taxes on soft drinks and on unhealthy snacks decrease consumption of those products but would be fought hard by commercial interests and anti-tax crusaders.

A bottle of whisky costs the same in Moosonee on the James Bay coast as in downtown Toronto, but fresh fruit is many times more expensive. Food subsidies for remote areas improve the consumption of healthy foods,[72] and might well reduce health care costs. But the new money would still have to be found in the short term, and where would it come from when most voters live in urban areas?

Getting the Lead Out in Toronto

The South Riverdale neighbourhood just east of downtown Toronto was the home to the Canada Metals plant for seventy years. Canada Metals was the country's largest secondary smelter of lead; it extracted already refined lead from scrap, particularly old car batteries. Tests by the Toronto public health department in the early 1970s showed that hundreds of Riverdale children had dangerous levels of lead in their bodies. However, the community was unable to advance its case with the province and found little assistance from neighbourhood doctors. In 1976, the South Riverdale Community Health Centre opened its doors to provide primary health care to the under-doctored community. But the new centre had an agenda beyond treatment. The health centre's environmental committee led the citizens' fight against lead pollution. Pressure from the residents led to the Ministry of the Environment's enforcing its regulations against Canada Metals, to a drop in emissions, to replacement of contaminated soil, and eventually to the closing of the smelter.

In other parts of North America, the main source of environmental lead was tetraethyl lead, a gasoline additive that increased engine performance. The South Riverdale Community Health Centre also co-operated with other groups to encourage the ban on lead in gasoline. As a result of these interventions, the average blood lead level of Riverdale children fell by over 90 per cent. The ban on lead in gasoline has resulted in major decreases in lead levels throughout the world. In retrospect, the high lead levels in Riverdale children from the 1930s to the 1970s likely caused an average 10-point drop in IQ as well as numerous behavioural problems.

The information that so-called low levels of lead pollution were dangerous took decades to affect governmental policy.[73] Initially, the lead industry and many public health authorities focused on education and individual interventions. Parents were admonished to wash their children's hands prior to eating and to vacuum their houses. Gradually, communities like South Riverdale formed alliances with public health departments and lobbied governments to implement environmental solutions, including the elimination of lead in gasoline, emissions controls, and soil abatement.

Sidewalk Safety

In the winter of 1994, a crafts program had just finished at Ottawa's Sandy Hill Community Health Centre. It was an icy night, and two seniors fell as they were making their way home. Further discussion and a few letters spurred a community meeting held in May 1994. The following year, continued community pressure led to the establishment of the Winter Sidewalk Safety Committee.

There are two parts to the program: personal safety and public policy. The committee educated people about safely navigating ice, including the appropriate use of canes and of special grippers that fit onto the bottoms of boots. The committee researched the most effective methods of clearing snow and ice. It concluded that it was important to clear the snow on boulevards between sidewalks and the street because melting water from the snowbanks led to ice formation. The city provided boxes with traction "grit" at key corners where keeping one's footing was often a problem. Political pressure from seniors ensured that the city kept the program in place when provincial cuts caused other budget reductions.

It Takes a Village

In 1996, Regent Park Community Health Centre executive director Carolyn Acker attended an international conference on community health centres in Montreal. She and board member Camille Orridge* took in a riveting presentation by Dr. Jack Geiger, one of the founders of community-oriented primary health care. Geiger described the development of an innovative primary health care project in the Mississippi Delta in the 1960s.[74] The community development aspects of the project especially impressed Acker and Orridge. For example, there were no financial institutions in the health centre's 1,300-square-kilometre, 14,000-population catchment area. Representatives of the health centre visited all the local banks and told them that whichever of them opened a branch in the community, hired residents as tellers, and provided fair mortgages would get all the centre's business. It worked. The community got the bank.

After Geiger showed a video of the establishment of the Mississippi Delta centre, he mentioned that one of the young girls shown receiving services had since become its executive director. This part really stuck with the folks from Regent Park. They knew that very few kids in

---

* The dynamic Orridge is the executive director of the Toronto Community Care Access centre, a home care agency.

Regent Park (colloquially called "the Park") thought they would ever become executive directors. Well-intentioned city planners had created Regent Park after the Second World War. They bulldozed hundreds of houses in the east downtown Cabbagetown neighbourhood and put up public housing. The planners had wanted a mixed neighbourhood. Unfortunately, Toronto's shortage of affordable housing led to the prioritizing of existing public housing for the poorest of the poor. Over the years, the area deteriorated physically and socially. Now over 80 per cent of the Regent Park residents are on social assistance. It is one of the poorest neighbourhoods in Canada. More than half its residents are immigrants, and 70 per cent are visible minorities. Not many kids see themselves finishing high school, never mind running a health centre.

Acker and Orridge left Montreal with a new goal for the Regent Park Community Health Centre: "community succession." They wanted the kids in Regent Park to become the doctors, nurses, and administrators of the future. But first, they concluded, they needed to help the kids from the Park finish high school.

Regent Park kids do reasonably well in elementary school, but they have to leave their community for high school. There they find themselves in an unfriendly world where students and teachers have negative views about the Park. The kids from the Park have less money than most other students, but they still have to pay for transit tickets, lunches, and a dizzying list of fees that the strapped Toronto education system has levied to make up for provincial cutbacks. Mike Harris's mean government also cut welfare payments by 22 per cent in 1995. As a result, kids from the Park dropped out at twice the rate of other Toronto students.

The community health centre started Pathways to Education in the fall of 2001 on a shoestring, with only two months of funding. Now it has a little bigger cushion, but its goals are ambitious. Pathways distributes free transit tickets, provides money for various school fees and other expenses (such as photocopying), and sets aside $1,000 per high school student per year to be used for post-secondary education. Eventually the project will require $2.4 million per year to be self-sustaining.

The program features mentoring, tutoring, financial assistance, and advocacy. Tutoring is available from two sites with over 150 volunteer tutors. There are also seventy mentors. The results so far have been sensational enough for Pathways to garner several awards.[75] Ninety-five per cent of eligible kids participate in Pathways. Serious attendance problems (which are strongly correlated with dropping out) declined by 50 per cent. The number of kids considered at risk academically was also cut by 50 per cent. Program manager Norman Rowen tells the story of one girl who was considered a troublemaker in grade 9. Now, in grade 10, she is excelling academically and says she wants to be a lawyer. She babysits two young siblings, and when she starts to study, the six-year-old reads too while the three-year-old pretends to read.

Acker admits that Pathways didn't have to be run by the health centre. But she says that in Regent Park, the community health centre was the logical organization to do so. She also adds that there is no question in her mind that Pathways is a preventive health program.

Real Welfare Reform

Debates on social welfare policy mirror those on the nature of good and evil. Some maintain that if we give recipients of social assistance better services, they are more likely to become independent. Others claim that mollycoddling those on the dole just encourages them. These voices claim that we need to be "cruel to be kind" in order to make welfare recipients independent. They advocate time limits for welfare, more checks for fraud, and workfare.

There are two major problems with the tough-love approach. The first is that the vast majority of those on social assistance in Canada are the children of single parents. If we treat parents roughly, it's the kids who feel the lash. Another problem with tough love is that many of these single parents (overwhelmingly mothers) have been badly treated all their lives—one more kick in the pants will likely kick them down, not up. In fact, the System-Linked Research Unit at McMaster University has documented that one-half of single parents on social assistance are depressed.[76]

The Mac unit conducted a fascinating study that proves the effectiveness of a "soft-love" approach to those on social assistance. Working with the Hamilton-Wentworth Department of Social Services, they randomly assigned social assistance recipients to various interventions that they thought might improve their lives. One group received a package of child care, recreation, and skills development. Another group received employment retraining, while a third had regular visits from a public health nurse, who worked with them to develop a structured problem-solving approach to family issues. Another group received no interventions, and yet another received all of them.

At the end of two years, all the intervention groups were more likely to have left welfare than the control group, only 10 per cent of which discontinued social assistance. Twenty-five per cent of the group with the comprehensive services left welfare. And this relative two-and-a-half-fold increase in welfare departure didn't cost anything. After the decreased welfare payments were factored into the equation, they more than paid for the enhanced services.[77]

Professor Gina Browne, director and founder of the System-Linked Research Unit, concludes from a decade of research that "it is as or more effective and as or less expensive to offer health-oriented, pro-active, intersectoral community services to people with synergistic risks than to provide services on demand in a piecemeal, sectoralized or separately-financed manner."[78]

Developing a Conscience for the Health System
There are increasing examples of the integration of public health with health care. Manitoba, for example, has developed a provincial registry and follow-up program for childhood immunizations;[79] Manitobans no longer have to rely upon tattered immunization cards and family physicians' charts for their immunization record.

And the British Columbia Cancer Agency has run the continent's oldest and largest cervical cancer screening program for over fifty years; it has helped reduce the rate of invasive cancer by one-half to two-thirds.[80]

In some regional authorities, the public health approach is gradually becoming the overall approach to health care. As described in chapter 1, the public health officers within the Saskatoon, Edmonton, and Calgary regional health authorities were in central positions to control the influenza epidemic in the winter of 2000. Dr. Cory Neudorf is Saskatoon's chief medical health officer, but he is also the vice-president for corporate support for the regional health authority. He is intimately involved in developing services based on the needs of the population—the essence of public health.

The Saskatchewan Human Services Integration Forum

Saskatchewan established the Human Services Integration Forum in 1994. It includes associate and assistant deputy ministers from eleven ministries and secretariats. The development of the forum was spurred by a 1993 investigation of twenty-seven child deaths, which concluded, like Gina Browne, that broad social policy initiatives were required in order to address the issues. The forum focuses on promoting better service integration. It has links with nine regional intersectoral committees, which expanded beyond government membership to include such third parties as health districts, school divisions, colleges, band councils, police, and housing authorities.

The forum supports a number of initiatives, including Saskatchewan's Action Plan for Children. The Action Plan has established the Children's Advocate Office, co-ordinated interdepartmental budget planning, supported the development of an early childhood initiative, and funded more than three hundred interdepartmental prevention and support grants to local groups. The forum also provides overall policy co-ordination to several provincial initiatives, including Integrated School-Linked Services, the Aboriginal Policy Framework, the Culture and Recreation Strategy, the Saskatchewan

Training Strategy, the Restorative Justice and Aboriginal Justice strategies, Saskatchewan Assisted Living Services, and Health's Strategy for Intersectoral Collaboration. The most recent focus is Schools Plus, a plan to use the schools as a place to integrate services for children and families.

Sherbrooke Goes Healthy

Sherbrooke is a bustling city of 140,000 located 150 kilometres southeast of Montreal. In July 1987, the Sherbrooke regional health authority (RRSSS) supplied $20,000 to hire a co-ordinator for its Healthy City project. She met with a variety of municipal officials over the next several months, and in November 1987, the Sherbrooke municipal council established a project steering committee made up of the city's general manager, the directors of the city's services and public relations, the directors of both of the city's community health centres (CLSCs), and the public health department. In May 1988, the city adopted a resolution making it a Healthy City. The city put up $15,000, each CLSC put up $2,500, the public health department put up $10,000, and the RRSSS renewed its commitment. The original partners were soon joined by many others—the chamber of commerce, the Catholic school board, the transit commission, and two post-secondary institutions.

The Healthy City project established a number of concrete ventures. Working groups were established for each, and they developed action plans for their enterprises, which were then approved by the steering committee and the municipal council. Projects completed include a youth recreation centre, a handbook for architects and construction contractors to make them more aware of interior design issues for the elderly, and "Yes to the Environment," which fosters innovative, co-operative solutions to the city's environmental problems.

One long-term effect of a community consultation on children was the creation of a variety of CPS, or "church-park school" projects. These ventures attempt to foster increased co-operation between the different key institutions and community organizations within three targeted neighbourhoods.

In 1992, after completing its first eight projects, the Healthy City Committee decided to energetically pursue a single long-term priority: fighting against poverty. A working group chaired by the mayor, Jean Perrault, organized visits to the poor areas by business people and public managers, published a guide to help businesses and institutions adopt hiring and service policies that favour the poor, and set up a data bank of unused equipment to be offered to community associations that work with the poor. The city also investigated methods of reducing staff overtime to create new job opportunities, especially for youth.

Creating a Positive Feedback Loop for Health

To break out of the local arena, we need to use local action to promote political action at higher levels. In Vancouver's DTES, the initial harm reduction programs such as needle exchange started with a few users. But citizens' groups such as VANDU linked with public health and pushed the issues up the line. Eventually the public debate resulted in political change and in a new mayor who wants to push the envelope further. In Toronto, concern about a local lead smelter helped ensure regulations to protect all Canadian children from lead pollution. In Ottawa, concerns by seniors at a community health centre led to a citywide program to reduce falls. In Sherbrooke, concerns by local health workers at a community health centre led to a city-wide intervention to reduce poverty.

Governments can complete the circle by providing resources to public health, community health centres, and citizens' organizations. This stimulates more local action and creates a positive feedback loop for health. The origins of public health in Canada, as in Britain and the US, lie with social reformers who were leaders in their local communities.[81] Analyses of successful healthy community projects in Quebec have concluded that involvement of public health and community health centre personnel has been key to successful local projects.[82] Many health advocates argue that community action is the lifeblood of public health. Professor Toby Citrin from the School of Public Health at the University of Michigan claims that "communities are essential to the future of public health."[83] New Zealand epidemiologist Dr. Robert Beaglehole claims that the empowerment of local communities is "a necessary step in the rejuvenation of public health."[84]

The steps involved in starting a bonfire provide a useful metaphor for this process. You can't start a fire by holding a match to a pile of logs. The fire must be started with small sticks, the kindling. As the kindling catches fire, bigger sticks are added until, finally, the large logs are laid on. Community-level action is the kindling that starts the fire for population health. However, without larger logs (higher-level action), the fire will soon burn out.[85]

There are some special lessons here for the reform of primary health care services. Better care for chronic illness, as described in chapter 5, can dramatically reduce complications. Treating alternate-level-of-care patients in more appropriate settings can improve individual outcomes and save resources for the system. Better teamwork, as described in chapter 9, can make our existing number of physicians and nurses go much further. But even if we implement all these reforms, we will still miss the biggest prize: preventing illness entirely.

That's why the programs with the most potential are those that link primary prevention directly with health services.* Regent Park, South Riverdale, Sandy Hill, and Sherbrooke community health centres are examples that integrate treatment and prevention.

---

* The concept of community-oriented primary health care was actually pioneered by Dr. Sidney Kark in South Africa in the 1940s.

Quebec's Quiet Public Health Revolution

It is hard to believe that only forty-five years ago, Quebec was one of the most backward parts of the country with some of the least developed public health services. Now Quebec is considered to have the most effective public health services in Canada. It's one of the few provinces with modern legislation.[86] Since 1998, Quebec has had a National Institute of Public Health, which, like the US Centers for Disease Control supports communicable disease control with a flying team of experts.

But Quebec's public health system's concerns are broader than infectious disease. Quebec is the only province with a network of local community health centres that integrate treatment services, social services, and local public health—the CLSCs (*centres locaux services communautaire*). The CLSCs are based upon the World Health Organization definition of primary health care,[87] which is very similar to the concept of community oriented primary healthy care. In the third world, this might mean drilling a well to provide safe water. In Canada, it might mean helping inner city kids finish high school or preventing aboriginal kids from developing diabetes.

While some other provinces have adopted and then ignored goals for their health programs, Quebec's health policy has reflected its public health goals since the 1980s. The public health system is charged with "exerting a positive influence on major health determinants, in particular through trans-sectoral coordination." CLSCs have a mandate to work with their communities and citizens' organizations in developing neighbourhood health plans based upon the provincial goals. Quebec's public health system has the architecture to effectively promote local action on the social determinants of health. Communities are then able to transmit political pressure upward to promote higher-level policy change.

Conclusion: Public Health = Democracy

Public health and prevention are mainly responsible for the health improvements of the past 150 years. Unfortunately, there is little pressure to prevent anonymous deaths in the future when there are so many identifiable victims suffering now. Canada's public health services are in crisis. The SARS outbreak is just a mild taste of the epidemics we face if our governments cannot overcome their petty jealousies to implement a Canadian disease control service.

However, public health must broaden its focus beyond germs if it is to be successful. Housing, education, gender, and the environment all play a major role in determining the health of Canadians. Health services must work with communities and other sectors to influence these determinants. Public health's opponents claim that this amounts to political interference in health policy while supporters quote Virchow's dictum—"health is politics." Effective public health services don't rely only on quarantine and vaccination. They give power to people, which is the definition of democracy. Controlling HIV in the DTES requires epidemiology and democracy. Ann Livingston, VANDU's indefatigable co-ordinator, says her organization teaches drug addicts "citizenship 101." Her motto echoes that of public health workers throughout history. "All people, no matter how criminalized and hated, deserve a chance to live, and a chance to make a better life for themselves."

Your Community and Prevention

- Do your country, province, and community have overall strategies for health, including goals and measurable targets?
- Does your province have a cabinet-level coordinating committee for human services?
- Could your community's public health system cope with a SARS like outbreak *and* another serious problem at the same time?

- Do local public health and primary health care services have a mandate to link with citizen groups and engage in intersectoral action for health?
- Does your community's (or province's) primary health care strategy integrate prevention and public health?
- Does your community offer comprehensive health and social services to people on social assistance?
- Does public health have a mandate to protect watersheds as well as test water?
- Does your community have HIV/AIDS prevention programs including school-based education, outreach with sex workers, and special programs for those who use intravenous drugs including needle exchange, low threshold methadone treatment, and safe injection facilities?
- Does your community have an organized program to encourage healthy living like the Kahnawake Schools Diabetes Prevention Project? Does your community permit junk food in schools?
- Does your community have an organized falls prevention program?
- Does your community have a program like Pathways 2 Education to help poor kids get through high school and into post-secondary education?
- Does your community have an organized approach to poverty like Sherbrooke Quebec?
- Is public health involved in evaluating and guiding the treatment system?

Chapter 9

What's Up, Doc?
Improving Access with Teamwork

Shirl Schilbe was living in Port Lambton, a scenic town on the shores of Lake Huron, when she had her heart attack in 1999.[1] She decided that she should move back to her native London to be closer to her specialty medical care. However, a year later she still had not been able to find a family physician. In 2000, there were no London family physicians taking new patients. Three years later, there were only two.[2]

In 1999, the Quebec College of Family Physicians estimated that 300,000 Montrealers lacked a family doctor.[3] Local doctors claim that 25 per cent of Sudbury's population does not have a family doctor.[4] Opposition critics blame the Nova Scotia government for not doing more to address the doctor shortage in their province.[5]

Everyone in Canada seems to be convinced that there is a drastic shortage of doctors and that it is getting worse. But Canada actually has more doctors than ever before. So what is happening to these doctors? Have they disappeared into some black hole?

This chapter examines the doctor shortage and diagnoses why we perceive a doctor shortage when there are more doctors all the time. Then it offers a number of examples of innovative programs that demonstrate that we can dramatically improve access to physicians if they are used differently. It's not the absolute number of doctors that determines access. It's how they practise. Like other parts of health care, our problems with access to physicians appears to be at least as much about lack of management as lack of resources.

What Are the Numbers?

According to the latest data from the Canadian Institute for Health Information (CIHI), there were 59,412 doctors in Canada in 2002, up by almost 900 from the year before.[6] The number of physicians per capita ratio rose from 152 per 100,000 in 1981 to 195 per 100,000 in 1993, a 28 per cent increase.[7] During this time, there continued to be media reports of "dangerous doctor shortages." In the mid-1990s, in an unprecedented fashion, the ratio then dropped to 185 (in 1998) before rising to 189 in 2002, roughly 3 per cent below the peak.

A recent CIHI report further analyzed these numbers and concluded that after adjusting for various demographic changes in the general Canadian and physician populations,* the functional doctor–patient ratio had declined by 5 per cent from its all-time peak in 1993.[8]

It is regularly claimed that Canadian doctors are fleeing to the US—a massive medical brain drain. However, only a small proportion of Canadian doctors leave the country in any one year. The outflow actually peaked in 1978 when 873 Canadian doctors departed and only 192 returned for a net loss of 681, or 2.7 per cent of all physicians. In 2002, 500 doctors left Canada while 291 Canadian doctors returned, for a net loss of only 209, or 0.3 per cent of the physician workforce.[9]

Of course, there are different numbers in different provinces and regions. Quebec has 14 per cent more doctors per capita than the Canadian average, and Saskatchewan has 19 per cent fewer. From 1998 to 2002, there was an 11 per cent increase in the number of

---

* More new physicians are women, who tend not to work the same hours as men, and it is claimed that an older population requires more medical services.

doctors per capita in Alberta but 1 per cent decrease in Ontario family doctors. Nevertheless, the stories of perceived shortages are the same everywhere.

What Are Doctors Doing?

If Canadian doctors are not running away to the US, and if the physician per capita numbers are basically the same as they have been for ten years, then why do we perceive there to be a shortage? Has someone kidnapped them?

The answer is that doctors are working in an increasingly inefficient structure. Even if the numbers of doctors doubled, unless we were to change the structure in which they work, Canadians would still have inadequate access.

The Fee's the Thing

Most Canadian doctors receive the vast majority of their income from fees for service. As Dr. Gabor Maté, a Vancouver family physician and columnist notes, "Our fee-for-service medical system actively punishes doctors who spend time with patients and financially rewards those who practise superficial medicine in profit-motive walk-in clinics, who see minor problems and refer more challenging cases to the emergency ward."[10]

Fee-for-service is piecework. The more patients a doctor sees, the more she makes. But the fee schedules, which predate medicare, also pay much more for procedural than for cerebral services. Put more crudely, fee-for-service pays doctors much more to cut and prod than to listen and think. As a result, doctors can maximize their incomes by seeing patients quickly and doing more to them.

For example, in Ontario,[11] a gastroenterologist earns 62 per cent more for a complete endoscopic examination of the colon than for a consultation[12] and an ophthalmologist receives nearly nine times as much for a cataract extraction and lens insertion than for a consultation.[13] In each case, the consultation would take longer than the procedure. The Ontario Health Insurance Plan (OHIP) pays an obstetrician/gynecologist 25 per cent more for a hysterectomy than for a normal vaginal delivery even though the delivery takes more time and is fraught with more danger.[14]

Compare the impact of the current fee-for-service system on two family doctors with contrasting practice styles. Dr. Do-Right delivers babies and works in the ER and hospital. She visits patients at home and helps them die with dignity. She also has patients in the local nursing home and takes call every fourth night. She does much of her work on the telephone, talking to patients, home care nurses, social workers, and others. But, like most provinces, hers doesn't permit billing for phone calls. She has taught her patients to manage their own minor illnesses, so the only patients she sees in person are those with complicated problems. As a result, she can only see three to four per hour. She employs a nurse to provide better care for her patients, but she cannot bill for the services the nurse provides. Even in a province with a high fee schedule, Dr. Do-Right's annual billings would be less than $200,000 for a sixty- to seventy-hour week. After her overhead, she would barely clear $100,000.

Dr. Do-Right can look across the corridor and see Dr. Make-Good, who never leaves his office, where he sees eight patients per hour, forty hours per week. After regular hours, his answering machine refers patients to emergency departments or walk-in clinics. He doesn't employ a nurse, doesn't talk to patients on the phone, and hasn't taken call since he was in training. Dr. Make-Good would bill approximately $400,000 per year and take home over $300,000.

One night, Dr. Do-Right's pager awakens her at three in the morning. One of her hospital patients has taken a turn for the worse. As she pulls on her clothes and looks for the keys to her ten-year-old clunker, her new baby begins to cry and her spouse exclaims in exasperation, "If you leave me again, just stay out. Dr. Make-Good has two Mercedes in his driveway and he never has to leave his family in the middle of the night!"

Of course, Dr. Do-Right and Dr. Make-Good are caricatures. Most family doctors are somewhere in the middle. But these practice portraits illustrate the stark choices available to doctors, choices that aren't available to nurses, teachers, or others whom we pay through the public purse. Doctors are not employees. They are independent contractors who can set up shop where they want and see the patients they want to see, and who are paid for the services they render.

Of course, doctors who practise in hospitals have to maintain privileges and this requires some responsibilities. But the increasing numbers of family doctors who don't do any hospital work are pretty much free to run their practices in any way they see fit. These perverse incentives have been with us for decades, but now the flight is on. An Ontario study of family physician practice patterns between 1991 and 1997 found fewer family physicians working in hospitals or nursing homes, delivering babies, or providing house-call services.[15] There was a 55 per cent increase in the proportion of family doctors who did nothing other than see patients in their offices.

The disparities in medicine are not confined to family practice. There are similar inequities within and between specialties. Because doctors are paid so much more to do than to think, doctors who have more gadgets in their bags make far more money than those who just use their heads. Geriatrics, pediatrics, and psychiatry are some of the specialties that find themselves on the short end of the fee stick. According to CIHI, in 2000/1 pediatricians earned 22 per cent less than other specialists and psychiatrists were the lowest billing of all doctors, 34 per cent less than the specialist average.[16] Dr. Tilak Malhotra, a pediatrician in Prince Albert, notes that treating children can take twice as much time as a similar adult case: "A child can't give you a history. You have to spend time with the patient but also with the parents."[17]

Geriatricians face problems similar to those of pediatricians. They have to spend a lot more time with their patients and their patients' families to take a proper history, and they perform few fee-rich procedures on them. Dr. Willie Molloy, the Hamilton geriatrician who designed the "Let me decide" advance clinical directive discussed in chapter 4, says that many geriatricians are so fed up with their low pay that they have left the field and just practise general internal medicine. He claims that when young doctors see that geriatricians make so much less than other doctors, they choose another specialty.[18] It is important to stress that these disparities have nothing to do with medicare. In North America, fee schedules have always rewarded procedures more than cognitive services.[19]

And the Winner Is . . . Ophthalmology

Ophthalmologists are the fee sweepstakes winners. In 2000/1 they billed 50 per cent more than the average for all specialists. In Saskatchewan, ophthalmologists billed more than three times as much as pediatricians. In Manitoba, one of a few provinces that publish the list of all doctors' billings, ten of the top twenty-eight billing doctors were ophthalmologists in fiscal year 2001/2.[20]

That's because one of Canada's most popular operations is cataract surgery and it pays big bucks. Cataract surgery used to take hours to perform with patients required to spend seven to ten days in hospital to recover. Now, due to technological advances, it takes experienced operators less than fifteen minutes to perform the surgery and patients typically recover at home. But in Ontario, the operation usually pays more than $400.* That's the equivalent of over twenty regular office visits to a family doctor.

There are very few Canadians who know about these disparities. Dear reader, you are in an elite group. However, other doctors know. It drives them crazy. One general surgeon recalls being awakened to remove a bleeding Meckel's diverticulum (a small pouch in the lower intestine) before the patient, a child, bled to death. "I was

---

* OHIP pays $405.50 for the cataract extraction and $100.75 for the insertion of an interocular lens.

called out at 5:00 a.m. to remove a two-year-old's bleeding Meckel's, s——ing my pants until the Meckel's was in the dish and kid stable. All this for about two-thirds of a cataract."

In the United States, these disparities resulted in the federal government's Commission for Medicare and Medicaid* implementing a resource-based relative value scale (RBRVS) in the 1980s. A team of physicians and statisticians looked at every item in the fee schedule and assessed how much training and skill were required for its performance. Then they rebuilt the fee schedule from scratch. Not surprisingly, there were large increases for family doctors and geriatricians but decreases for specialties like ophthalmology.

In Canada, physicians are equally concerned. Dr. Larry Erlick, the current president of the Ontario Medical Association, asks, "Why do some physicians receive 2–3 times the income of others? We all are expert in our own fields, dedicated to excellence and prepared to provide top quality patient care."[21] However, it has been impossible for doctors to find a solution themselves. In the early 1990s, the Ontario, Alberta, and British Columbia medical associations each spent over a million dollars to prepare RBRVS reports. However, when the boards of these associations received the reports, they didn't act. The potential losers screamed and the potential winners didn't have the stomach for the fight. In 1997, the OMA and the provincial government agreed to appoint former Manitoba deputy minister Dr. John Wade to redo the RBRVS report. Within a few months, the specialists within the OMA voted that no fee should go up or down by more than 3 per cent per year, effectively neutering the whole process.

Dr. Wade soldiered on. His draft report, released in 2001, recommended reducing the cataract fee to $131 but suggested doubling the fee for some neurosurgical procedures and increasing fees for

---

* In the US, Medicare is a national program that covers the elderly and those with certain illnesses (such as end-stage kidney disease). Medicaid is the program for the medically indigent, but it covers only a fraction of those without private health insurance.

geriatrician consultations by 70 per cent.[22] He eventually tabled his final report in 2002, but it appears destined to sit on the shelf with the others.

What Are the Prescriptions?

Teamwork Goes for Gold

The present fee-for-service payment system creates huge disparities in income between doctors, and poisons their professional relationships. It also causes terrible problems for patients. Provincial medicare plans pay doctors little or nothing for essential services such as home care and palliative care, with the result that it is frustratingly difficult in many communities to find doctors willing to take on these tasks. Fee-for-service also penalizes doctors who are good team members. Most provinces don't pay doctors to discuss cases with home care nurses or other providers, and those that do don't pay much. When Dr. Do-Right hired a nurse, she cut her throat twice. First, she pays the nurse out of her overhead, and second, she can't bill for the services the nurse performs. As a result, very few family doctors practise with nurses, and home care staff across the country complain about the difficulty of communicating with doctors.

The US National Institute of Medicine's *Crossing the Quality Chasm* identified the creation of high-functioning teams as one of the key solutions to health care's woes. We may think of heroic individuals (usually doctors) when we think of health care, but in reality, as Dr. Donald Berwick, president of the Institute for Healthcare Improvement says, teams, not individuals, deliver health care to patients with serious or chronic illnesses. Our women's and men's hockey squads inspired all Canadians with their gold-medal victories in the Salt Lake City Winter Olympics. They would not have won a single game if the players had competed as individuals. Canada won gold because our stars played as team members.

Specialists or Generalists or Both?

In the early 1990s when Bill and Hillary Clinton attempted to revamp the US health care system, there was considerable concern among specialists that the reforms would control access (and costs) by putting pressure on primary care providers to decrease referrals. The specialty groups fought back partly by supporting research that indicated that outcomes were better if specialists managed complicated health problems.[23] However, other research indicated that generalists' patients did better if they had two or more illnesses. A US study showed that patients with rheumatoid arthritis had better arthritis outcomes if they were followed by a rheumatologist but were more likely to get routine preventive care if they were followed by a generalist.[24] Toronto's Dr. Donald Redelmeier demonstrated that Ontario residents being treated for one chronic condition (such as emphysema) were less likely to get good care for other illnesses.[25]

Eventually, some researchers studied the obvious and demonstrated that patients did best if specialists and generalists work together in what are termed "shared care" arrangements. A recent study showed that specialist-managed heart attack patients did better than generalist-managed ones. But patients did best if a specialist/generalist team jointly managed them.[26] Other research indicates that shared care provides better outcomes for obesity treatment[27] and diabetes.[28]

Not surprisingly, embedding specialists and family doctors in multidisciplinary teams improves outcomes even more than just linking doctors together. As we mentioned in chapter 6, doctor/nurse practitioner teams provide better-quality care to nursing home residents.[29] Multidisciplinary teams have also been found to provide better-quality care for congestive heart failure,[30] depression in the elderly,[31] community management of severe mental illness,[32] rheumatoid arthritis,[33] hyperlipidemia,[34] diabetes,[35] and young people with physical disabilities.[36]

Many doctors are keen advocates of teamwork. Dr. Philip Berger, the chief of Family and Community Medicine at Toronto's St. Michael's Hospital, notes that when his department established interdisciplinary teams, nurses became the team chairpersons: "The designation of nurses as the chair of the team of course resulted in a shift of power away from the physicians to the nurses. But this was not a shift of power for the sake of shifting power. It was a shift to the health professional who is most often at the centre of the patient's care and the health professional most often available for patients."[37]

However, team-building is a new concept for health care, where decision-making all too often seems patterned on the military. It wasn't too long ago that nurses had to stand when a doctor entered the room. Other sectors have realized the importance of flattening hierarchical structures, and health care is catching up. But sometimes it seems to be achingly slow. Not all physicians are ready to work in equal relationships with other professionals. A recent survey showed that 36 per cent of Canadian doctors said that the physician's role should be to lead the team.[38] A US survey of students showed that most doctors, nurses, and social workers in training believed that an interdisciplinary team approach benefits patients, but the physicians in training tended to believe that the team's primary purpose was to assist physicians.[39]

In September 2001, nurses at the McGill University Health Centre walked off the job in protest after an orthopedic surgeon violently grabbed an operating-room nurse's wrist, causing tendon and nerve damage. Subsequent media reports noted that this assault was not an isolated event.[40] Alberta studies showed that more than one in three nurses reported verbal abuse and one in six physical abuse *in their five most recent work shifts*. While most abuse came from patients, one in eight episodes involved a physician as the abuser. Debbie Forward, president of the Newfoundland and Labrador Nurses Union, says the operating rooms have a particularly troubling incidence of abuse: "Surgeons throw things around the room, they grab nurses, they use degrading language, and they swear." Forward says the most troubling episode with which she is familiar involved a surgeon who choked a nurse until he was restrained.

Teamwork Triumphs in Saskatchewan

In chapter 8, we introduced you to Dr. Tony Hamilton from Beechy, Saskatchewan. In 1995, Dr. Hamilton was one of three doctors serving the southwestern Saskatchewan towns of Beechy, Kyle, and Lucky Lake. However, Kyle's doctor died, and then Lucky Lake's retired and promptly died. These tragedies left Dr. Hamilton as the only physician to serve over 3,200 people. The newly created health district tried to recruit another physician to no avail. Fortunately, in 1996, Joanne Perry had just graduated as one of the first nurse practitioners from the new program at Saskatchewan's Institute of Applied Science and Technology. That year, Dr. Hamilton left fee-for-service payment for a contract with the health district and started working with Perry. Their team was an immediate hit.

Dr. Hamilton retired a few years later but his successor, Dr. J.C. Cooper, now works with three nurse practitioners, one in each town. These four professionals work in a high-functioning team with the rest of the regional staff, including public health, mental health, and home care, as well as two long-term care facilities. As a result of this arrangement, Dr. Cooper can maintain a practice more than twice as large as the national average. Depending upon the location, 80 to 98 per cent of non-emergency patients can be given an appointment within forty-eight hours of calling for one.

Some doctors are concerned that if they don't see their patients for every concern, no matter how trivial, they won't maintain an effective relationship with them. However, Dr. Hamilton, back in Beechy for six weeks while Dr. Cooper takes a needed vacation, scoffs at such claims. He says that it is much more professionally rewarding to have the time to work up a complicated patient than to spend one's time with minor illnesses. He notes that he recently had the time to address the case of young boy with attention deficit disorder and met with his parents and teacher. He claims that he couldn't possibly have afforded to do this without being part of a team.

This project is dynamic and is continuing to evolve and to measure its progress. But it is a wonderful example of what can be achieved when health care services are planned around the needs of patients by the team that will be caring for them.

Quebec: L'équipe nouveau

Ormstown is a quiet picture-postcard town of four thousand, 80 kilometres southwest of Montreal. In the late 1990s, Guy Rho, executive director of the hospital, and Guy Deschenes, executive director of the *centre locale des services communitaire* (CLSC), thought there must be a better way to improve the efficiency and effectiveness of the health services in their region. They looked at some innovative models in the northeastern US and talked to the three family doctors in nearby Huntington. Eventually, the doctors joined with the hospital and the CLSC in a new project, which was funded by the federal government's Health Transition Fund. The Ormstown CLSC was one of the few in Quebec that did not have its own physicians, so the Huntington doctors had always had a close relationship with it. Dr. Raymond Lemieux and his colleagues were keen to deepen the relationship if it improved care for their patients.

Michelle Bigras, a CLSC nurse, started working with the doctors, but at the start neither she nor the physicians knew what she should do. Gradually, Bigras has worked out her role with the doctors and the other staff. She sees almost any type of patient, although she does refer more complicated patients to the physicians. She removes sutures, deals with patients with urinary tract infections, and manages all the patients who are on anti-coagulation therapy.

Dr. Lemieux notes that Bigras isn't just a physician-substitute. She also complements the doctor. For example, she educates asthmatics to make sure they understand how to use their inhalers properly. It often requires quite a bit of time, but it hadn't been done before. We know from chapter 5 that better teaching for asthmatics can dramatically improve their control and lessen hospitalizations. Dr. Lemieux notes that physicians don't have to do everything and that nurses do some things better, such as patient education. As a result of the teamwork, the three doctors find their time goes further.

Teamwork Takes Off

We mentioned the innovative Taber, Alberta, primary health care project in chapters 4 and 5. Taber is a town of about 7,500 located between the Rockies and Alberta's Badlands. Including the surrounding rural area, about 13,500 people use the town's health services. Dr. Rob Wedel realized in the early 1990s that there was a coming crisis in access to health care for people living in rural areas. However, it took almost ten years for his dreams to become reality. Now Dr. Wedel and the other doctors work with a nurse and a nurse practitioner and are better integrated with the regional staff, including home care, public health, and mental health. As a result of this teamwork, the doctors manage roughly 50 per cent more patients than the national average.*

Dr. Ed Hudson was always hooked on teamwork. Dr. Hudson's father started practice in Hamiota, a small town in western Manitoba's picturesque Assiniboine Valley, in 1907 when there was a typhoid epidemic. The junior Dr. Hudson was destined to carry on his father's good works, but the Second World War detoured him to the Pacific and European theatres of war. After the war, he took up practice with his father and Dr. Keith Hames. The Hudson-Hames partnership was always looking for new ways to get their hard work done. In 1972, after Dr. John Hastings's national report extolled the virtues of interdisciplinary practice, Drs. Hudson and Hames and the town of Hamiota approached the Manitoba Ministry of Health to establish a community health centre. By 1974, the centre was up and running. Over the years, there have been many changes, but the board and staff of the centre have never deviated from their commitment to high quality and accessible care.

Like other effective teams, the Hamiota group has a full meeting every morning. It takes only fifteen to thirty minutes to identify "who's hot and who's not," but this simple tactic ensures that everyone is

---

* There are eight doctors amounting to roughly six full-time equivalents.

familiar with the key issues of the day. It also serves as a wonderful platform for staff education.

The granddaddy of Canadian health centres is the Sault Ste. Marie Group Health Centre, which was discussed in chapter 5. It isn't the oldest interdisciplinary health centre in the country,* but it is the largest. The clinic features sixty-four doctors, eight nurse practitioners, ninety-six registered nurses, and fifty-two other professional and technical staff. The clinic provides comprehensive care to over fifty-six thousand patients.

The Somerset West Community Health Centre in Ottawa established its own walk-in clinic to better serve those of its patients who require same-day appointments. The clinic is very popular and on busy days can see over forty patients. One of the doctors is assigned to back up the clinic, which is run by a nurse practitioner. Clinical co-ordinator Dr. Dona Bower recalls how other doctors warned her that physicians would still have to see the patients anyway. However, shortly after the clinic started, a study showed that 93 per cent of patients did not require a doctor's consultation. Nurse practitioner Jennie Humbert works relief at Somerset West but also co-ordinates the nurse practitioner program at the University of Ottawa. She says that the morale of nurses is always higher in places where they can work up to their full potential. She notes that without the nurse practitioners in the clinic, the doctors would be overburdened and many patients would end up needlessly using emergency departments.

You will recall Dr. Russell Goldman from chapter 4 as a young Toronto family physician with the Mt. Sinai Hospital palliative care program. Dr. Goldman was struggling to manage sixty patients until he tried out a pilot project with Toronto's home care agency, the Community Care Access Centre. For the past two years, Dr. Goldman has been working with the same two nurses instead of having to deal with different nurses for each of the patients he sees. This teamwork

---

* That honour is usually claimed by Winnipeg's Mt. Carmel clinic, which opened in 1926.

has permitted him and the nurses to know each other better and to work together more effectively. A full evaluation has been completed, although the Ministry of Health hadn't yet released the results at the time of writing. But Dr. Goldman thinks the project helped his patients a lot. Although he is busy, he can now provide care to one hundred patients, a 67 per cent increase in his caseload since before teamwork.

Shared Care: Better Use of Specialists

While there are slightly fewer family doctors per capita in Canada now than there were ten years ago, the number of specialists has continued to increase. There are now 93 specialist physicians per 100,000 Canadians, up from 89 in 1993. Specialists could also be much more efficient if they worked in teams with family doctors, nurses, and other care providers. Traditional specialty practice in Canada is based on seeing patients who are referred by family doctors for one-hour consultations. This is very inefficient because frequently a family doctor needs only a quick phone call with the specialist to clarify a specific issue.[41] Occasionally the specialist needs two hours to finish a complicated consultation. Some specialists provide ongoing care to patients that could be provided by family doctors with some intermittent coaching from the specialist. Our present complement of specialists could greatly extend their range, with the appropriate supports.

The Hamilton health service organization (HSO) Mental Health and Nutrition Program is an excellent example of a program that integrates specialty expertise with primary health care. HSOs are family practices in which the doctors are paid on the basis of capitation instead of fee for service. *Capitation* is literally per head funding: the Ontario Ministry of Health pays the HSOs a certain amount of money per patient per month depending upon their age and gender. Many HSOs have since joined the newer Ontario Family Health Network program.

The Hamilton program started in 1994 and now includes 23 full-time equivalent (FTE) mental health counsellors and 2.2 FTE psychiatrists working with 87 family doctors in 36 practices at 51 different sites. These practices include 180,000 patients, roughly 40 per cent of Hamilton's population. The family doctors refer patients to mental health counsellors, who work in the practices, and both professionals liaise with the psychiatrists. The psychiatrists visit the family doctors' practices and can see patients for traditional consultations. However, most of their time is spent meeting with the family doctors, mental health counsellors, and other professionals to discuss cases as a group. This allows a psychiatrist to provide input into the care of many patients instead of only the few that he or she could see in regular consultations.

The psychiatrists are also available by telephone at very short notice. This permits family doctors or counsellors to provide instant assistance to the other professionals. Dr. Nick Kates, the psychiatrist who is the program's director, notes that the family doctors don't call often but that it is a tremendous comfort to them that there is a specialist available by phone when they need one.

Dr. Bob James's family practice is located in a renovated century house in the historic community of Dundas, just west of Hamilton. He finds that the program helps him provide better care to his patients. He recalls a teenager in his practice who was a real diagnostic dilemma. He had had a head injury as a young boy, and had difficulty in school with teachers and was bullied by other students. After seeing the boy and his family with the visiting psychiatrist, they concluded that he had a rare form of autism. With the appropriate therapy, he is now functioning well and his behaviour is much more socially appropriate.

Darlene James, Dr. James's wife, is a social worker who works as the mental health worker in his practice. She really enjoys working in a family-practice environment after years of working in hospitals. Darlene notes that in hospital, social workers tend to feel like "guests in the house of medicine," while she feels at home in primary health care. Of course, this attitude is fostered because the Jameses' team gives new meaning to the term "family practice."

In 2000, Hamilton family doctors made over four thousand refer-rals to the program, greatly increasing their patients' access to men-tal health services. The youngest patient has been four and the oldest ninety-eight. One in eight patients is under eighteen years of age. The counsellor deals with 75 per cent of the patients without involv-ing the psychiatrist directly. The psychiatrists see only 15 per cent of the patients alone and another 10 per cent with the counsellor. Popu-lation surveys have shown that the prevalence of psychiatric disorder is 25 per cent.[42] However, relatively few people with psychiatric disorders actually receive mental health services. The Hamilton pro-gram increased the numbers of patients receiving mental health care by 900 per cent in its first year.

The program has increased access in a sustainable fashion, making the best use of all the different professionals. Since the implementa-tion of the program, referrals by family doctors to psychiatric outpa-tient clinics have fallen by nearly 70 per cent.[43] The psychiatrists are helping far more patients because they are not limited to providing care in one-hour sessions. As Darlene James notes, one size does not fit all: "Primary health care cannot afford a Procrustean bed."*

Hamilton's McMaster University was established in the 1960s to challenge conventional medical school curricula. "Mac" has also attracted some of the world's best clinical investigators and is con-sidered the North American home of so-called evidence-based medi-cine. The HSO Mental Health and Nutrition program stands out among health care services by routinely using sophisticated instru-ments to assess patients' condition after care. And most patients show considerable improvement, despite typically using only one or two sessions.[44]

The nutrition side has been with the program since 2000. Previ-ously it was run out of the Henderson Hospital. There are seven FTE

---

* Procrustes was one of many ancient Greek rogues who were bested by Theseus. Procrustes seized travellers and made them fit his iron bed by stretching those who were too short and lopping limbs off those who were too tall.

dietitians who see more than 5,500 referrals per year, mainly for diabetes and hyperlipidemia.

Dr. Kates feels that his program could be a model for other kinds of shared care. He feels that the particular advantage of his program is that it directly integrates specialized services into primary health care settings. The co-location of staff has dramatically improved communication between the different providers, who, like Darlene James, feel they are really part of the team. He also feels that the program benefits from central administration, which has facilitated evaluation, research, and quality improvement.

Shared care psychiatry has taken off in many Canadian communities since the College of Family Physicians and the Canadian Psychiatric Association released a paper on shared mental health care in 1997.[45] Dr. Jack Haggarty helped start a shared care mental health program in Thunder Bay, Ontario. A McMaster graduate, he knew Dr. Kates and had been familiar with the Hamilton program. When Dr. Haggarty decided to return to Thunder Bay after a couple of years in southern Ontario, he spent two weeks with Dr. Kates. As he says, the intention was to build on a good model, "stealing" as many good ideas and instruments as possible.

Dr. Haggarty's deal with his employer, the Thunder Bay Regional Hospital, included being able to establish a shared care program. Thunder Bay has nothing similar to Hamilton's network of non-fee-for-service family practices, but there are several large group practices. One of them, the Fort William Clinic, was keen on the idea, and Dr. Haggarty based two mental health counsellors there. The clinic has twelve physicians and over thirty thousand patients. Dr. Haggarty spends half a day there every two weeks and is available at other times by cellphone. He also measures each patient's symptoms and disabilities and has documented substantial improvements.

The doctors at the Fort William Clinic are paid on a fee-for-service basis, but the psychiatrists are salaried and this seems to be the necessary factor. The family doctors do lose some income when they spend time with the counsellor or the psychiatrist, but, so far at least, they are so thrilled with the better care their patients receive that it hasn't been an issue.

There are shared care programs in Calgary, North Bay, Halifax, and other communities. Dr. John Fraser, a family doctor at Halifax's North End Community Health Centre, claims that shared care has opened up mental health services to those who would otherwise have suffered without care. Now, he says, "I see patients getting better."[46]

Making Shared Care Standard:
The Northwest Territories Shows the Way

So far, there has not been much application of shared care beyond psychiatry. However, the Northwest Territories may be showing the way forward. In chapter 5 we highlighted the NWT diabetes program, which is an excellent example of shared care. All sixteen of the medical specialists* in the Northwest Territories (population 42,000) are on alternate payment plans, and this has facilitated their involvement in primary health care settings. For example, Dr. John Morse, a specialist in internal medicine and the medical director of the Stanton Regional Hospital (the only secondary care centre in the NWT), provides backup to family doctors and community nurses for endocrinology and gastroenterology. He flies into Fort Smith (a town of 2,500 on the NWT–Alberta border) every six weeks to see patients, perform endoscopies, and discuss patients with doctors and nurses.

Telephones and Telehealth

Health care personnel can also increase their productivity by doing more work over the telephone. A Dartmouth University group found that telephone calls were just the prescription to decrease clinic congestion and increase follow-up. The investigators, led by Dr. John Wasson, told half the patients in the study to double the length of time between their follow-up visits. For example, if they had been coming

---

* General surgery, obstetrics/gynecology, otorhinolaryngology (ENT), pediatrics, anesthesia, psychiatry, internal medicine, ophthalmology, orthopedics, and radiology.

every six weeks, they were booked every three months. But in the meantime, the staff kept in close touch with them by telephone. The patients in the control group came in according to their original schedules. After the researchers crunched the numbers, they showed that the telephone follow-up patients were much less likely to be hospitalized and their overall health care costs were 30 per cent lower.[47]

A number of studies have found that patients greatly appreciate being able to speak with a nurse before deciding whether to go to an emergency department or other health facility. A British experiment found that nurse telephone advice after regular office hours reduced patient visits to primary care centres by 38 per cent, home visits by 23 per cent, and the need for telephone advice from doctors by 69 per cent.[48] Other patient outcomes were slightly better in the nurse advice group. The province of Quebec has had a provincewide nurse telephone advice line (Info-Santé) since 1994. The nurses are based in the province's network of 160 CLSCs, although after hours, the calls are routed to a regional number. An evaluation of Info-Santé showed a very high rate of satisfaction; 76 per cent of callers said that without the service they would have gone to an emergency room or a doctor's office.[49] New Brunswick, British Columbia, and Ontario also have provincewide services, and other provinces are actively engaged in planning similar services.

Teamwork Promotes Equality

Teamwork promotes equality among different health professionals. As a result, teamwork promotes efficiency. Our present system is very inefficient because specialists perform tasks that could be performed by family doctors, family doctors do work that could be done by nurses and other health workers, and providers waste their time doing things that patients and families could do for themselves. Other sectors have moved away from hierarchical structures because they waste human resources at every level.

Teamwork and the move away from fee-for-service also make doctors more collegial with each other and promote sustainable practice. Taber's Dr. Wedel notes that before he and his colleagues left fee-for-service, there were high billers and low billers, even though they all worked hard. But after the implementation of the alternate payment plan, all the doctors are making within 10 per cent of each other. This has improved morale among the physicians.

Graham Scott, a former Ontario deputy minister of health, noted in a report to the Ontario government in 1995 that traditional fee-for-service practice is a major cause of physician shortages in rural areas: "For example, where a community can support six physicians but has only three, if they are young and energetic or workaholics they can almost manage an on-call schedule of one in three, and they can generate a very high income. This can create an incentive for resident physicians to discourage new physicians from coming to the community even though there is sufficient patient demand to assure an adequate income. This approach is dysfunctional as it will lead to the loss of most of these physicians when the pressure becomes too much—often a function of age."[50]

Dr. Steven O'Brien, a family doctor who practises in rural Prince Edward Island, concurs with Scott's analysis. He is now part of a salaried four-physician team after over twenty years of fee-for-service practice. He says that the new payment plan has improved physicians' lifestyles. "There's probably work enough for three doctors in a fee-for-service arrangement, but in order to have a good lifestyle you need four doctors. And in order for it to be divided equally, then everybody has to be in a salaried system."[51] Dr. O'Brien makes a little less now but claims that his improved lifestyle is more than sufficient compensation: "Doctors working here have always made plenty of money but had no time to enjoy it."

Conclusion

Your Community
and Access to Professionals

- Do your community's family physicians work in group practices that include shared twenty-four-hour call?
- Do your community's family physicians work in interdisciplinary teams with nurses, social workers, midwives, and other professionals?
- Do your community's specialists work in shared care arrangements with family doctors and other primary health care practitioners, or do they spend the vast majority of their time in traditional consulting practice?
- Does your community offer telephone advice to prevent unnecessary visits to emergency departments and doctors?
- Do your community's doctors and primary health care centres offer e-mail contact?

Teamwork is the key to dealing with the access problems Canadians face every day. We might still need some additional doctors, nurses, and other professionals, even if we were to use them to their full capacity. But we would meet many additional needs by maximizing teamwork. And we might surprise ourselves and find that we don't need as many new bodies as we think we do now. We will return to the discussion of teamwork in chapter 14 when we discuss how to redesign the health care system.

Chapter 10

Canada on Drugs

Fifteen-year-old Vanessa Young was a popular student at Oakville Trafalgar High School. She did have some of the usual adolescent problems, and perhaps a few others. Like many young women who constantly see rail-thin models presented as the ideal body form, she suffered from bulimia. On Saturday, March 18, 2000, she seemed to have exorcised that demon. She carried a healthy 63 kilograms on her 155-centimetre frame. Her father, Terence, a former member of the Ontario provincial legislature, remembers Vanessa standing in his den asking if she could go out with some friends when she suddenly collapsed. Attempts by her father and ambulance workers eventually revived her heart, but she never regained consciousness and she died that Sunday afternoon. A life full of promise, gone in a moment.[1]

That Saturday evening passed like the fog of nightmare for Terence Young. But he noticed that the doctors at Oakville-Trafalgar Memorial Hospital kept mentioning cisapride, a drug Vanessa had just started taking for stomach bloating. When he asked about the drug, one of the doctors simply said, "They dish it out like water."

Not long after Vanessa's death, her sister Madeline decided to find out a little more about cisapride and searched for information about it through her school's computer. She was shocked at what she read. First, doctors weren't supposed to prescribe the drug to children younger than sixteen years of age. Second, doctors weren't supposed to prescribe cisapride to patients with bulimia or other vomiting disorders. In fact, there were so many concerns about cisapride that the manufacturer, Janssen-Ortho, had written a warning letter to all Canadian doctors in September 1998, four months before Vanessa received her first prescription. The letter warned doctors to be careful about prescribing it for patients with "uncorrected electrolyte disturbances" such as might result from bulimia. The month that Vanessa died, Janssen announced that it was withdrawing cisapride from the US market. The company would make the same announcement in Canada two months later. By 2000, there were 314 cases of potential heart arrhythmias and 80 deaths in North America associated with the drug. It struck Terence Young how even a rare chance of death was too big a price to pay to remedy bloating and gas. In fact, the Health Canada release in May 2000 notes with understatement, "Alternative therapies are available to treat the gastrointestinal disorders for which cisapride is used." TUMS, anyone?

Physicians widely prescribed cisapride. In 1999, the last full year that Janssen sold cisapride in Canada, it racked up sales of one million prescriptions totalling $77 million. This was enough to make cisapride the fifteenth-biggest seller in the country.

It would be nice if cisapride were an isolated example, but it's not. Since 1993, seven drugs have been introduced into North America and then withdrawn from the market, contributing to over one thousand deaths. Between September 1997 and September 1998, nearly 20 million Americans took at least one drug that the FDA withdrew from the market during this time. There is a 10 per cent chance that regulators will withdraw a new drug from the market or place new warnings on it in the first seven years it is on the market.

The sad story of Vanessa Young reminds us that prescription drugs present a complicated story. New medications have revolutionized the treatment of many diseases. Every day, prescription drugs save lives and enrich others. However, medicines also contribute to the deaths of thousands of Canadians every year while their costs stretch public and private health budgets to the limit. The issues are usually defined as a lack of resources, money, and pharmacists. However, this chapter outlines that the real issues here are similar to those in other areas of health care: quality, quality, quality.

Why Is Canada's Drug Bill Soaring?

Increasingly, Canadians are concerned that they cannot afford the medications they need.[2] Within a couple of years, Canada will spend more for prescription medications than for doctors' services. Prescription drugs have been the fastest growing component of health costs since 1975. And only 36 per cent of the costs of prescription drugs are paid for publicly, compared with 71 per cent for overall costs and 90 per cent or more of the costs of hospitals and doctors.[3] Canada's annual prescription drug bill reached $14.6 billion in 2002.[4]

Under the Canada Health Act, the provinces have to provide first dollar coverage (that is, with no user charge on deductible) for medically necessary care from doctors and in hospitals. Canadians get their medication for free while in hospital. But once out of hospital, we have to pay for some or all of our own medicines. Gradually, provinces have built up their outpatient pharmaceutical coverage, typically starting with tuberculosis and other communicable diseases. The picture across the country resembles a patchwork quilt, with some provinces providing universal programs with user charges while others cover only certain diseases (such as cancer or diabetes) or socio-economic groups (such as the elderly or those on social assistance).

There is a sad irony that some Canadians are suffering for want of needed medication while others are dying from the side effects of drugs prescribed for trivial purposes. This reality seems remote from the usual storyline we hear about pharmaceuticals:

1. Prescription drugs are wonder products. They dramatically improve our health while side effects are kept carefully under control.

2. Quality costs big bucks. If we want to continue the stream of life-saving products, we need to pay more and more all the time.

There is another version of this storyline. Prescription drugs are double-edged swords: they can kill as well as heal. Also, the best drug doesn't always cost the most money. Sometimes the best therapy is only pennies away.

Prescription Drugs Save Lives but Are Also a Major Cause of Death

In April 1998, University of Toronto researchers published an article in the *Journal of the American Medical Association* (*JAMA*) that reviewed all the individual studies examining adverse drug reactions (ADRs) in hospitalized patients.[5] The conclusion: ADRs in hospital kill over 100,000 Americans every year, making this the fourth leading cause of death after cardiovascular disease, cancer, and injuries. The report used US studies, but author Dr. Bruce Pomeranz, a University of Toronto professor of physiology, claimed the results could be extrapolated to Canada, meaning roughly 10,000 deaths each year from hospital ADRs in this country.[6]

Community drug therapy can also be dangerous. A 2003 Harvard study found that 5 per cent of all elderly people suffered an ADR from a prescription received from an ambulatory clinic in a one-year period.[7] Thirty-eight per cent of these were classified as serious or life-threatening, and nearly 1 per cent were fatal. This would mean that one in every two thousand seniors dies every year from an ADR related to an ambulatory care prescription. Another 2003 Harvard study found that 25 per cent of ambulatory patients reported an ADR within four weeks of receiving a prescription.[8] In this study, nearly 4 per cent of patients had a serious ADR.

ADRs are a big problem in this country, too:

- A Montreal study showed that ADRs accounted for 10 per cent of emergency department visits by elderly people.[9] Twenty per cent of the others were taking medications that had a potential for an ADR.

- Another Quebec study showed that half of all seniors received a potentially dangerous prescription in one calendar year.[10] Thirty per cent were taking long-term benzodiazepines (valium-like drugs) contrary to clinical guidelines. McGill University investigator Dr. Robyn Tamblyn claimed that 20 per cent of hip fractures in seniors were caused by falls due to these long-acting sedatives.[11]
- An Alberta study found that over one-quarter of that province's seniors had taken a non-steroidal anti-inflammatory drug (NSAID) like ibuprofen during the previous year.[12] The authors evinced concern that these medications could be responsible for many ADRs every year. Over 2,600 Alberta seniors filled a prescription for two NSAIDs on the *same* day.

While some Canadians take too many drugs for their own good, a lot of us aren't getting the medicine we need. For example, as lamented previously, fewer than one-third of people with hypertension are receiving proper treatment,[13] and unrelieved pain is endemic in health care institutions.[14]

The paying public might well want to know why there are apparently so many quality issues in a sector that is regulated up the wazoo. It appears that poor-quality prescribing (particularly in community settings) results from three key factors:

- *Drug companies' marketing practices overwhelm doctors' lack of knowledge and training in pharmacology.* Drug companies spend more than twice as much on marketing as they do on research and development.[15] Almost all of these resources are poured into the promotion of new medications to doctors, particularly the opinion leaders within a particular community. The industry maintains an army of detailers who visit doctors' offices presenting their drugs' benefits in glossy colour while the side effects are in fine print. Canadian doctors have deficient training in clinical pharmacology, the basic science of drug prescribing.[16] Once in practice, doctors may claim they get their information on the use of drugs from medical journals and conferences, but, when tested formally, they appear to be influenced by the pharmaceutical companies' marketing efforts.[17]

- *Patients do not have easy access to purveyors of non-drug therapies.* Many disorders can be treated solely with non-drug therapies, and others are treated more effectively when non-drug therapies are used to complement pharmaceutical therapy.[18] However, physicians—particularly family physicians—have restricted access to psychologists, social workers, dictitians, rehabilitation therapists, chiropractors, and other professionals who provide non-pharmaceutical therapies. Furthermore, these services are usually not covered by provincial medicare plans.
- *Pharmacists are the experts in medication, but, outside of hospitals, they typically work in isolation from doctors and other professionals.* Better use of pharmacists can lead to better outcomes for patients.[19] More about this shortly.

Patent Protection Is Not the Major Cause of Escalating Drug Costs

Brian Mulroney insisted that Canada had to extend its length of patent protection for new drugs to allow us to participate in the US–Canada and North American free trade agreements. So we dutifully extended patents for twenty years. The legislation also permits the brand-name companies to prevent the entry of generic competitors for three additional years simply by applying for an injunction during patent litigation.* While some claim we need extended patent protection, to ensure innovation, lengthened patents are not required to guarantee the development of new drugs.[20]

---

* This legal hammer is not available for other litigation cases. Typically, the litigant has to wait until the case is won before it can halt the operations of a competitor.

Fifty out of the seventy-seven anti-cancer drugs that have been approved for use in the United States were developed with help from the National Cancer Institute.[21] A study of the twenty-one drugs introduced in the United States between 1965 and 1992 that were considered by experts to have had the highest therapeutic impact on society found that public funding of research was instrumental in the development of fifteen.

However, while patent protection is an important public issue, longer pharmaceutical patents aren't the cause of spiralling drug costs. Even the strongest opponents of patent extension claim that lengthened patents add only about 1 to 3 per cent, or $150 to $500 million, to the country's drug bill.*

Newer Isn't Necessarily Better, But It Is More Expensive

Despite the prevailing wisdom that high-quality therapeutics cost big bucks, we're overpaying for what we're getting. Costs are spiralling upward because doctors tend to overprescribe drugs, particularly to the elderly, and they tend to prescribe new, expensive drugs when a cheaper alternative is available. For example, a recent study showed that a forty-year-old high blood pressure medication, chlorthalidone, is more effective than two new medications while being less than 3 per cent of their cost.[22] British Columbia's per capita pharmacare expenditures for high blood pressure medication for the elderly increased by 250 per cent from 1986 to 1996.[23] Only 4 per cent of this increase was due to price increases; 96 per cent was due to the prescribing of newer, but usually less effective, medicines.

To reiterate, there is no question that advances in drug therapy have greatly benefited people. But most new drugs are great leaps sideways.

---

* The Canadian Labour Congress estimates an extra $3.6 billion to $7.3 billion in costs between 1993 and 2010 (http://www.clc-ctc.ca/hot-issues/billc91.html, accessed December 19, 2001). The Canadian Drug Manufacturers Association estimated $4.1 billion to $9.4 billion over twenty years (http://www.cdma-acfpp.org/issues/fed_monopolies.shtml, accessed December 19, 2001).

Very few new drugs are major advances or so-called category 2 drugs. The federally appointed Patented Medicine Prices Review Board (PMPRB) defines category 2 drugs as "the first drug product to treat effectively a particular illness or which provides a substantial improvement over existing drug products, often referred to as 'break-through' or 'substantial improvement.'"[24] From 1994 through 2000, the PMPRB approved only 30 new patents for breakthrough drugs compared with 570 new patents for category 1 and 3 drugs.*

Category 1 drugs are "line extensions," or reformulations of existing products (for example, a long-acting version of an existing drug). Category 3 drugs are defined as "a new drug or new dosage form of an existing medicine that provides moderate, little or no improvement over existing medicines." Category 3 drugs are referred to as "me-too" products because they are sometimes manufactured by changing only a small part of an existing drug; for example, adding one hydrogen atom to an existing drug allows a company to register a new patent. The drug companies then use their massive promotional budgets to convince doctors to prescribe these me-too drugs.

The constant parade of newer and better arthritis drugs demonstrates the downside of the way the industry operates. These drugs are called non-steroidal anti-inflammatory drugs, or NSAIDs, because they decrease joint inflammation resulting from arthritis but are not related chemically to steroids such as cortisone. NSAIDs are also effective painkillers. The original NSAID is Aspirin, which is often as effective as newer agents. Unfortunately, NSAIDs have a nasty tendency to cause gastrointestinal ulceration and bleeding. They can also cause other problems such as kidney failure and heart disease. In the last forty years, over twenty NSAIDs have been introduced into the Canadian market. Typically, each is described as a major advance in terms of safety, pain relief, or reduction of inflammation. Eventually,

---

* There were five more category 2 drugs approved in the next two years.

research demonstrates that the claims were exaggerated and the search for the Holy Grail of NSAIDs continues.

In the early 1980s, McNeil Laboratories marketed zomepirac as safer and more effective than Aspirin. Unfortunately, people taking zomepirac tended to develop severe allergic reactions. McNeil Laboratories removed zomepirac tablets from the market in March 1983.[25]

Syntex introduced another NSAID, ketorolac, into the Canadian market in 1991. In 1993, two professors of pharmacy at the University of Manitoba criticized Syntex's marketing, which referred to the drug as "unlike conventional NSAIDs."[26] In fact, professors Robert Ariano and Sheryl Zelenitsky claimed, "Ketorolac is not a 'wonder drug' with a mysterious mechanism of action; it is simply another NSAID."

In the late 1990s, several companies were developing a new class of NSAIDs appealingly called COX-2 inhibitors. Scientists at that point knew that NSAIDs had effects on two different pathways affecting key chemicals called prostaglandins. Some drug companies were betting that selective inhibitors of the COX-2 system would only reduce inflammation and not interfere with the COX-1 system, which could cause stomach bleeding and kidney failure. In 2000, both *JAMA* and the equally prestigious *New England Journal of Medicine* published articles that claimed that the COX-2 inhibitors celecoxib[27] (brand name Celebrex) and rofecoxib[28] (brand name Vioxx) were safer than traditional NSAIDs.

However, gradually the story unfolded that these glowing journal reports were missing some key data. The celecoxib investigators reported just the first six months of results from their study, but Dr. Jim Wright of UBC noticed that there were twelve-month data available at the FDA Web site.[29]

At the twelve-month mark, celecoxib patients had the same number of ulcers as the patients taking other NSAIDs. The advantage in the first six months was not maintained at twelve months. In fact, the FDA noted, "For upper gastrointestinal safety, and also for global safety, there does not appear to be any meaningful advantage for Celebrex." A later editorial in the *British Medical Journal* by three European scientists went even further, claiming, "Publishing and distributing overoptimistic short term data, using post-hoc changes to the protocol, while omitting disappointing long term data of two trials which involved large numbers of volunteers, is misleading."[30] Typical British understatement!

The rofecoxib paper reported comprehensively on gastrointestinal outcomes but not on cardiovascular outcomes. Rofecoxib did cause fewer ulcers and less gastrointestinal bleeding, but it caused more cardiovascular problems, especially blood clots.[31] All told, the adverse events causing patients to withdraw from the trial were the same.

In the meantime, celecoxib and rofecoxib broke the banks of public and private drug plans. The Ontario Drug Benefit Plan costs for NSAIDs increased by 150 per cent in just eight months—the equivalent of $43 million per year.[32] COX-2 inhibitors were responsible for all of the increase. Very few doctors tried their patients on another, cheaper NSAID before prescribing Celebrex or Vioxx. Manitoba had forecast that Celebrex would cost its public drug plan about $500,000 per year but spent that in the first six weeks after its approval.[33] According to anecdotal reports, in some communities more than half of seniors were taking it.

In fact, most seniors who take NSAIDs have osteoarthritis, which is due to wear and tear over time, rather than rheumatoid arthritis, which is due to inflammation. Most people with osteoarthritis could get better pain relief with fewer side effects if they avoided NSAIDs entirely and simply took acetaminophen (brand name Tylenol)— saving 97 per cent of the costs.[34]

Drug Companies Play Politics

At this point, an inquisitive reader might want to know what maintains this *Alice through the Looking Glass* World. Why are we brainwashed into thinking that the real issue is money when there are thousands of Canadians dying every year because of bad prescribing?

Why do we think that all new drugs are so marvellous when they are seldom much better than old ones and often more dangerous? It could have something to do with the fact that the large drug companies are some of the planet's most powerful political players. They always play hardball, and they aren't afraid to pitch inside.

Pharmaceuticals are the most profitable economic sector, with profit margins running 40 per cent higher than financial services, the next highest ranking group.[35] Pharmaceuticals may have the fattest profit margins, but they are also high risk. New blockbuster drugs typically have to go through long testing programs where things can and do go wrong. The federal government regulates new drug development, licensing, and patent protection, as well as spending hundreds of millions of dollars for drug plans for Native people, the military, and the federal civil service. The provinces regulate pharmacists, hospitals, and doctors, as well as paying for their own patchwork of provincial drug benefit plans. As a result, pharmaceutical manufacturers are major political actors in Canada. Whether a company is pressing the feds for a extended patent protection or cajoling a province to put a drug on a public drug plan's formulary, drug companies and governments see a lot of each other.

The pharmaceutical industry was a major contributor to George W. Bush's election campaign and has more registered lobbyists in Washington than there are members of Congress.[36] The *New York Times* says, "There is no lobby in Washington as large, as powerful or as well-financed as the pharmaceutical lobby." President W's defence secretary, Donald Rumsfeld, squeezed in an eight-year stint as CEO of drug-maker Searle between shifts working for Republican presidents.

The lobby is equally powerful in Ottawa, and the supporters of the industry are interchangeable with Canada's ruling elite, the Liberal party. Jim Keon, president of the generic drug trade group, the Canadian Drug Manufacturers Association, says, "For every lobbyist we can hire, they've got seven." Over the past five years, lobbyists for the industry have included former cabinet ministers and campaign strategists.[37]

Take the Money or Hit the Road

Besides currying favour with governments, drug companies use some of their enormous profits to butter up doctors and consumers. Former editor of the *New England Journal of Medicine* Dr. Arnold Relman claims that "the medical profession is being bought by the pharmaceutical industry."[38]

The industry bombards doctors with gifts, starting in medical school.[39] Doctors deny that free vacations and speakers' fees affect their professional judgment. But common sense suggests and research demonstrates otherwise. Doctors who get money from a drug company are much more likely to request that that company's drugs be added to hospital formularies[40] and to write favourable review articles about the company's products.[41]

Dr. Henry Stelfox and two colleagues from the University of Toronto found that 96 per cent of physician authors who wrote positive articles about calcium channel blockers (CCBs) had financial relationships with companies that made the drugs. That compares with 60 per cent of authors who had neutral views of CCBs and 37 per cent of authors who had a critical view.[42]

It is interesting to note that most of the authors of these overview articles, which make prescribing recommendations to other doctors, had financial arrangements with at least one company that made the drugs in question. By 2000, the US Food and Drug Administration had difficulty finding doctors to advise them who weren't already being paid by the industry.[43]

Consumer groups usually operate on a shoestring, so they have big ears when drug companies offer them hundreds of thousands of dollars. But if a consumer group does take industry funding, then is it truly independent? Karen DeKoning, a former president of the Canadian Breast Cancer Network, doesn't think so. The CBCN was founded in 1994 to bring the consumer voice to decision-making tables. Drug manufacturer Janssen-Ortho gave the organization $100,000 to fund advocacy workshops, including breakfast meetings on Parliament Hill.[44] DeKoning says that the grant came with no strings, but then, in November 2001, the company offered money for some specific projects. She says that Janssen wanted stories on the CBCN Web site about anemia, and they wanted to link the CBCN site to the Anemia Institute Web site, which Janssen also sponsors. (Janssen manufactures Eprex, which is used to treat anemia.)

Current CBCN president Barbara Heft claims that the organization is very careful about the way it takes money from drug companies. But Barbara Mintzes, a researcher at the University of British Columbia's Centre for Health Services and Policy Research, asks, "How well can you play a watchdog role about pharmas if they're financing you?"

Durhane Wong-Rieger, the executive director of the Anemia Institute, allows that there are some bad apples in the pharmaceutical industry, but claims, "The majority of pharmaceutical companies are open-minded, willing to have a good partnership with consumer groups, and a couple of companies are truly benevolent."

Wong-Rieger is also an outspoken advocate for allowing drug companies to advertise directly to consumers.[45] She claims that consumers don't blindly accept their doctors' views and are searching for other sources of information. Mintzes, who has written extensively about direct-to-consumer advertising, claims that advertising is designed to increase sales, not to provide unbiased information.[46] Mintzes and others have suggested that if the drug companies wanted to sponsor unbiased education, they could donate their money anonymously to an organization controlled by patients' groups.

No doubt Wong-Rieger sincerely believes her position, but her organization stands to benefit from its stand in favour of the drug industry. Denis Morrice, CEO of the Arthritis Society of Canada, also claims that drug-industry money can be useful and doesn't bias his organization. His society received $1.8 million from drug companies in 2000.[47]

While the companies can be very nice to their friends, they can react strongly to perceived threats.

Bristol-Myers-Squibb attempted to prevent the Canadian Coordinating Office for Health Technology Assessment (CCOHTA), a

Federal/Provincial/Territorial organization, from releasing a report reviewing cholesterol-lowering medications. The company objected to CCOHTA's assessment that the drugs were equivalent, claiming that this conclusion would cause pharmaceutical plans and consumers to use cheaper drugs. The court refused to grant an injunction and denied the company's appeal. But, the litigation forced CCOHTA to spend one-eighth of its annual budget defending itself in court.[48]

McMaster University's Dr. Anne Holbrook chaired a committee for the Ontario Drug Benefit plan on proton-pump inhibitors, a type of gastrointestinal drug. The committee filed an interim report saying that there was no difference clinically between omeprazole (brand name Losec) and two competitors. Then omeprazole's manufacturer, AstraZeneca, sent a letter to Holbrook asking her to "refrain from finalizing and distributing the guidelines" and warning that if she persisted, the company would take "appropriate legal proceedings."

AstraZeneca spokesperson Sheila Frame claimed that the other drugs were not equivalent to Losec. Furthermore she asserted that Ontario had no jurisdiction to make these decisions, saying that the responsibility lay with Health Canada and the Federal government.[49] AstraZeneca never pursued the issue further but Dr. Holbrook says she still considered the letter to be a threat.[50]

What's the Prescription?

Public Insurance Would Save a Lot of Overhead
As we discussed in chapter 2, public health insurance is more efficient than private insurance because it has lower overhead costs. We could save about 10 to 20 per cent of Canada's total drug bill simply by putting prescription drugs under the Canada Health Act.[51] However, these savings would be one time only and would still leave us with costs increasing at 15 to 20 per cent per year.

It's the Quality, Stupid!

The main reason for unsustainable drug costs is poor-quality prescribing and therapeutics. However, governments and private payers are almost completely focused on cutting costs, which in practice means shifting costs to consumers through user fees. This is completely contrary to *Crossing the Quality Chasm*'s Rule 9, which states, "The health care system should continually decrease waste (goods, services, and time) instead of focussing on cost reduction." If we focused on reducing wasteful prescribing, we could avert thousands of premature deaths and tens of thousands of hospital admissions, and reduce costs to boot. There are three general directions for needed reforms:

1. Better use of non-pharmacological therapies
2. Improved quality of prescribing
3. Reduced costs of medications dispensed

Non-Pharmacological Therapies

North Americans tend to think there is a pill for every ill. With more direct-to-consumer advertising, we are continually told that health and happiness are only one prescription away. However, there are lots of non-drug therapies that should be better used. For example, diet and exercise can effectively treat mild to moderate hypertension.[52] Cognitive behavioural therapy, a version of structured problem-solving, can effectively treat mild to moderate depression.[53] Spinal manipulation, by chiropractors or other professionals, is as effective as or more effective than traditional medical management of low back pain.[54] And, as we have noted in other chapters, dietary fibre, plastic hip protectors, self-management support, and other non-pharmacological approaches have very useful roles but are also underutilized.

Canadian practice guidelines typically identify non-drug therapies as part of comprehensive care,[55] but most physicians have poor access

to other professionals, such as social workers, dietitians, physiotherapists, and chiropractors, who provide non-drug therapies.

Chronic Pain: Getting the Needle and Solving Problems

Pain is troublingly common. A 2001 survey of nursing home residents in Ontario, Saskatchewan, and Manitoba found that 50 per cent
had pain and nearly 25 per cent experienced pain daily.[56] US studies
estimate that 20 per cent of all adults have chronic pain.[57]

Dr. Linda Rapson is trying to improve our odds against pain.[58]
Dr. Rapson's mother-in-law got her interested in acupuncture over
thirty years ago. Shortly after Rapson entered family practice in
Toronto, her mother-in-law recommended she take an acupuncture
course, thinking it might help with the pain she herself suffered from
a degenerative spinal disc. Now, Dr. Rapson is chairperson of the
Ontario Medical Association's complementary medicine section,
runs an acupuncture clinic, and treats palliative care patients at
Casey House Hospice and spinal cord injury patients at Toronto's
Lyndhurst Centre. In her spare time, she advocates for better integration of traditional and modern medical techniques.

Although the Chinese have used acupuncture for over two thousand years, it was virtually unknown in North America until New York
Times reporter James Reston claimed in a 1971 article that acupuncture had successfully relieved his post-appendectomy pain.[59] Scientific respect grew when it was shown that acupuncture stimulated the
body to produce endorphins. Acupuncture raises the body's pain
threshold,[60] improves cardiorespiratory fitness,[61] and has been found
to be useful for patients with osteoarthritis[62] and kidney stones.[63]

Dr. Jeff Ennis took the proverb "Physician heal thyself" so seriously that he shifted careers. He had graduated from the McMaster
medical school in 1988 and trained in psychiatry in New Zealand
before returning to Hamilton with his physiotherapist wife. But he
was experiencing so much pain from a series of back problems that
he was not sure he could continue working. His wife convinced him
to work at the pain clinic at Chedoke Hospital. After five years as

co-director, he struck out on his own and established a pain program at downtown Hamilton's St. Joseph's Hospital.[64] He runs five group sessions each year. Each group has about a dozen participants and involves 150 hours of classes.

Dr. Ennis's approach to pain incorporates cognitive behavioural therapy. The main part of the program is a half-day group session divided into three parts. In the first part, the group discuss their goals as well as barriers and facilitators to attaining them. The second part focuses on information and education. The third part is devoted to specific pain-relieving modalities, including hypnosis and other relaxation techniques. A number of studies have shown that cognitive behavioural therapy is effective in relieving pain,[65] and Dr. Ennis's experiences validate them. But the main approach of the program is simply helping people get on with their lives despite their pain. Ennis notes that they don't start their sessions by discussing how they are feeling because "we already know everyone feels kind of lousy."

We could relieve a lot of suffering if we used acupuncture, cognitive behavioural therapy, and other non-drug modalities for the millions of Canadians who suffer chronic pain.

Getting to the Heart of the Problem
Coronary heart disease (CHD) is the most common cause of death in Canada. The past thirty years has seen the development of many effective surgical and pharmaceutical treatments. However, we've known for a decade that combining an ascetic diet and a vigorous but contemplative lifestyle can reduce angina and heart attacks as effectively as surgery for some patients.[66] Even a moderate health-promotion regime can reduce the amount of medication or surgery required by cardiac patients.[67]

Rehab isn't just for the fifty-year-old executive who's had a mild heart attack. Ontario research shows that older patients with heart failure markedly improved their quality of life after exercise training.[68] Unfortunately, only 10 per cent of eligible coronary heart disease patients participate in a rehabilitation program.[69]

The Toronto Rehabilitation Centre's cardiac program is North America's largest cardiac rehabilitation centre, treating 1,600 patients per year. The first heart transplant recipient to run the Boston Marathon was one of the centre's patients. The program includes

- *Fitness evaluation and individualized exercise prescription.* Patients must take at least one of the centre's classes every week, as well as completing four other sessions per week.
- A *lecture series* for patients and their families, covering a variety of topics related to living with coronary heart disease.
- *Peer group support* for patients who are accommodating them selves to a chronic illness that requires major lifestyle change.

Improving the Quality of Prescribing

While poor-quality prescribing is a terrible problem costing lives and money, it is also a terrific opportunity. If we could eliminate the prescribing of unnecessary drugs and ensure that the cheapest agent was used when a drug was necessary, we could afford many more of the true blockbusters when they are really needed. There are two basic approaches here: the first is to decrease the effects of drug company marketing, and the second is to deal with the structural problems that promote poor prescribing.

No Free Lunch
Since drug company marketing adversely affects doctors' prescribing, then staying away from such promotion could improve prescribing. Doctors start their contact with drug-company representatives in medical school, and the links get stronger in post-graduate training. The drug companies know what they're doing. The more contact, the more likely those doctors will prescribe the way the drug companies want them to.[70]

In the early 1990s, Dr. Gordon Guyatt, a McMaster University respirologist, championed a process that established formal guidelines for contact between post-graduate medical trainees and drug-company representatives. The guidelines did not eliminate contact but clarified that companies should not pay for non-educational benefits (such as free lunches), should have their material vetted before presentation, and should not be responsible for program content.

Dr. Guyatt was only the chairperson of the internal medicine residency program, but he soon found his whole university embroiled in conflict.[71] He claims that an official of the Pharmaceutical Manufacturers Association of Canada (now Rx&D) met with him and tried to convince him to make the guidelines more permissive. When Dr. Guyatt clarified that the guidelines would not be changed, the official suggested that this decision might compromise the funding the drug industry provided for research as well as education. Later, when internationally renowned researcher Dr. David Sackett was talking with this official about research funding, Sackett says that the official claimed that the university's position on drug-company-supported education meant that he would no longer provide funding for research.

Eventually, the McMaster guidelines were implemented. Dr. Guyatt continued to debate the issue with a friend, Dr. Allan Detsky, physician in chief at Toronto's Mt. Sinai Hospital. Detsky didn't think the guidelines would be that useful. So he and some colleagues designed a study that examined the attitudes to the usefulness of drug-company information among McMaster internal medicine graduates pre- and post-guidelines, as well as a control group, graduates of the University of Toronto, which never had any guidelines. The results, published in *JAMA*, showed that Mac post-policy grads were less than half as likely as the other two groups to find drug-company information beneficial in guiding their practice.[72] They were more skeptical about commercial sources of information. Mac grads who had been exposed to the new policy also saw fewer drug reps in their offices.

Unfortunately, doctors don't usually know about the various

guidelines for interchange published by universities, the Canadian Medical Association, Rx&D, or other organizations. Researchers at the University of Manitoba found that 88 per cent of Canadian psychiatry trainees were unaware of any formal guidelines or policies concerning interactions with the drug industry.[73]

Even when doctors or drug companies break guidelines about inappropriate interactions, they usually don't get caught. When they do get caught, the penalties are so small that they essentially amount to licence fees for bad behaviour.[74]

Recently, Rx&D attempted to increase the moral suasion provided to its members by publishing detailed reports of misbehaviour. Dr. Joel Lexchin, a Toronto emergency-room physician and a noted expert on pharmaceutical issues, says that he is all in favour of more transparency, but he questions whether openness will deal with the main issue, "that companies not attempt to bribe doctors."[75]

There is now an organization of doctors and scientists that is trying to promote more independence from the drug industry. Dr. Bob Goodman, a New York City internist, founded No Free Lunch in 1999 to expose inappropriate drug-industry marketing practices and to support doctors to "just say no to drug reps."*

Pharmacists: An Underutilized Resource

The public is accustomed to seeing the pharmacist as simply a dispenser of drugs rather than as a skilled professional with at least five years of post-secondary education including four years of pharmacy. But in the past twenty years, hospital pharmacists have become key players within multidisciplinary teams. One study demonstrated that when pharmacists were members of the clinical team and made ward rounds with doctors and nurses, the teams identified seven times as many adverse drug reactions as did teams without a pharmacist.[76] In

---

* More information can be found at http://www.nofreelunch.org.

Canadian hospitals, pharmacists increasingly make rounds with doctors and are receiving more respect for their expertise.

Outside of hospitals, there are few examples of such high-functioning teams. Doctors and pharmacists can practise in the same community for thirty years without talking for more than ten minutes on professional issues. Pharmacists spend the vast majority of their time filling prescriptions without adding much of their professional value. Part of the problem is payment. Typically, pharmacists are paid only when they dispense a prescription, not when they provide advice. However, payment isn't the whole story: in Quebec, pharmacists can bill for providing other professional interventions, but they do so only with fewer than 0.5 per cent of prescriptions.[77]

Sometimes even small doses of pharmaceutical information can be effective in improving prescribing. An Ontario study provided mailed feedback to physicians on their prescribing of antibiotics, along with educational material to alert doctors to more appropriate antibiotic prescribing. The experimental group reduced costs and increased the use of first-line drugs.[78]

But simple education is usually not enough.[79] Interventions that combine a number of different approaches are more effective.[80] These include academic detailing and the integration of pharmacists into clinical teams.

Academic Detailing: Using Marketing for Good

In the early 1980s, Harvard researchers demonstrated that so-called academic detailing could improve physicians' prescribing.[81] In academic detailing, pharmacists visit doctors' offices and use the same techniques as drug-company detailers, including sophisticated communications strategies and glossy materials left with the doctors. But the information they provide is non-biased. The program wasn't cheap, but it saved $2 for each dollar it spent.[82]

Bob Nakagawa, currently director of clinical pharmacy services for the Fraser Health Authority in British Columbia, started the first

Canadian program of academic detailing out of North Vancouver's Lions Gate Hospital in 1993. Its present director is Anne Nguyen. The program publishes a newsletter on a particular topic, and then Nguyen visits the doctors. An evaluation of the program using a control community in the BC southern mainland found that there had been enough savings from better prescribing to offset the costs of delivering the program.[83]

This type of program has spread to several other provinces. In Saskatchewan, the Saskatoon District Health Board pharmacy program runs the program RxFiles, with financial support from the Department of Health. RxFiles develops its topics from speaking with physicians. It now contacts over 30 per cent of the province's family doctors, including over 60 per cent in Saskatoon, Regina, North Battleford, Prince Albert, and some rural areas.

The Alberta Drug Utilization Program started in 1999. It has conducted two academic detailing campaigns—one for anti-infectives and another for gastrointestinal drugs—in three small communities south of Edmonton. The programs accredit all their activities with professional organizations so that doctors can pick up coveted CME points toward their continuing certification. They start with a group presentation from a Calgary- or Edmonton-based specialist and then visit each doctor three times over the next few months. The first two visits are from a pharmacist, while the final visit is made by a semi-retired Edmonton internist.

Dr. Harold Lopatka, a pharmacist who runs the Alberta program, says that we have just started to scratch the surface of quality improvement. He notes that it took the Australians fifteen years to get where they are now. Australia launched its National Prescribing Service in March 1998 as the follow-up to a previous initiative, Quality Use of Medicines. The Australian federal government provides almost $4 million (roughly $3.5 million in Canadian dollars) for the National Prescribing Service.

DEANS Drives Nova Scotia Drug Utilization

Dr. Michael Allen is a Halifax family doctor who is director of special projects for continuing education in Dalhousie University's Faculty of Medicine. He is also the chair of the management committee of the Drug Evaluation Alliance of Nova Scotia, or DEANS. DEANS uses academic detailing as one tactic within a broad strategy to improve the utilization of pharmaceuticals. DEANS identifies drug issues that have a major impact on the health of Nova Scotians, analyzes them, develops interventions that are based upon high-quality evidence, and then evaluates the impact of the dissemination of their information. According to Dawn Frail, a pharmacist with the Department of Health who works with DEANS, the organization tailors its interventions to its specific issues.

DEANS started its academic detailing program in 2001 with flu and pneumonia vaccination. The program employs two pharmacists and one nurse detailer. They have since done rounds on osteoarthritis and hormone replacement therapy and are planning one for osteoporosis. Dr. Allen says that the osteoarthritis unit introduced physicians to techniques to critically appraise drugmakers' claims.

Drug companies usually publicize their products by referring to the relative reduction of adverse events—"Drug X reduces heart attacks by 20%!" But the absolute reduction in risk may simply be from 1.0 to 0.8 per cent per year. In other words, instead of having ten chances in a thousand of having a heart attack, now you have only eight chances in a thousand of having one. It sounds a lot less impressive to express the results in absolute terms instead of relative ones.

It's even less impressive to point out that five hundred patients would have to take the medication constantly for one to benefit each year. The others would not have had a heart attack in any event or would have had one despite the medication they took. Expressing benefit in this way is referred to as the "number needed to treat," or NNT. It isn't surprising that drug companies focus on the reduction of relative risk. It makes their products look better. But usually the more important numbers to doctors and patients are the absolute risk reduction and the NNT.

DEANS is also educating pharmacists. Deb Barnhill, the co-ordinator of continuing education for Dalhousie's College of Pharmacy, sits on the DEANS management committee. She knew that women were asking as many questions of pharmacists about hormone replacement therapy as they were of physicians. She thought the materials produced for the physicians' academic detailing were excellent, and she came up with the idea of modifying them for pharmacists. She put together an advisory committee of pharmacists and physicians and reshaped the literature and presentations for pharmacists. In the spring of 2003, she conducted ten small-group educational sessions, which directly reached almost one-quarter of the province's pharmacists.

Barnhill thinks DEANS is wonderful and is very grateful that pharmacists have been so well included in its work. She sees a lot more interaction between physicians and pharmacists in the future. She also thinks more undergraduate interdisciplinary education would help the different professions get to know each other before they start their practices.

Pharmacists Make the Team

A next step in integration is to have pharmacists seeing physicians' patients in consultation. Dr. Jana Bajcar, a University of Toronto professor of pharmacy, combines her academic pursuits with practice as part of the St. Michael's Hospital family practice department. She sees a patient in the clinic or at home and then provides advice to the doctor regarding the patient's drug management.[84]

Dr. Renette Bertholet, a pharmacist in Red Deer, Alberta, started working with the fifteen-doctor Associate Clinic in July 2000. Like Dr. Bajcar, doctors refer patients to Dr. Bertholet and she conducts her consultation in the clinic or in patients' homes. In the first two years of the program, Dr. Bertholet saw seventy-four patients and identified 763 drug-related issues. She follows up most patients with another visit, and some she phones on a regular basis. She also designs continuing education sessions for the doctors.

Anti-coagulant therapy can protect patients who have had blood clots or are at special risk of developing a clot. However, they are tricky to use. Too much and the patient might bleed to death. Too little and he or she might develop a clot. A number of foods and other medications can interfere with anti-coagulant therapy. Physicians, particularly family doctors, tend to have a few patients on these medications and usually do not become expert in their use.

Jim Oxley, director of pharmacy services with Saskatchewan's Five Hills Regional Health Authority, developed an award-winning program where a pharmacist takes the lead in monitoring anti-coagulant therapy. Patients get their blood drawn in the morning and then the pharmacist talks to them by phone in the afternoon. While sixty per cent of patients within the normal range is considered acceptable, nearly 80 per cent of the Moose Jaw-based program's 300 patients attain that standard.[85]

We can create an even better environment to facilitate high-quality prescribing by embedding pharmacists directly into clinical teams. Susan Troesch has been a pharmacist for nearly thirty years, but the last few have been the most satisfying professionally. She always did enjoy her work as a manager of community pharmacy in Vancouver's East End, which included responsibility for a long-term care facility. It kept her on her toes. Older people with multiple chronic illnesses and polypharmacy stretch the curious minds of pharmacists like Troesch. But she was somewhat discouraged that she spent the vast majority of her time, in her words, "plugging and cranking"—filling prescriptions and making change. She longed for meaningful interactions with the doctors and other professionals who also treated the patients she saw.

A few years ago, she started volunteering at the Mid-Main Community Health Centre located in midtown Vancouver. She loved the opportunity to work with the centre's doctors, nurses, and other professionals. Mid-Main started in 1988 as an offshoot to the REACH community health centre a few kilometres east. It now provides medical, dental, massage, family counselling, clinical pharmacist, and nurse practitioner services.

Troesch works in a half-time position and provides services at the centre, on the phone, in long-term care facilities, and in patients' homes. She does everything but dispense medications. The doctors and other professionals refer clients to her for pharmacy consultations. She also follows up approximately fifteen patients a day. Some need regular monitoring of their anti-coagulants. Some have just had changes in their drug regimens. She spends a considerable amount of her time researching drug information. For example, recently a doctor asked her for advice about a diabetic who had early kidney damage and low blood pressure. As we described in chapter 5, Troesch also has a major role with the recently started diabetic groups in the centre. She is thrilled with the opportunities to practise her profession up to her potential and the rest of the team is very happy to have her on board.

Mildred N. is the kind of patient who is grateful for Troesch's presence on the primary health care team. Mildred's home care nurse asked Troesch to see her because she was worried about her sleepiness. Mildred was also depressed, anxious, and disabled as a result of a recent car accident.

When Troesch started to see her, Mildred was so sleepy that she could barely finish her sentences. She wasn't taking her painkillers on a regular basis. She waited until the pain was unbearable and then took too many. It turned out she was taking three different benzodiazepines as well as three different antidepressants. No wonder she couldn't stay awake! Troesch first got her to take her painkillers on a regular basis, which greatly reduced her pain and anxiety. Then she worked with Mildred to decrease her benzodiazepines. Gradually, she woke up and took charge of her life.

One of Troesch's pet peeves is the long-term prescription of benzodiazepines, or "benzos," as they are often called. Toronto researcher Ruth Cooperstock first described the problem of benzos for women over twenty years ago.[86] Cooperstock found that doctors often prescribed drugs to women for essentially social reasons. But the problem affects men as well. Up to one-third of seniors are taking these drugs, which cause falls, hip fractures, and a decline in cognitive function that can mimic dementia.[87] Typically, they are prescribed for a short-term problem such as temporary insomnia, even though there are many non-drug therapies that are as effective.[88] Benzos are very addictive, and patients quickly find that attempts to discontinue them result in more insomnia and anxiety.[89] Nothing thrills Troesch more than working with elderly people who have been written off and helping them wake up to the rest of their lives.

Unfortunately, Susan Troesch is a rare breed. There are very few pharmacists working as part of primary health care teams. At the REACH community health centre, the dean of primary care pharmacists is preparing to retire. Carol Lyster started at REACH over twenty-five years ago. She worked full-time and ran a dispensary as well as providing consults to doctors, nurses, and directly to patients. Dr. Sandra Witherspon, a long-time physician at REACH, introduced her patients to Lyster as a full member of the team and often passed on to her the follow-up of asthma and hypertension patients. Afshin Jaberi, a young UBC pharmacy graduate, is looking forward to carrying on Lyster's tradition as REACH's full-time pharmacist.

Technology Can Help with Safety

Patricia Johnston, a director of patient care at Riverview Health Centre in Winnipeg, proudly points out the new Pyxis medication system being used in the hospital. Studies in the 1990s had shown that medication errors could be greatly decreased with the use of automated systems.[90] Riverview has implemented a new system that uses a touchscreen and requires a fingerprint identification from the nurse dispensing the medication. Future refinements to drug safety include placing bar codes on patient bracelets and the same bar code on their medicine bottles. The nurse must scan both bar codes before dispensing the medication.[91]

Reducing the Costs of the Medications Dispensed

In 1969, the Trudeau government implemented a system of compulsory licensing that greatly facilitated the access to generic drugs in the Canadian market. Other companies were free to manufacture a generic copy of a brand-name medication simply by paying a licensing fee. During the 1980s and 1990s, Canada lengthened the period of patent protection, which increased the time that brand-name drugs retained their market exclusivity. As a result, it has been taking longer and longer for generic competitors to get to market.

However, as we have discussed, 95 per cent of new patented drugs are not breakthroughs. Over half of all new patented agents are so-called me-too drugs. The large number of drugs designed for the same therapeutic purpose offer wonderful opportunities to re-establish competition in the marketplace. There are over a dozen NSAIDs (anti-arthritis drugs) available in Canada. Given that some of these drugs work better for some people and others work better for others, there is usually no a priori reason to start with anything other than the least expensive drug.

Hospitals have historically used formularies, which limit the drugs available within an institution. The formulary committee decides which arthritis medications it will stock and which it won't. The hospital's doctors have to choose an arthritis medication from the formulary.

In the 1980s, some American health plans that paid for prescription drugs started using the formulary process outside of hospital. This process is usually referred to as "therapeutic substitution." Different drugs that treat the same illness are grouped together in a therapeutic class, and the most cost-effective ones are covered for first-line prescription.[92] Patients have the option of paying by themselves for drugs not covered.

British Columbia introduced its own version of therapeutic substitution, the Reference Drug program, in 1995. British Columbia's program requires patients to use the most cost-effective or "referenced" products unless their doctor completes a special authorization form and sends it to BC PharmaCare.[93] The BC government claims that it has saved $200 million in the program's first five years, with annual savings running at approximately $44 million per year.[94] Evaluation of the Reference Drug program has shown that it decreased costs for drugs without depriving patients of effective therapies.[95]

What Doesn't Work: Charging Patients for Drugs

We know that charging user fees for doctors and hospitals injures some patients. In Canada, we have evidence of the deleterious effects of user fees for drugs. In the mid-1990s, the Quebec drug plan began levying user charges on the elderly and poor, who had previously been exempt from these charges. Evaluators found that drug use decreased by 14.7 per cent among welfare recipients and by 7.7 per cent among the elderly.[96] Emergency-room visits increased 71 per cent. Visits to doctors' offices increased by 17 per cent. Emergency-room visits by social assistance recipients who were mentally ill increased by over 500 per cent. The policy was estimated to have caused an extra two thousand hospital admissions. A US study has also found that user charges for drugs for seniors led to decreased use of essential drugs and increased numbers of admissions to nursing homes.[97]

Conclusion: Just Say No to Poor-Quality Prescribing

Drug therapy is expensive, and the price keeps going up. As in other areas of health care, the real story is quality, not cost. Prescription drugs save many lives, but they also kill thousands every year. Present patterns of prescribing are a serious health hazard. However, there are many exciting programs developing in Canada that show we can fight the war on drug costs by focusing on quality.

Your Community
and Effective Use of Medications

- Does your community mount active surveillance for adverse drug reactions (ADRs)? Active surveillance can reveal one hundred times more ADRs than passive surveillance.
- Does your community mount active surveillance for inappropriate drug-industry marketing practices? Are there any consequences for bad behaviour?
- Do doctors, pharmacists, and scientists have to declare conflicts of interest when they provide advice to hospitals, other health care organizations, and your province on which drugs should be provided in formularies?
- Does your community offer a full range of non-drug treatments including, but not limited to, lifestyle change, physical therapies, and cognitive behavioural therapy?
- Does your community offer academic detailing by pharmacists in doctors' offices?
- Does your community ensure pharmacist consultations for patients with complex multi-drug regimens?
- Does your community have primary health care centres with pharmacists integrated into the interdisciplinary team?
- Does your province's drug plan use therapeutic equivalence to determine which drugs should be offered as first-line agents?
- Does your province bulk-buy its drugs? Does your country bulk-buy its drugs?

Chapter 11

Waiting for This, Waiting for That

Milo Craig went through a nightmare after suffering a fall on August 27, 2002. It was her last day at work at the United Church in Cartwright, in the rolling hills of southwestern Manitoba. She tripped on a basement drain and sustained a severe fracture of her upper left arm.[1] First she spent six days in the nearby Tri-Lake Health Centre waiting to see an orthopedic surgeon. Then she was transferred to Winnipeg—150 kilometres away—to see an orthopedic surgeon at Seven Oaks General hospital. He evidently thought the fracture would heal without surgery and transferred her follow-up to a surgeon in Brandon, closer to her new residence in Glenboro.

The Brandon doctor saw her three times over the next three months, when a CAT scan concluded that Craig should have surgery after all. However, he couldn't perform the procedure for another two months, and therefore referred her to another Winnipeg surgeon. When Craig saw this doctor three weeks later, he claimed to have a longer waiting list than the Brandon doctor. She couldn't talk to her Brandon surgeon for four weeks after that because he was on holidays. When she finally did see him, he referred her to a third Winnipeg doctor. Two weeks later, when Craig saw this third surgeon, he said he had a three-month waiting list, and, yet again, referred her back to Brandon. When contacted by the *Winnipeg Free Press*, a spokesperson for the Brandon Regional Health Authority noted that Craig could have had her surgery if she had accepted the Brandon doctor's original end-of-January slot. Unfortunately, as of February 12, 2003, she was still facing a two- to three-month wait for care.

Milo Craig's situation is, fortunately, not the norm. But it is common enough that waits and delays are Canadians' number-one concern about their health care system. Up until twenty or thirty years ago, patients with complicated problems were often admitted to hospital for "investigations." They would have all their tests and see all their different specialists within a few days. Today, such patients are rarely admitted. Too often they have to wend their way through a maze of outpatient tests and specialist visits. There has been an explosion in the number of specialists, which has exponentially increased the referral possibilities.

Waits and delays are the biggest political issue facing medicare. A 2003 five-country survey found that Canadians were more likely than Americans, Australians, Britons, or New Zealanders to report undue waits for procedures* and difficulty seeing a specialist.[2] Parading waiting-list victims through the legislature is a provincial opposition party's favourite weapon. In 1999, the Manitoba Conservative government lost power partly because the NDP focused on "hallway medicine"—people waiting undue periods for hospital beds after being designated for admission. Then, in 2003, the popular Doer government cruised to re-election over the disorganized opposition parties. The only issue on which the NDP seemed vulnerable was hallway medicine, which the opposition claimed was still present four years later.

In a world where a pizza comes in thirty minutes, it's hard for Canadians to accept that they have to wait months, or longer, for health care. Another shock is that there is little information about how long people actually do wait. Even so, it is unequivocal that far

---

* It is not clear from the survey whether Canadians did, in fact, wait longer, but they were more concerned.

too many patients are waiting much longer than is clinically acceptable. Canadians shouldn't have to accept this poor level of service.

The public appears confused about what causes delays. A 2000
Ontario Medical Association review of public opinion found that
over three-quarters of Canadians considered waste to be a major system problem.[3] However, the preferred option wasn't better management but, rather, more funding—public funding, by the way.

When Canadians like Milo Craig have problems accessing the system, it is obvious that there are serious management issues. It appears
that simply phoning the Winnipeg doctors and inquiring about their
wait times would have prevented two needless trips to town.

This chapter discusses the causes of waits and delays. It turns out
that we are badly mismanaging patients' flow through the system.
Or, perhaps more appropriately put, we generally *aren't* managing
people's flow through the system.

Are We Really Waiting Too Long?

With all the attention focused on waiting lists, one would think that
we would actually know how long people are waiting. In fact, there
are very few waiting lists in the way people imagine them. The average Canadian thinks health care queues are like those at a popular
restaurant where one signs up with the maître d', who deftly ensures
that the various parties get their appropriate tables in an expeditious
fashion. We imagine that somehow there must be maître d's for the
various services to which we are referred.

This active, central management does occur for a few procedures
in a few centres, but they are exceptions. Individual doctors keep
most waiting lists, such as they are, on file cards or other ephemera
somewhere in their offices. Whether you're waiting for a visit to a
family doctor or one to a specialist, whether you're anticipating a
simple test or sophisticated surgery, it's likely that your doctor or her
receptionist will be the one deciding when you get your care. Recent

analyses of waiting lists in Canada and other jurisdictions have concluded that there are no consistent criteria for placing patients on lists, that there are a variety of methods for measuring waiting times, and that there is little auditing of lists.[4]

There is very little scrutiny of whether patients really need surgery.[5] According to retired surgeon Charles Wright, real practice often varies from accepted clinical practice guidelines. All hospitals have quality assurance mechanisms, but vigilance varies markedly from place to place. Wright says that it would be relatively easy to monitor whether surgery is appropriate and beneficial but claims that, in general, surgeons aren't keen to have more scrutiny.

Even when someone measures wait times, the methods used vary tremendously.[6] Sometimes the measured wait time starts when the family doctor makes an initial referral to a specialist. Sometimes the clock starts ticking after the first visit with the specialist, sometimes only after a specialist has booked a surgical date. The differences in accrued time can vary by 200 to 300 per cent, depending upon which measurement is used.

Audits of lists are critically important. Studies of surgical wait lists in other countries have found that 20 per cent to 50 per cent of patients on the lists are not in fact candidates for surgery.[7] Their clinical condition may make them inappropriate candidates for the procedure—they may even have died. Or they may have already had the procedure, or not want it, or be on more than one list.

Missing all these key data, the political playing field is wide open to both hyperbole and oversight. During the last few years, some studies claim, the situation has been getting worse, while others claim improvement.[8] As a result, authorities typically make funding allocations according to political rather than evidence-based rules.

Some of Canada's best-known researchers in the area of waiting lists recently concluded, "The current Canadian 'non-system' of physician-controlled lists makes it impossible for managers to manage and actually 'puts patients last.'"[9]

How Much Do Patients Really Suffer Because of These Delays?

Many people waiting for hip and knee replacements experience considerable pain and disability. It doesn't affect their vital status to wait an extra few months, but recent data indicate that patients who wait shorter times for knee replacements have better outcomes.[10]

What about those awaiting heart or cancer care? Many people erroneously believe that once you are told you need heart surgery you will die if you don't get it quickly but will have normal life expectancy if you get it right away. However, even for very high-risk heart-surgery patients, bypass surgery increases survival chances by only 5 to 10 per cent per year in absolute terms.[11] High-risk patients are typically fewer than 20 per cent of all patients. For many, the survival benefit is closer to 1 to 2 per cent per year. Many others are having their surgery to relieve pain and disability, but the procedure won't lengthen their lives. Despite the talk about droves of deaths on heart-surgery waiting lists, only one in two hundred Ontario heart-surgery waiting list patients dies before having surgery.[12] The death rate of waiting-list patients is actually lower than that for heart patients who aren't waiting for surgery.[13]

Certain cancers, such as acute leukemias, kill rapidly without treatment. In Canada, people with these kinds of cancers or with high-risk heart conditions don't wait long for care. If you have a less serious case of heart disease or cancer, it might actually be nice to have two or three weeks to get your affairs in order, arrange care for children, cat, or partner, and contemplate life. That's because even "routine" surgical treatments for heart disease or cancer have mortality rates of 1 to 2 per cent; those involving complicated surgery can have death rates of 10 per cent or even more.

What happens if patients with slow-growing cancers like breast, colon, and prostate have to wait for care? It is technically correct that each extra day confers some extra risk of the cancer's spreading, but the danger is very low. Some studies show no decrease in survival if breast cancer patients wait three to six months for surgery,[14] while others show that these delays worsen survival by about 2.5 per cent per year.[15] It looks like a few weeks' wait has negligible risk.

The country's top court will soon rule on the urgency of surgery. On May 8, 2003, the Supreme Court of Canada agreed to hear the case of George Zeliotis, an elderly man who says he had to wait months in excruciating pain for a hip replacement through the public health system.[16] Zeliotis and a Quebec physician, Dr. Jacques Chaoulli, contend the province is violating their right to offer and receive private health care.

The concern about the urgent need for surgery has fuelled the demands for what are called "care guarantees." In Britain and Sweden, patients who cannot get care within a certain time frame within their own areas are free to go to other regions or even out of the country for care. In Canada, Roy Romanow considered recommending a similar practice but ultimately rejected it. And, of course, some, such as *Calgary Herald* columnist Danielle Smith, feel that the only cure is a private system.[17]

But Don't Waiting Lists Automatically Mean We Don't Have Enough Resources?

Canadians think that waiting lists indicate a lack of resources.[18] In a recent editorial, McGill University surgeon Jeffrey Barkun suggests that many Canadians see waiting lists as "the result of a societal compromise between the founders' promise of universal access to care and reality of currently committed resources."[19] It's just common sense that if there is a wait for something, there isn't enough of it, right?

In fact, a waiting list usually doesn't mean that there is insufficient capacity to meet the demand. Consider the office of Dr. Frazzle, family physician. He really loves family practice. He likes being part of the day-to-day lives of his patients. But after ten years of practice, he is worn out and discouraged. He used to dream about getting old with his patients, but now he jokes that his practice might kill him first.

Dr. Frazzle has a four-to-five week wait before he can see routine patients. Every morning he faces a nearly full schedule, and yet through the day, at least fifteen to twenty people phone to book appointments. Many of them should be seen within a few days, not weeks. His staff try to squeeze in some, but refer the majority to walk-in clinics. Most of these patients still come to see him a few days later because the ER and walk-in clinic doctors always tell patients to "check in with their family doctors in a few days." Dr. Frazzle tries to accommodate them, but once they get into his office, they seem to raise six other problems. Too often he gets home late for dinner. Isn't a family doctor supposed to have a family of his own?

Surely Dr. Frazzle has too little capacity to meet his demand. Doesn't he?

Dr. Frazzle's office has had that four- to five-week wait for several years. It's longer when he comes back from holiday and shorter just before he goes away. But it's always pretty close to one month. While discussing this issue over coffee at a conference, Dr. Frazzle hears that some colleagues keep a few slots open in their schedules every day to see urgent patients. He decides to give it a try. He keeps two appointments free at the end of the morning and afternoon clinics and asks his staff not to book them until that day. For a couple of weeks it looks like this new plan will work. He is seeing more of his urgent patients and reducing referrals to walk-in clinics. But soon his wait for routine visits increases because of fewer open slots. And he is surprised to find on many mornings that his staff have already filled the coveted urgent openings. It turns out that they sometimes hoard them for patients they like or fear.

Dr. Frazzle's response is to create super-protected emergency slots that only he can fill. Soon he is spending at least thirty minutes every day assessing the urgency of patients—discussing them with his staff, talking to patients on the telephone, trying to find care for patients he can't see, and so on. This isn't why he went into medicine. That job working nine to five at the downtown varicose-vein-stripping clinic is starting to look mighty attractive. Better pay, no overhead, no phone calls.

While it is easy to understand why Dr. Frazzle feels overwhelmed, it seems like he must be pretty close to meeting his demand. His practice is near equilibrium—the number of patients seen every day pretty much matches the number who wish to be seen. His average wait has stayed at one month for years. If he could somehow deal with his backlog, Dr. Frazzle could see all his patients the day they phone for an appointment, whether they were routine, urgent, or super-urgent.

Water Flowing Downhill: Moving to Advanced Access

Dr. Frazzle's situation is analogous to a river flowing into a reservoir backed up behind a hydroelectric dam. The amount of water entering the reservoir (patients wanting to be seen) matches the volume flowing through the turbines (patients seen). At times, when increased flow is allowed (when a doctor works hard before a holiday), the reservoir shrinks, and during periods of heavy rain (during a doctor's holiday), the reservoir gets bigger. But year to year, it is roughly the same size.

Rating the urgency of patients and taking the most urgent first certainly helps avoid problems that can occur when sick people have to wait too long. But this churning of the reservoir to cull the urgent means that patients deemed routine then have to wait even longer. Some of these get sick while they wait and then they need reprioritizing. As Dr. Frazzle found, soon a doctor can spend thirty minutes or more every day just reprioritizing patients.

Whenever a practice is in a steady state with a stable wait-list length, it is theoretically possible to eliminate waiting. If the clinicians can drain the reservoir by servicing the backlog, then patients can get same-day care. This technique of wait-list reduction leading to same-day appointments has come to be called *advanced access*.

Advanced Access Opens a Practice

A few years ago, Dr. David Crookston felt like he was Dr. Frazzle. The University of Toronto grad works at the Sault Ste. Marie Group Health Centre. He has about 1,400 regular patients and also works in the emergency department and has administrative responsibilities. Up until June 2001, Dr. Crookston had a one-month wait for routine appointments. Group Health has a very large centralized appointment centre, but if his patients didn't like how long they would have to wait, they would phone Dr. Crookston's nurse and plead their case. Many would go to Group Health's internal walk-in clinic or to the Sault hospital's ER. The doctors there told Dr. Crookston's patients to check in with their regular doctor in a few days. He felt like Dr. Frazzle. It was stressful.

Then Dr. Crookston decided to try out advanced access. Originated by former California family physician Mark Murray, advanced access radically recommends that the best solution to office congestion is to see every patient as soon as possible.[20] This concept is counterintuitive, but it's worked for Dr. Crookston and thousands of other doctors.

The director of Group Health's appointment centre, Lucy Fronzi, had been encouraging Dr. Crookston to consider advanced access. She had seen one of Dr. Murray's presentations and realized that advanced access could reduce patients' waits and improve doctors' working conditions. She also supervises twelve full-time employees in the appointment centre, and without a change she might have had to ask for more staff. They spend much of their days explaining why the waits are so long and listening to patients' complaints. One half-time position was devoted solely to making changes in the schedule.

Is There a Capacity/Demand Mismatch?

The first step to advanced access is to assess demand and compare it to capacity. Dr. Murray has calculated that on an average day in an average practice, 0.8 per cent of patients will call to be seen. For a practice of two thousand patients, that means roughly sixteen calls per day. This does not include the patients who are being followed for acute or chronic problems or who are already booked for routine care such as pap smears. Practices with a lot of sick or elderly patients will have higher call rates. Practices that teach self-care will get fewer calls than those that encourage dependency.

It is important to study demand as it occurs through monitoring phone-call and walk-in volume. Studying appointment books simply displays historical use, not present demand. Once the practice knows approximately how many calls it gets per day, it can assess whether the existing capacity can meet practice demand.

Despite the one-month wait to see him, Dr. Crookston's practice was in steady state. He confirmed this after he started his road to advanced access.

Working Down the Backlog to Same-Day Care

The tough part comes after the advanced access practice matches its demand to capacity, when it must work down its backlog. This requires extra work temporarily to drain the reservoir of demand that has built up behind the dam of the old practice style. Dr. Crookston worked an extra hour or two a day for a month, all the time enlisting his patients in the project. He promised them that things would be much better soon. Some practices temporarily bring in additional staff to reduce backlog. This is the most difficult part for clinicians because they are working harder but the administrators are already reaping some benefits from shorter wait times. Backlog cleanup requires temporary new resources and strong leadership support from managers and senior clinicians.

Dr. Crookston found that he could eliminate the backlog faster if he could manage his demand better. Like other advanced access physicians, Dr. Crookston discovered that one of the best ways to shape his demand was to ensure that his patients could see him when they had urgent problems. This tactic eliminates the demand for follow-up visits created when a walk-in or ER doc tells a patient to "check back in few days with your regular family doctor." While seeing his own patients for episodic care, Dr. Crookston reduces the demand for future care by dealing with their other problems as well. This is referred to as "max-packing." You will remember that in chapter 5, Seattle's Dr. Elizabeth Lin max-packed diabetes and depression follow-up onto her patient Amanda's visit for a sore shoulder.

After the backlog is eliminated, the next step is to decrease the number of appointment categories. Dr. Frazzle made things worse for himself when he created urgent and then super-urgent categories. Intuitively it seems correct to treat the most seriously ill first, just like triage on a battlefield. And if there is truly not enough capacity to treat all, then we must make some hard choices about who gets care. But if everyone is going to be treated at some point, it's better to treat them all sooner rather than later. Dr. Murray says the key question for managing demand should be, "Is the patient's personal clinician present today?" If the answer is yes, then the patient sees his or her regular provider. If not, the patient can decide with a nurse whether to see someone else today or to wait to see his or her regular clinician. Some clinics use only two appointment categories, short and long. Two short appointments can be combined for the equivalent of one long.

Dr. Crookston also found that his visits became shorter. When people had so much trouble seeing him, they would load up every problem they could find and bring them to the consultation. Now that they know they can come back any time, they focus on the most important issues without the pressure to do everything at once. Like other advanced access practices, Dr. Crookston found that his no-show rate plunged to essentially zero. Once practices get waits beyond a week or so, no-show rates escalate rapidly. Most report at least 10 to 20 per cent no-shows. Dr. Crookston found that his total demand actually dropped while his and his nurse's morale soared.

Reshaping Demand

While Dr. Crookston's demand matched his capacity, other practices will have to actively shape demand to make it more manageable.

Dr. Murray relates a story of Dr. F. who was part of an eight-doctor practice that moved to advanced access.[21] Dr. F. had over 2,500 patients, many of whom were chronically ill, while the other physicians averaged only 1,600 to 1,800. When the practices monitored their calls, Dr. F. found she averaged 24 calls for appointments each day but could keep only 12 slots open. When she tried to open more slots for same-day appointments, she found that she had to book her routine appointments further and further in advance.

It was clear that Dr. F.'s existing capacity did not meet her existing demand. Working with her practice manager, she first closed her practice to new patients. She was a very popular community doctor, but there was no point taking on new patients when she couldn't service her current ones. An underutilized nurse practitioner moved from another practice to form a care team with Dr. F. A nurse who was no longer needed for telephone triage (because of the move to advanced access) also joined them to assist in the management of patients with chronic illness.

Other methods to reduce demand include increasing the use of telephone and e-mail communication. In chapter 5 we mentioned a Group Health Centre physician, David Fera, who started seeing his diabetic patients in groups, improving their quality of care and reducing the time required per patient.

These same demand-modification tactics can also be used in specialty practice. At present, most specialist visits are forty-five minute to one-hour consultations. But some patients require two hours and many others need their family doctor to have only a five minute telephone call with the specialist to fix their problems. The Hamilton HSO Mental Health and Nutrition Program described in chapter 9 is a perfect example of this approach. The program has dramatically increased access to mental health services: the numbers of patients receiving mental health services has increased *nine-fold*. It has simultaneously reduced referrals by participating family doctors to local psychiatric outpatient clinics by two-thirds.[22]

Better Access and Better Care through Teamwork

Just imagine if we could get other specialists working in shared care arrangements. There are long wait times to see cardiologists in most parts of Canada. What if we could link up cardiologists to family doctors in a fashion similar to that of the Hamilton HSO Mental Health and Nutrition Program? If family doctors could speak on the telephone with a cardiologist for five to ten minutes, many referrals would be unnecessary, and others would be better planned and productive. What if cardiologists could spend time with groups of primary health care practitioners discussing cases once or twice a month, just like the Hamilton psychiatrists do? Over time, the primary health care providers would acquire much more expertise in managing cardiac patients. What if we established similar programs for orthopedics, neurology, and other specialties where waits are problematic? What if we had more doctors working together in group practices to facilitate shared care?

Even when advanced access is working well, practices still need to have contingency plans in place for occasions when demand temporarily outstrips capacity. Winter is busier than summer. Mondays are busier than Wednesdays. Sometimes several clinicians will need to be at a meeting, leaving a clinic short staffed. In these situations, staff should protect remaining capacity by limiting or eliminating booked appointments.

Advanced access is still a new concept, but gradually other doctors are testing the waters. Victoria family doctor David Attwell is very happy with the effect on his practice.[23] He claims that these techniques can help decongest emergency departments by nipping problems in the bud. Attwell asserts, "An upper respiratory infection doesn't become pneumonia for an old person, which then leads to heart failure, which then leads to a very expensive hospital visit."

More Complicated Access Problems: From the Russian Chicken Three-Step to Breast Care in Sault Ste. Marie

Advanced access techniques offer exciting promise for reducing waits in ambulatory care settings, but what about delays for surgery and other diagnostic and therapeutic procedures?

For many Canadians, waiting for care has begun to look like the Russian chicken three-step—the way Russians supposedly bought chickens in 1985. In the apocryphal story, our hardy comrade would have to line up for two hours to get a chicken voucher stamped. Then and only then could he get into the second line and wait two hours to show the voucher and get a chicken. Finally, our Russian friend would face two hours of waiting in a third line to hand over his voucher, buy the chicken, and leave the store.

Astute readers will note that if we allowed our comrade to line up just once and then have his voucher stamped, receive his chicken, pay, and then hand over his voucher, he could avoid two out of three waits. This would reduce his waiting time by 67 per cent.

Much cancer care in Canada looks like the Russian chicken story. For example, to be screened for breast cancer, first a woman has to line up for a mammogram. This delay usually isn't too long, but then she has to wait for the radiologist to read the X-ray and then for the report to get back to her family doctor's office. If it is positive, then and only then can her family doctor refer her to a surgeon for a biopsy. After the biopsy, the pathologist reads the slide and sends the report back to the family doctor's office. If the biopsy is positive, then and only then can the family doctor refer the patient to surgery. At each step, the patient might have to wait weeks or even months for the next visit or investigation.

Tommy Douglas identified this issue years ago: "I have a good doctor and we're good friends. And we both laugh when we look at the system. He sends me off to see somebody to get some tests at the other end of town. I go over there and then come back, and they send the reports to him and he looks at them and sends me off some place else for some tests and they come back. Then he says that I had better see a specialist. And before I'm finished I've spent within a month, six days going to six different people and another six days going to have six different kinds of tests, all of which I could have had in a single clinic."[24]

Today, many people find it takes them six months, not just one, to get through their six appointments.

The Sault Reduces Breast Cancer Waits

In the late 1990s, the Ontario Breast Screening Program and local providers were concerned that women in Sault Ste. Marie were facing long delays to have breast cancer surgery. A committee was convened to examine the issue, and it included Teresa D'Angelo, who was working in medical records at the Group Health Centre, and her husband, Joe, who was working at the local hospital. One of the committee's first tasks was to map the flow of patients through the system. They found that the delays accumulated mainly at the transition points—from mammogram to biopsy, and from biopsy to surgery. Sometimes the report would take too long to get back to the family doctor. Sometimes, the radiologist, after reading the mammogram, would decide the woman needed more X-rays, taken from different views. In the D'Angelos' words, there was a lot of "ping ponging" of patients between different posts along their diagnostic journey.

The D'Angelos thought that if they could eliminate some of the separate wait times, they could reduce the overall delay for care. Instead of being referred back to their family doctors to await a further referral, Sault women with suspicious mammograms now get immediate ultrasound examinations and, if necessary, biopsies. Within a few days, the patient and her doctors know if she has cancer. If she does have cancer and needs surgery, she gets her operation within a week or two. Within a few months, the wait times from mammogram to the final diagnosis of breast cancer plunged from 107 to 18 days.

This process is sometimes referred to as *facilitated referral.* Instead of being continually bounced back to their family doctors for the next step in the referral process, potential Sault cancer patients are assisted by a "navigator." Once a patient is in the system, a radiation technologist is assigned as her navigator to facilitate her movement through the system. The navigator sets appointments, makes sure the X-rays and other tests are at the specialist's office on time, and answers her questions.

A few years ago, Dr. Ivo Olivotto, now the director of the Victoria Cancer Clinic, found that using a similar approach reduced the time from a positive screening mammogram to diagnosis by 60 to 70 per cent.[25]

Winnipeg, Montreal, and several other communities have centralized wait-list management of breast cancer workups with salutary results. To quote Dr. Pasteur Rasuli, an Ottawa radiologist, "The development of comprehensive breast centres is an effective means of streamlining the management of patients with abnormalities detected through clinical examination or mammography by minimizing the number of visits and decreasing the overall waiting time to final diagnosis."[26]

You Can Climb Mount Baldy Yourself, but You Need a Sherpa for Everest

Mount Baldy, at a towering 831 metres, is the highest point in Manitoba. It's not too difficult to climb Mount Baldy. In most parts of Canada, if you decided to climb Mount Baldy in the morning, you could do it all by yourself before sundown. Just fly to Winnipeg, drive two hours west on the Trans-Canada Highway to Brandon, one hour north on Highway 10, half an hour west on Highway 5, another half hour north on Highway 366, and you're there. Take out your camera and document your ascent!

On the other hand, even in 2003, summiting Mount Everest takes a lot of help. The vast majority of Everest's conquerors are rookies. Very few make a return trip. Even experienced mountaineers don't really know if they are more suited to take the route up the North Col or the Western Cwm. Sherpas help them up the mountain.

The Sherpas are a Tibetan tribe that has lived with Sagamartha (their name for Everest) for over five hundred years. When New Zealander Edmund Hillary summited the mountain in 1953, he wasn't alone. Tenzing Norgay, a plucky Sherpa guide, was with him. Sherpas also carried most of the supplies that Hillary's team needed. If you were climbing Everest, would you try it alone or would you hire a Sherpa?

In the health care system, we don't always need Sherpa guides or navigators. Just as most of us can climb Mount Baldy ourselves, so we can deal with our own cut fingers—try some pressure, ice, and elevation, and if the bleeding doesn't stop, find a doctor's office or ER where we can get a few sutures. But if we get a serious condition like cancer or heart disease, most of us feel like we're climbing Everest without Sherpas.

Case Management Unclogs Saskatoon's Hospitals

Client Care Co-ordinator Cheryl McNally was facing a bed crunch at Saskatoon's Royal University Hospital, and Eloise J. didn't think she was ready to go home. The seventy-seven-year-old had mostly recovered from a fractured hip, but she lived alone in a small town 200 kilometres southwest of Saskatoon and was afraid of being by herself. Fortunately, as a co-ordinator of out-of-region transfers, McNally knew exactly what to do. She spoke to a nurse at the Leader Hospital just a half-hour drive from Eloise's home and found that, as usual, the small rural facility had extra beds. She asked the Leader Hospital nurse to alert the doctor on call that he would shortly be getting a telephone call, and then she sought out Eloise's physician. The Saskatoon doctor was soon talking to the Leader doctor, and shortly after that Eloise was recovering her strength closer to home.

McNally is one of fifty case managers who work for Client/Patient

Access Services, or CPAS, but you can think of her as a Sherpa guide or navigator. McNally's particular responsibility is dealing with out-of-region transfers to and from other acute care facilities. Much of her time is spent dealing with patients like Eloise who are leaving the Royal University Hospital to convalesce in a rural hospital. She also deals regularly with other university teaching hospitals in western Canada to arrange sophisticated care not available in Saskatchewan. For example, sixty-six-year-old Will G. had been waiting for two weeks to be transferred to the Vancouver General Hospital for an advanced cardiac procedure. McNally phoned the Vancouver cardiologist's secretary and confirmed that the specialist would take the patient. Then she phoned the ward manager at Vancouver General to establish that they would also take the patient. Within forty-eight hours, Will was on his way to Vancouver.

Sue Melrose, CPAS's director, is both the past and the future of case management. She originally trained as a social worker and worked as community case manager. Case management is commonplace in community settings. Home care services such as quick response teams or assertive community treatment teams, described in chapter 6, rely upon case management to ensure that patients move expeditiously through the system. Sue Melrose works with her definition of case management as "a collaborative process which assesses, plans, implements, coordinates, monitors and evaluates options and services to meet an individual's health needs through communication and available resources to promote quality cost-effective outcomes."[27]

Up until 2000, CPAS was purely a community service. Melrose and other CPAS workers had become increasingly frustrated with continual gridlock in the city's hospitals and suggested that better case management within hospitals might help decongest the institutions. That summer, Melrose and some seconded staff started the CPAS hospital pilot.

Melrose was shocked to see the lack of co-ordination within hospitals. Staff lurched from crisis to crisis in what seemed like a war zone. As in any war zone, black markets quickly developed to distribute scarce commodities. For example, when clerks in admitting tried to find beds for new patients, units would refuse patients who didn't meet their strict criteria. Some nurses and doctors habitually hoarded beds to ensure that they could meet their own needs. They made secret deals with staff on other wards. After standoffs that could last hours or days, general managers and even vice-presidents would get involved in the negotiations. Savvy ward nurses would wait until after four o'clock to deal with on-call managers instead of the more knowledgeable regular staff. Etcetera, etcetera.

Sue and the others were appalled to see the lack of attention to details that resulted in misuse of beds. She relates a story of a family member who drove 300 kilometres to Saskatoon to see her relative in the hospital and then drove home just in time to answer the ringing telephone: someone from Saskatoon was calling asking her to drive back to town to take her loved one home. Patients would wait days to see a specialist and then the doctor couldn't complete his consultation because a key test or X-ray hadn't been performed.

Melrose concluded that case management was as needed inside as it was outside the hospital. The Saskatoon region formalized the CPAS hospital component in April 2001. The CPAS co-ordinators quietly began to dismantle the unofficial processes that had grown like cancers. The maternity ward wasn't usually full, so they worked with the staff to make them comfortable taking care of low-intensity post-surgical patients. Pediatrics agreed to take patients a few years older than their traditional eighteen-years cut-off. Adult wards agreed to take patients who might be only sixteen years old.

Initially, Melrose reports, there was push-back from staff, especially doctors. Cheryl McNally notes that she has been referred to as the "doctor police" because some physicians think she nags them so much. But like Corporal "Radar" O'Reilly, who was at least one step in front of his superior officers at the 4077th MASH unit, the CPAS co-ordinators are typically in advance of the doctors. Clinicians tend to focus on the task at hand as opposed to the subsequent ones. But, as Sue Melrose says, "What's the big deal about planning two to three days ahead?" Gradually, CPAS won over many physicians because the co-ordinators proved they could help them and their patients by freeing up beds. Hearkening back to her social work experience, Melrose says it's like any community-development exercise—you have to show people you can help them and then they will help you.

One measure of CPAS's success is the small number of Saskatoon patients waiting for long-term care beds. In the early 1990s, there were often over two hundred persons waiting for long-term care beds, with over fifty in hospital beds. Regionalization and subsequent better co-ordination reduced the wait list to fewer than thirty. In the late 1990s, this wait list grew to over fifty. However, with the advent of in-hospital CPAS, the wait list plunged. Now there are over twenty vacant beds in the long-term care facilities, and general manager Dave Gibson says they are considering closing some beds. As opposed to those in cities like Toronto, Saskatoon hospital patients don't wait for nursing home beds. When patients are designated for a long-term care bed, they are typically there within twenty-four hours.

However, Melrose notes that although CPAS has developed creative detours around barriers, ultimately the region will have to re-engineer its processes to build upon CPAS's success. For example, the Saskatoon region was one of the first established in Canada, in 1992. But the city's three hospitals are still not fully integrated. Most of the surgeons are located at the Royal University Hospital (RUH) because of their academic affiliations. But this means that RUH is frequently overloaded even when there are free beds at City Hospital. One CPAS co-ordinator admits she has been tempted to tell patients in the hallways of the RUH emergency department that they wouldn't have to wait if they took a cab to City Hospital.

CPAS has had considerable success in temporarily moving patients and staff from RUH to City, but ultimately the region will have to grapple with moving entire programs. This is similar to what happens after implementing advanced access in ambulatory care. As the immediate problems recede, the permanent ones reveal themselves.

What About Family Doctors?

Some readers at this point may wonder about the role of the family physician in the co-ordination of care. The ideal of the family doctor embodied in Norman Rockwell's paintings or the 1970s TV drama *Marcus Welby, M.D.* was always rare and is getting rarer. A dwindling minority of family doctors agree with Dr. Elliot Halparin, a family doctor in rural/suburban Georgetown, 100 kilometres northwest of Toronto, that family doctors should co-ordinate all care. Dr. Halparin and some of his colleagues continue to see patients in hospital, nursing homes, the office, and even their own homes. This puts them in an excellent position to co-ordinate the physician's aspects of care. But it is almost impossible for even the most Welby-like family doctor to intimately know the social services system, the education system, and the justice system in addition to the health system. And, as Cheryl McNally demonstrates, professional case managers at the regional level even have knowledge about medical services that family doctors couldn't possibly maintain. For example, CPAS has ongoing information about the availability of neonatal intensive care unit beds not only in Saskatoon but also in Edmonton, Calgary, and Winnipeg. These other cities have larger referral areas and consequently greater numbers of specialty beds and greater surge capacity than Saskatoon. It makes sense to share, especially when some of the Saskatchewan patients referred to Saskatoon might actually live closer to these other cities.

As we discussed in chapter 9, family doctors are increasingly restricting their practices to the office. The provinces still remunerate the majority of family doctors on a fee-for-service system, which pays inadequately, if at all, for telephone calls. Some provinces are experimenting with special fees for the elderly, who often require considerable co-ordination of care. But most physician time devoted to case management is uncompensated.

Some Toronto physicians recently came up with a creative way of getting around this dilemma. Most family doctors have approximately 1,500 patients. Doctors Rochelle Schwartz and Sharla Lichtman aim for 150. How do they make a living? No problem! They charge their patients $2,500 a year,* which includes a fitness checkup and prescription, a physician's evaluation, a mental checkup from a social worker, and a nutritional evaluation from a dietitian.[28] Finally, the patient gets a health program that fits like a glove. According to the *Globe and Mail*'s Margaret Wente, you also get Dr. Schwartz or Dr. Lichtman any time you need them, 24/7. If you need a specialist, they will find one. Dr. Lichtman reports that she once spent eight hours on the telephone to get a patient an urgent MRI.

This situation certainly appears to work for the doctors. "This means I can be home for my kids at four," Dr. Lichtman happily notes. But even if their practice works for them and their patients, it's too impractical to implement nationwide. We would need over 180,000 new family doctors, more than six times the present complement.

Despite the thousands of hours of time that family doctors volunteer to co-ordinate patient care, the reality is that the system seems impenetrable to most patients with complicated illnesses. The good news is that with a little case management and some application of queueing theory, we could dramatically reduce waits and delays in the Canadian health care system. Given the CPAS example, it should be eminently possible for Canadians to get an MRI without a physician's whole day being devoted to the process.

---

* Yes, reader, I agree. This does seem to be contrary to the Canada Health Act, but the feds haven't done anything. *Plus ça change, c'est la même chose.*

Still Waiting . . .
for the Health System to Use Queueing Theory

Let's consider our breast cancer example again. It doesn't take more system resources if a woman has her mammogram and biopsy on the same day instead of bouncing around the system for three months. The resources are simply used all at once, today, instead of in dribs and drabs. In fact, because transitions can be resource-intensive, there are always savings when services are provided in tandem. If the ultrasound is directed by the same radiologist who has just read the mammogram, he doesn't have to worry about his notes being misinterpreted by a colleague. This is one of the principles that comes out of queueing theory: we need to do today's work today.

This discussion will seem startlingly familiar to readers engaged in business, engineering, statistics, or advanced mathematics. Agner Krarup Erlang, an engineer who worked for the Copenhagen Telephone Exchange, published the first paper on queueing theory in 1909.* Since then, queueing theory has been used to optimize the performance of everything from Disney World to downtown traffic. Wherever people or products arrive, have something done to them, and then leave, applications derived from queueing theory can help make the process more efficient.

Assembly lines take advantage of queueing theory in their design. Just imagine an auto plant designed like the health care system. A man would tighten a bolt on one side of the plant and then a porter would move the vehicle shell to the other side of the plant so the next part could be installed by someone else. Then the porter would have to move the vehicle to the far corner to have yet another bolt tightened. If work is reorganized into an assembly line, there is no more time required per worker per part. In fact, there is less time required for transitions. The overall time required for assembly is dramatically

---

* For more on queueing theory, see Dr. Myron Hlynka's *Queueing Theory Page* at http://www2.uwindsor.ca/~hlynka/queue.html.

reduced because the intervals the vehicle spends between workers shrinks from minutes to seconds.

Of course, we don't want to treat patients like cars or cow carcasses. All the same, some of the best-known health care institutions in the US use exactly this approach. And no one accuses them of veterinary medicine.

John Crispo, professor emeritus of political economy in the Faculty of Management at the University of Toronto, relates a recent trip to New York's famed Memorial Sloan-Kettering Cancer Center for assessment of his prostate cancer. Pressured by his wife to get a second opinion, he went into the hospital in the morning, had scans, blood tests, physical examinations, and meetings with oncologists and psychiatrists, and was out in time to enjoy an evening in Manhattan.

The fabled Mayo Clinic has always operated this way. People from the far corners of the world descend on the small town of Rochester, Minnesota, looking for some of the best health care services on the planet. They can't stay for months bouncing around between appointments, so they also get their services all at the same time. It's a mistake to think that this kind of service costs more just because it is used in elite centres like Sloan-Kettering or Mayo. The costs of the services actually go down when they are provided with one-stop shopping.

Britain is far ahead of Canada in using these methods, but even there, the *British Medical Journal* laments, "Hospitals have largely failed to use one of the most potent methods currently available for improving the performance of complex organizations."[29]

Mine Eyes Have Seen the Light: Cataract Surgery in Toronto
The Trillium Health Centre was created from a 1998 merger of the Queensway General Hospital in west Toronto and the Mississauga Hospital 5 kilometres farther west. The Queensway site was renovated as an ambulatory care centre, and in October 2001, the largest free-standing day-surgery facility in North America opened there.

The Surgicentre houses eight operating rooms in a 23,000-square-foot facility. Managers Kim Stephens-Wood and Evelyn MacLean proudly show off their new baby. The facility does over 3,000 cataract operations a year and has the capacity to perform over 25,000 other day procedures.

Cataract patients attend a pre-surgery clinic, where an anesthetist ensures that they are indeed low risk. When they come back for their procedures, they first meet a nurse in a private counselling room to ensure they are properly prepared. Then they have their surgery, which typically takes only fifteen to twenty minutes, and go into the post-op area. After they are cleared to leave this area, the same nurse who met them at the beginning takes them to the recovery area, lined with recliner chairs. When they are well enough, the nurse clears them to go and then calls them the next morning to make sure they're recovering on schedule. Every step in the process is carefully planned around the patients and their needs, to ensure effective, efficient patient flow.

The Surgicentre is bright and lined with windows, and has areas for families, including children. Patients had input into the design, ensuring fully private assessment rooms and real plants beside the recliners.

Right-wing ideologues often claim that we need to introduce private-sector management and the profit motive to improve the efficiency of health care in Canada. For example, the Cambie Surgical Corporation, a for-profit surgery centre in Vancouver, boasts that it achieves efficiencies "that one cannot duplicate in the administratively overburdened structure of a major public institution."[30]

Private cataract surgery clinics helped revolutionize care in western Canada and became a focus of political conflict in Alberta. But the for-profit sector has no monopoly on quality improvement. Trillium and other non-profit health organizations are taking advantage of queueing theory and are moving patients faster. In fact, the Calgary Regional Health Authority, a very public organization, has one of the largest quality improvement initiatives anywhere in North America.

The Real Alberta Advantage:
Quality Improvement in Calgary

Some organizations devolve quality improvement to a separate department, where it languishes. However, the staff of the Quality Improvement and Health Information (QIHI) department of the Calgary Region see themselves as consultants to other departments that, logically, should own the quality improvement process in their area. As a result, the region has completed dozens of separate projects and trained hundreds of staff in quality improvement methods. Each department's quality improvement physician is responsible not only to his director, but also to the QIHI medical director, Dr. Ward Flemons.

Health Care Gets an Eleven-Step Recovery Plan
The Calgary region uses an eleven-step model to develop quality improvement initiatives.[31] The first step is to establish a project team, which should include all those affected by the process. For example, the team dealing with leg and lung clots (deep vein thromboses, or DVTs, and pulmonary embolisms, or PEs) had a main working group, an evidence working group, and a data collection working group. These groups included representatives from respirology, hematology, radiology, the laboratory, and the emergency department. Step two is to collect background data. The clot group looked at the total number of patients who presented with possible clots, by hospital and by the tests performed.

Step three is to develop problem or issue statements. The clot group noted that the diagnostic process varied from patient to patient for no apparent reason. Possible clot patients who presented to the ER had to return for follow-up the next day, but many came at night, when key diagnostic services were not available. Many patients with possible clots never returned for their full diagnostic workup.

Step four is a formal diagramming of the entire patient journey. This part often shocks staff because typically they know only their own part of the process. The whole patient pathway is almost always at least as tortuous as Tommy Douglas's experience. As Sue Melrose notes, "Most things are done in the health care system for the convenience of providers." From the individual provider's perspective, everything might look fine. When the provider goes to her waiting room, there is someone to see who will move on to the next way station. But to patients, the same process might be experienced as an endless, terrifying series of merry-go-rounds.

Step five is to determine the root causes of the problems. This involves critically examining the patient flow for bottlenecks. The review of clots found lack of access to timely diagnostic tests and poor access to family doctors for follow-up as well as other problems. Step six is to verify the causes of delay with data. The clot group focused on the lack of standardization of the diagnostic process and on the difficulty of accessing timely diagnostic testing. Step seven is to critically review the literature. The clot group focused on the diagnostic workup and proposed that the region's physicians use the Wells score, which divides possible clot patients into low-, medium-, and high-risk groups.

Steps eight, nine, ten, and eleven are selecting solutions, implementing solutions, measuring results, and evaluation. Those familiar with quality improvement techniques will recognize here the iterative plan-do-study-act (PDSA) cycle. Because change is so difficult, especially in large organizations like health systems, people use the PDSA method to slice the transition into digestible pieces. Each innovation is tested to ensure it works.

For example, try putting alerts about needed follow-up on all diabetic patients' charts for a week and see if that makes a difference in their follow-up. It might seem that small alterations wouldn't make much difference, but organizations can engineer major improvements in service through successive quick cycles of change. To quote the Great Helmsman, a journey of a thousand miles starts with a single step. (There is more about the PDSA method in Appendix A.)

In 2003, the Calgary Health Region launched 38 new quality

improvement projects, seventeen for patient safety and twenty-one for patient flow.

The foremost advocate for such approaches to innovation in health care is Boston pediatrician Donald Berwick, who is the founding president and CEO of the Institute for Healthcare Improvement (IHI). Dr. Berwick has been a champion for quality all his professional career. He has continually noted that health care systems perform far below their quality potential and that poor quality is often directly responsible for poor cost control.

Berwick founded IHI in 1991, and it has grown to be the world's most prominent organization concerned with quality improvement in health care. IHI sponsors conferences and workshops and has acted as consultant to a number of countries and health organizations. IHI has helped redesign the UK's National Health Service cancer and cardiac care.*

The Cardiac Care Network of Ontario

One of the most cited examples of wait-list management in Canada is the Cardiac Care Network of Ontario. During the late 1980s, concern over reports that heart patients were dying while awaiting surgery led to investigations of Ontario's cardiac surgery wait lists. These inquiries revealed many familiar problems, such as no central wait list and no standards for rating the urgency of a case. Subsequent consultations with cardiologists, cardiac surgeons, epidemiologists, family doctors, and consumers led to the creation in 1990 of the Cardiac Care Network (CCN).† The CCN convened an expert group, which developed an urgency rating scale to ensure that urgent patients would be properly triaged.[32]

---

* For more on IHI, see http://www.ihi.org.
† For more information on the Cardiac Care Network of Ontario, see its Web site, http://www.ccn.on.ca/.

CCN's structure includes a co-ordinating body (with doctors, ministry representatives, and so on) and a network of member centres, each with a regional cardiac care co-ordinator who assists patients through the system. With the support of organizations such as Toronto's Sunnybrook Hospital's Institute for Clinical Evaluative Sciences, CCN maintains a comprehensive database on cardiac surgery, angioplasty, and cardiac catheterization. The CCN uses its data to promote continuous quality improvement. Whenever a hospital's mortality rates are significantly higher than other hospitals', the findings are drawn to the hospital's attention and follow-up analyses are conducted.

Implementing the CCN has contributed to Ontario's having some of the best cardiac surgery outcomes in the world. From 1994/95 to 1999/2000, Ontario's bypass surgery operative mortality fell 32 per cent (from 2.8 to 1.9 per cent) and length of stay decreased by 15 per cent (from 8.1 to 7.2 days), while the numbers of operations performed increased by 33 per cent (from 5,811 to 7,731).[33]

Hospitals regularly update data on patients waiting for care, and the CCN posts the information on the Internet. Patients or their doctors can request treatment according to where wait times are shortest. However, this patient-shifting almost never occurs. For the first three months of 2003, the average wait time for outpatient heart catheterization* in the Greater Toronto Area varied from a low of eight days to a high of thirty-seven days. Across the province it varied almost eight-fold, from eight days to sixty-three days. One would think that if patients or family doctors were using this information the wait times would tend to equalize themselves.

The regional co-ordinators provide a single point of contact for information for patients with questions or concerns, but they don't really act like Sherpas.

---

* An X-ray of the heart and coronary arteries, which is the first step toward surgery.

Western Canada Gets Involved

In 1997, the federal government's National Forum on Health reviewed waiting lists and concluded, "Most waiting lists for elective surgery are unstructured, many are padded, few are standardized, and even fewer are evaluated. They are therefore quite meaningless."[34] This led to a Health Canada study on waiting-list issues in 1998 and, later that year, to the establishment of the Western Canada Waiting List Project (WCWL). The WCWL is a consortium of the four western provinces, their medical associations, seven of the largest regional health authorities, and four health research centres. It is based at the University of Calgary and has funding from Health Canada's Health Transition Fund.*

The WCWL project's main goal has been to develop urgency rating scales for cataract surgery, children's mental health services, general surgery, hip and knee replacement, and MRI scanning. The project has used similar consensus processes as Ontario's Cardiac Care Network to develop these indicators. As we go to press, the project has developed most of the instruments, but their use will still be voluntary for the surgeons.

We Need to Think Outside the Box

The Cardiac Care Network of Ontario has done world-class work. Until the Ontario Ministry of Health established the CCN, low-risk patients at no vital peril sometimes had their surgery months before those at great risk. There were no comparisons of performance between different organizations in order to continually improve performance. The CCN has produced excellent data, which have been used for planning[35] and research.[36] It is one of the most successful quality improvement programs in the country.[37]

But the CCN's wait management techniques are limited in their

---

* For more about the Western Canada Waiting List Project, see http://www.wcwl.org.

application to other clinical situations. The reason is that the CCN breaks one of the cardinal commandments of queueing theory: Thou shalt not create multiple lines according to urgency. Dr. David Naylor, dean of medicine at the University of Toronto, wryly notes that queueing theory is a "conspicuous area of underuse" for the Canadian health care system. Naylor was one of the original researchers involved in the establishment of the CCN. He claims that cardiac surgery is different from most other services because of the degree of urgency for some patients. He also notes that it is prone to demand/capacity mismatches because the Canadian hospital system has so little margin.

What this really means is that there are problems, which accrue because patients are not widgets under the complete control of an industrial engineer. Any industrial engineer will tell you that nothing stalls efficient flow faster than product variation. On an assembly line, if the vehicles sometimes arrive a metre above a worker's head and sometimes below his waist, that worker has to expend time and effort moving up and down. This variation can slow down a line. And if the worker can't cope with the variation, the line might stop dead.

A British study shows that even small variation in patients' conditions after heart surgery can dramatically affect the demand for post-op ICU beds. The researchers found that 90 per cent of heart patients stayed less than forty-eight hours in the ICU after surgery.[38] If all patients used less than two days of ICU care, the heart service would need only eight ICU beds. But if even a few patients require longer ICU stays, this could gum up the works unless there are more ICU beds. If only 10 per cent of patients stay in the ICU longer than two days, then ten ICU beds are required to prevent cancellations of surgery 94 per cent of the time. The service would need twelve beds to prevent cancellations 99 per cent of the time.*

---

* Interestingly, Naylor points out that assuming a Monday-to-Friday surgical schedule but full ICU staffing on weekends, the congestion could be ameliorated by scheduling complicated cases for later in the week so they could have extra ICU time over the weekend for recovery.

Canadian hospitals typically run at greater than 95 per cent capacity, so heart surgery is still cancelled because of lack of post-op ICU beds. And, given that some heart patients are urgent and others are much less so, there are occasions when choices need to be made about who will go first. However, if hospitals ran at 90 per cent capacity and patients could be shared between hospitals,* then very few operations would have to be cancelled. It might even be possible to move heart surgery to advanced access.

Since most of the time Canadians do get their care eventually it makes sense to work down the backlog and then go to just-in-time servicing.

Establishing multiple urgency ratings can help temporarily, but soon it becomes counterproductive. Our intrepid Dr. Frazzle temporarily improved his access to urgent patients when he saved specific slots for them. But the situation quickly soured because the non-urgent patients were simply pushed further into the future.

That's the main reason why Ontario's Cardiac Care Network is not the right model for the management of most Canadian wait lists. And that's why the Western Canadian Waiting List Project is unlikely to be the answer to waits for the five services with which it is working. If the WCWL sponsors can gain the surgeons' co-operation, the project will collect, for the first time, important before-and-after data on surgical patients. But developing more categories of urgency will not reduce waiting times. Just ask Dr. Frazzle. The real solution is to do today's work today.

Join the Queue . . . in Britain

Dr. Richard Steyn first became interested in queue management as a general practitioner in rural Scotland in the 1980s. His practice essentially used advanced access techniques, although he didn't realize it at the time. His patients faced no waits when they wanted to see

---

* Most Canadians live within a four-hour drive of two hospitals that perform heart surgery.

him or one of his partners. But he noticed that waits in cities were several weeks long for GPs and months long for specialists. In the 1990s, Dr. Steyn completed his training as a thoracic surgeon, and in August 1999, he was appointed consultant thoracic surgeon at Birmingham Heartlands and Solihull NHS Trust.

Shortly after taking his appointment, Dr. Steyn was one of four physicians who attended a lecture by Dr. Kate Silvester. Dr. Silvester is not your average doctor. She originally trained as an ophthalmologist but tired of it. Then she trained as a manufacturing systems engineer and worked for seven years as a management consultant. Since 1999 Dr. Silvester has worked for the Modernisation Agency, which is the key organization leading the redesign of the National Health Service. Like the other physicians, Dr. Steyn was very skeptical about Silvester's approach and her disdain for urgency ratings. He had come to the meeting hoping it would lead to care by urgency, sometimes referred to as "carve-outs."

After the meeting, Steyn tried to prove Silvester wrong. He hit his computer and modelled the results of different queue-management methods. Eventually, he proved Silvester right. As his interest in queueing grew, he got involved in a project to reduce wait times for lung cancer workups and then, in December 2001, he was appointed national clinical lead for demand and capacity with the Modernisation Agency. He now travels the world, lecturing and consulting on demand and capacity management and queueing theory.

Dr. Steyn sympathizes with doctors who think they're on a battlefield. With the chaos in most health care systems, it's understandable that busy physicians simply put their heads down and move on to the next patient. He says that if doctors ever want to get off their endless treadmills, they need to learn about queueing theory and advanced access techniques.

Unclogging Colonoscopy in the Midlands

In Birmingham, an evaluation of the delays for colorectal cancer treatment showed that the major bottleneck was colonoscopy. On average, it took 120 days to get an appointment. When the investigators looked further, they found that there were several different endoscopists, each with his or her own waiting list; several had sorted their patients into various urgency categories. All told, there were seventy-three separate queues. The Birmingham endoscopy service had all the problems of Dr. Frazzle's practice—long routine waits, constant prioritization and reprioritization, stress, stress, stress. Because the waits were so long, patients often didn't show up for their appointments, sometimes because they had gone elsewhere— or died. The staff would scramble to find another patient, but too often the available slots weren't filled. This compounded the problem because, according to another law from queueing theory, you cannot carry forward unused capacity but you do carry forward unmet demand.

Eventually, after a lot of education and a fair bit of cajoling, the endoscopy service went to one list, centrally managed. General practitioners and other referring physicians can still ask for a specific endoscopist, but then the patient gets a later appointment than if the referral is simply made to the endoscopy service. Just like Dr. Crookston, the endoscopy service had to work down the backlog, but soon the average wait had been cut by 75 per cent.

Dr. Steyn says that a few doctors were the main barriers to the change. These physicians claimed that the service was disrupting the sacrosanct doctor–patient relationship. Steyn thinks that some were really concerned about the impact on their private practices. In Britain, specialists can practise inside and outside the public system at the same time. If they develop long waiting lists in the public system, they can then suggest that patients see them privately, which allows them to bill higher fees.[39]

Dr. Steyn also has no patience for doctors who claim that some doctors are much better operators than others. He says that a department that has doctors who aren't performing properly has serious management issues. As to patients' preferences, Steyn claims that very few patients have specific preferences for individual specialists.

Most are thrilled to get earlier appointments, and they still have the choice of waiting to see a specific doctor.

Straightening the Lines to Care

In 2002, the waits for CAT scans in Newfoundland plummeted from twelve to fourteen weeks down to one to three weeks.[40] A new high-speed scanner at the Janeway health centre helped. But Shawn Thomas, the director of diagnostic imaging for the St. John's region, claims that another factor is mainly responsible for the rosy picture: "The success of our approach involves using our resources wisely and looking at diagnostic imaging as one huge department within the region, not a number of smaller departments at individual sites."

Thomas explains, "What was happening was that requisitions for CAT scans were flowing into the three X-ray sites, and some sites were overutilized and some were underutilized." St. John's was having the same problems as the Birmingham endoscopy suite—multiple queues and long waits. And St. John's solved their problems the same way, with a single queue.

Dr. Naylor agrees that, in general, putting patients into single queues for services instead of into multiple queues for individual doctors is the way forward. It will require better information systems. He also agrees with Dr. Steyn that the private-practice mentality is antithetical to such approaches. That's because a single queue treats operating time as a public good, while the private-practice system treats it as private property. We tend to think of medicare as a public system, but the title of a 1986 book by Dr. Naylor, *Private Practice: Public Payment*, more accurately describes the true situation.

It took several publicized deaths and decades of controversy before Manitoba confronted its lack of planning for heart surgery.[41] Noted Edmonton heart surgeon Arvind Koshal's August 2003 report condemned the overall lack of management of the heart surgery program. It recommended consolidating surgery at St. Boniface Hospital, closing the smaller program at the downtown Health Sciences Centre, and implementing a centralized wait list. Winnipeg Regional

Health Authority CEO Dr. Brian Postl says that previously, some surgeons had told the RHA to "drop dead" when asked to participate in the central list. Decades of reports had failed to solve the mess, but Health Minister David Chomiak promised that Dr. Koshal's report would be implemented in its entirety.

There is no fixed method for allocating operating room (OR) time in Canada. Usually, individual surgical departments make this key public-policy decision. Sometimes it's democratic and transparent. Sometimes it's autocratic and opaque. In some departments, the time is shared equally and new operators are given referrals by other surgeons, who shorten their lists. But usually, OR time is given according to historical volumes or the length of wait lists.

Saskatchewan wait list researcher Steven Lewis notes that this system penalizes honest doctors and rewards those who pump up their lists with questionable surgical candidates. He recalls one surgeon who acquired half the OR time in one community by stuffing his list with patients whose problems his colleagues didn't think merited surgery. Allocating OR time according to these methods also penalizes doctors who share patients with their colleagues.

Like Dr. Steyn, David Naylor disputes the claim that some doctors are so much better than others that they deserve more time. Naylor does admit that certain very complicated patients might benefit from having their surgery from "Dr. Goldenhands," but he says these cases are the exceptions and could easily be dealt with as such. Naylor says that any doctor who maintains that there are significant differences in the quality of care provided by different members of her department is admitting to inadequate quality assurance processes.

Conclusion

In this chapter, we have looked at medicare's Achilles heel: long waits for care. It turns out that despite all the concern and controversy, our information systems are so inadequate that we don't really know how long patients wait and we don't know the impact of these delays on their health.

Your Community and Waits and Delays

- Does your community measure waits and delays throughout the system?
- Does your community or province post wait times for different practitioners and for different services on the Internet?
- Do ambulatory clinics in your community, including family doctors' offices, have waits beyond one or two days? Are they using advanced access techniques?
- Do medical specialists participate in shared care arrangements with family doctors and primary health care centres?
- Does your community have wait-list co-ordinators for cardiac care, cancer care, orthopedics, neurology services, and other specialty services? Do these people facilitate access like a Sherpa guide?
- Does your community have comprehensive programs to deal with waits and delays, including for diagnostic and therapeutic procedures, special treatment units, medical specialists, and patient transfers?
- How does your community apportion operating time? Is it allocated democratically and transparently, or autocratically and opaquely? Do new doctors have to struggle to build up their practices, or do the older surgeons share their lists?
- Does your community centralize its wait lists under one manager, or are they kept by individual clinicians?

The good news is that there are untapped resources we could use to reduce and, often, eliminate waits. Wait lists are not usually a result of lack of money, and they can't be solved by simply adding money. We do need to buy more diagnostic equipment and do more joint replacements, but as with other problems in our health system, fixing waits and delays requires better management rather than large wads of cash.

In the last chapters, we will extend our discussion of waits and delays to system redesign. Single community queues for services show tremendous potential to reduce waiting, but we can't get there without re-engineering the system.

Part III

Developing a
Canadian Agenda for Quality

Chapter 12

Beware of Snake Oil:
The Private Sector Has No Panaceas

The previous nine chapters have shown that we already have the solutions to most of the apparently intractable problems facing our health care system. However, we don't usually hear about them. The most commonly offered remedies are a lot more money and privatization. The last three chapters outline how we can develop a Canadian agenda for quality. The first step is to avoid the siren calls for market solutions.

Our twenty-year blind love affair with the private sector seems to be on the wane; but a number of Canadians still believe that you only have to replace the word "public" or "non-profit" with "for-profit" and you have automatically made something 15 per cent more efficient. Adam Smith knew this was a myth over two hundred years ago, but that doesn't stop some modern-day economist wannabes from claiming that if we lift the regulatory shackles, the market's invisible hand will erase all human woes.

Markets are the most efficient mechanism to provide most goods and services, but all markets require a court system to enforce contracts. And most businesses require some form of public-policy framework. Governments regulate capital acquisition through stock markets because otherwise charlatans will beat out honest financiers. Honourable manufacturers can't compete with those that are willing to pollute the environment or reduce labour standards. Business needs government environmental and labour regulations to maintain a level playing field.

Furthermore, markets just don't deal effectively with some goods and services. For example, we publicly fund and administer fire services. We don't rely upon people to purchase firefighting insurance. What if everyone but one on the block had such insurance and his house caught on fire? Would we wait until the fire moved to someone else's house before we called the firefighters? And would different fire services compete with each other? It sounds like a nightmare.*

This chapter examines the public-private mix for health care. It doesn't look as though the private sector is any panacea for medicare's problems.

Financing the System:
A Private Bureaucracy Costs More Than a Public One

In the US, where most people rely upon private health insurance, each of the roughly one thousand companies selling policies has its own actuaries, sales and marketing people, computer systems, and so on. The administrative costs also add up in hospitals and even in doctors' offices. The average US doctor needs a full-time person just to do billing and reconciliations. An average Canadian doctor's secretary, on the other hand, spends just a couple of hours a month on these tasks. Huge resources are devoted in the US to screening out sick people to prevent them from acquiring insurance, denying claims, and fighting appeals. As a result, the US system has three and a half times Canada's per capita cost for administration despite tens of millions of people being without insurance.[1]

User fees are often suggested as a solution to Canadian medicare's woes, although it is unclear what problem they might solve. Some

---

* Of course, people do buy coverage for fire damage, but fire service is another matter entirely. I am indebted to Toronto journalist and author Linda McQuaig for this story.

claim that user fees would save money by reducing frivolous use of the system. Others claim that they would bring in much-needed revenue. Clearly, they cannot accomplish both missions! In fact, user fees tend to discourage the poor and the elderly from entering the system. But there are no overall savings. Nature abhors a vacuum, and the health care system detests unused capacity. As a result, any beds or doctors freed up because the sick poor can't get desperately needed care end up being used by the well-to-do for more trivial matters.[2]

We even have a natural experiment from Saskatchewan to back this up. When medicare started under the CCF government in 1962, there were no user charges to see a doctor. However, Ross Thatcher's Liberals came to power in 1964 and implemented user fees for doctors and hospital care in 1968. The NDP eliminated the charges after it won the election of 1971. Afterward, researchers were able to look at changes in use over time by different groups. They found that there had been a small drop in use of doctors' services, but there was no change in overall health care costs because there was no change in hospital use, which was responsible for the vast majority of expenditures. Further analysis revealed that the poor and the elderly reduced their visits to doctors but that there was an increase in the use of doctors by middle- and upper-income groups.[3]

Some claim that user fees are benign because they discourage only frivolous use. However, a US study involving quite healthy adults showed that user fees led to a 20 per cent increase in risk of death for people with high blood pressure because they were less likely to see a doctor and get their blood pressure under control.[4] The same study showed that user fees were just as likely to discourage appropriate care as inappropriate care.[5]

Some Canadians, such as Fraser Institute executive director Michael Walker, claim that user fees in Sweden "manage demand without cutting people off."[6] However, if you cut a Swede, he bleeds. Research shows that if you charge a relatively less well off Swede for health care, he will be less likely to get it.[7] As Saskatchewan premier Lorne Calvert notes, "The problem with user fees is that if you set the costs too high, you deter people from obtaining necessary health services, but if you keep the fees low and waive the cost for people with low incomes, the administrative costs soon outweigh any financial benefit."[8]

The scientific evidence supporting publicly financed care is long and strong. So why do brain-dead ideas like user fees keep coming back? University of British Columbia professor Bob Evans is one of the world's most respected health economists. He and his colleagues have repeatedly examined this issue and refer to user fees and like ideas as "zombies."[9] The scientific evidence repeatedly kills them, but, just like zombies, they keep bouncing back to life to wreak havoc. Evans notes that private finance strategies (from user fees through private insurance to medical savings accounts) all tend to benefit the wealthy, the healthy, and those who want to sell services. At the same time, private finance tends to disadvantage the poor and the sick. With the political support of the rich and of aspiring business people, it is not surprising that these zombies are so resilient. They will always be brought back because of whom they serve.

For-Profit Delivery: An Illusion of Innovation

Depending on the exact wording of the survey, approximately two-thirds of Canadians are opposed to so-called two-tier medicine, in which the wealthy pay privately to jump queues in the public system for doctors and hospital care.[10] The current hot public issues concern the extent of public coverage (especially home care and pharmacare) and whether public authorities should contract out their publicly funded clinical services to for-profit corporations.

The terminology can get tricky here because private organizations already deliver most health care in Canada. In Ontario and Quebec, almost all hospitals are private but non-profit. In other parts of the country, hospitals are owned mainly by regional health authorities, which are quasi-governmental bodies, but there are many independent, private non-profit hospitals as well.* Most doctors are in private practice, although more are becoming employees all the time. According to economists, doctors' offices are not the same as other small businesses because they are governed by professional norms as well as by the bottom line. Bob Evans refers to doctors' practices as "not-only-for-profit" enterprises to distinguish them from for-profits and non-profits.[11]

During the 1980s and 1990s, hospitals contracted out non-clinical services (such as laundry and food) as well as laboratory services. There was very little evaluation of these policies. Former Prince Albert Parkland Health Authority CEO Stan Rice published one of the few assessments of private lab care.[12] Prince Albert saved more than 40 per cent when the health authority took over the private lab services.

It is only in the past five years that there has been a major thrust to contract out surgical and other clinical services. Some claim that as long as the public pays, it doesn't matter who delivers the service, but others claim that profit is incompatible with care. In May 2002, a group led by Dr. P.J. Devereaux, a McMaster University cardiologist, published a review of all the individual studies that had compared the mortality rates of for-profit and non-profit hospitals.[13] The group found fifteen studies that met their rigorous requirements. Adults had 2 per cent higher death rates in for-profit hospitals, while the infant mortality rate was 10 per cent higher. The investigators estimated that if all Canadian hospitals were converted to for-profit status, there would be an additional 2,200 deaths per year. This is higher than the number who die every year from suicide, colon cancer, or car accidents. The likely cause of the higher death rates was that the for-profits tended to have fewer staff and less well trained staff. These factors have been found to be associated with higher death rates in other studies of the quality of hospital care.[14]

---

* In Winnipeg and Vancouver, most hospitals are independent private non-profit organizations, while in most other cities and provinces, they are owned by regional health authorities.

Devereaux's group published a second paper, in the *Journal of the American Medical Association*, in November 2002, comparing for-profit and non-profit dialysis care.[15] In the US, roughly three-quarters of dialysis is conducted in for-profit facilities and one-quarter in non-profits. However, all care for end-stage kidney disease in the US is paid for publicly by the federal government's Medicare program. So the researchers were investigating exactly the situation that Canadian proponents of for-profit care recommend for Canada: public payment but delivery by whoever submits the best bid.

The investigators found that patients attending for-profit dialysis clinics had 8 per cent higher death rates than those who got their care at non-profits. For-profit clinics had fewer staff and less well trained staff. They also dialyzed patients for less time and used lower doses of key medications. These results suggest that in the US there are 2,500 premature deaths every year for people on dialysis because their care is being provided in for-profit clinics.

A review of the performance of for-profit and non-profit nursing homes found that for-profit homes tended to have poorer quality than non-profits.[16] For-profits averaged fewer and less well trained staff and had higher staff turnover. The for-profits also had more violations of US federal regulations for care, higher rates of skin ulcers, pneumonias, falls, and fractures, and greater use of restraints. They also spent less on food. The review included one Canadian study, from Manitoba, which came to similar conclusions.[17] Residents in for-profit facilities in Manitoba had higher rates of hospitalization for four conditions (dehydration, pneumonia, falls, and fractures) that are sensitive to poor quality of care in nursing homes.

There is little comparative peer-reviewed literature comparing for-profit with non-profit home care, but the few studies available also found poorer quality in for-profits.[18]

Other US studies have also produced damning evidence on for-profit care. For-profit US health maintenance organizations (HMOs) rated lower than not-for-profit HMOs on all fourteen quality indicators measured by the National Committee for Quality Assurance.[19]

The Harvard researchers who conducted this study estimated that there would be six thousand more breast cancer deaths annually in the United States if all HMOs were for-profit.

It also appears that for-profit care tends to be more expensive than non-profit care. American public hospitals are 25 per cent less expensive than private for-profit facilities. Private non-profit hospitals are 12 per cent less expensive than for-profits.[20] Fifty-three per cent of the difference in cost between public and for-profit hospital care is due to higher administrative charges in commercial facilities.

A study of US Medicare* costs found that health spending was higher and increasing faster in communities where all beds were for-profit than in communities where all beds were non-profit.[21] Spending grew fastest in those communities that converted all their beds to for-profit care during the study period. Spending fell the most in those communities that converted all their beds to non-profit care.

Recent rhetoric claims that private markets for the finance and delivery of health care should lead to more efficient health care.[22] However, with over 75 per cent of health care costs being personnel, the literature indicates that for-profit providers tend to skimp on staffing, leading to poorer outcomes. At the same time, their costs tend to be higher because of extra administrative expenditures, which include 10 to 20 per cent profit margins.

From Justice Emmett Hall's 1964 Royal Commission on Health Services to the 2002 Romanow Royal Commission, Canadian inquiries have consistently concluded that health care is not a normal market good. Asymmetry of information between providers and patients prevents consumers of health care from being fully informed, a key factor for the establishment of any market. The consequent public-policy reactions of legislation and regulation (for doctors, hospitals, drugs, and so on), which are necessary to protect

---

* The American Medicare program insures all people sixty-five years and older, as well as those with certain chronic illnesses. In general, the coverage is not as comprehensive as the Canadian version and patients have to pay considerable out-of-pocket costs.

consumers, present further barriers to the establishment of traditional markets. And, as the US system bears witness, fraud is still a
major concern despite expensive regulatory controls.[23] That is why
all developed countries except the US have opted for mainly public
and overwhelmingly non-profit systems.

For-Profit Services Create Problems
with International Trade Treaties

Canada has asked that health care be reserved as a public service under
the North American Free Trade Agreement. However, the US does not
accept that Canadian health care is a public service. Experts differ in
their level of concern about this issue. However, they all agree that the
more commercial health care activity Canada allows, the more difficult it will be to maintain that health care is, in fact, a public service.[24]
Roy Romanow concluded that no one really knows with certainty how
significant trade issues are for medicare. He advised the federal government to be more mindful of the risks of permitting more commercial involvement in health care delivery.

Economists distinguish between small firms owned by professionals, who are ruled by professional norms as well as by the bottom
line, and large publicly traded corporations, which have a fiduciary
responsibility to maximize profits for shareholders. Unfortunately,
NAFTA and other trade agreements do not.

PFI to P3s:
Perfidious Financial Idiocy to Public-Private Pickle

Advocates for more private-sector involvement in health care suggest that governments contract with commercial firms to build and
manage hospitals and other health facilities. In 1992, the British
Conservative government introduced the Private Finance Initiative,

or PFI, to facilitate the building of public works. The concept has since spread like malaria and is widely being touted in Canada under the name of "public-private partnerships," or P3s. The Ontario government used a P3 to build Highway 407 north of Toronto and planned to use P3s to build hospitals in Ottawa and Brampton.* British Columbia and Alberta are also actively investigating using P3s to build new health facilities.

The concept behind P3s, as stated by their proponents, is that the private sector provides the capital and takes on the risks while the public sector reaps the benefits. The schemes' proponents purr reassuringly about the symbiotic relationship between the private and public sectors that will generate extra value for taxpayers and shareholders alike.

However, these reassurances sound eerily like late '90s Wall Street's attempts to calm investors with words like "synergy" and "convergence" while stocks climbed to perilous heights. In the cold reality of morning, we know that high-tech stocks are subject to the law of gravity. We also know that many of the leaders of high-flying companies never believed their own pap. We were being taken for a ride.

It appears that P3s cannot defy gravity either. The risks are not transferred to the private sector. The public is still on the hook. The Ontario provincial auditor concluded, regarding Highway 407, "We observed that, although cited as a public-private partnership, the government's financial, ownership and operational risks are so significant compared to the contracted risks assumed by the private sector that, in our opinion, a public-private partnership was not established."[25]

In Australia, government has had to bail out two P3 hospitals.[26] The Victoria state government had to buy the La Trobe Hospital from a private firm because it was losing so much money, it could "no longer guarantee the hospital's standard of care." Private companies might go bankrupt or one of their officers might abscond with

---

* As we go to press, the new Ontario Liberal government has not yet decided whether to abrogate these contracts.

their assets, but patients will still need care. There is no way of transferring that risk to the private sector.

Another problem with P3s is that the private sector pays higher costs for capital than the public sector. Allyson Pollock and her colleagues at University College in London have dissected the experience of the PFI in Britain and conclude that the PFI capital costs are twice what they would have been if the hospitals had been publicly constructed.[27] To quote Richard Smith, the editor of the *British Medical Journal*, "The schemes produce more problems than solutions, partly for the simple reason that private capital is always more expensive than public capital."[28] As a senior doctor in one of the Ontario hospitals due for a P3 partnership puts it, "Of course it will cost more, but it was the only way the government would let us build our new hospital."

When the Nova Scotia government announced its decision to end its P3 program used to build schools, Finance Minister Neil LeBlanc noted that the previous government had used the P3 concept to push the expenses off the province's books, not because it was a good idea.[29] Far from transferring risk, the P3 schools program in Nova Scotia cost taxpayers an additional $32 million, which, LeBlanc noted, could have built three additional schools. It looks as though P3s are yet another private-sector chimera. They are certainly no saviour.

What Should Be the Role of the Private Sector in Health Care?

Clearly there is some role for the private sector in health care. Even the most ardent supporters of medicare don't advocate a government monolith that extends from insurance through hospital ownership to drug manufacturing. Let's consider the issue methodically for a few moments.

If a Service Is Needed, Then It Should Be Publicly Financed

At present, roughly 70 per cent of the system is publicly funded. The public purse picks up 90 per cent or more of hospital and medical services. The coverage for other services varies widely across the country. In general, coverage improves as one moves west within Canada for home care, long-term care, and pharmacare. Someone in Nova Scotia could pay tens of thousands of dollars a year for drugs and nursing home care while a person in Manitoba wouldn't have to spend more than her old age pension to get the same services.[30] In fact, in many provinces sick people have to pay down their savings and go on welfare before getting publicly funded care. Sounds eerily like the United States, doesn't it?

This doesn't make any sense. The whole idea of medicare was to prevent people from having to resort to charity care. For that matter, why is there no coverage for dental care and vision care? These are also essential health care services, and Hall recommended children's dental and vision programs forty years ago.* The same economics that concludes that a Canadian-style single-payer system is more efficient and more equitable for hospital and physicians' care also applies to these other services. In all cases, there are major administrative savings (in the order of 20 per cent or higher) when one moves from a multi-payer to a single-payer system. Canadian public drug plans cost less to administer than do private plans, just like Canadian public hospital insurance costs a lot less than American private hospital insurance.[31]

Emmett Hall also recommended coverage for home care and pharmacare forty years ago. At that time, many European countries covered most bills for home care, pharmacare, long-term care, and other goods and services, including hearing aids, eyeglasses, and dental care. Now even more do. But the Liberal government of the 1960s was split, and so we ended up with only doctors' services being covered. We have been waiting forty years for the federal government

---

* As a result, in supposedly classless Canada the best way to identify someone's class at birth is to look at his or her teeth.

to implement Justice Hall's eminently reasonable recommendations. Oh, by the way, in case anyone is keeping count—the Liberals have been in power for thirty of the past forty years.

The Closer You Are to Patient Care, the More You Need Non-Profit Services

Economists note that it is hard to contract privately for health care services if they are characterized by low contestability, high complexity, low measurability, or susceptibility to cream skimming.[32]

- *Low contestability* means that conditions make it difficult for firms to enter the market. For example, not that many companies could afford to buy a hospital, attract doctors, and meet all the regulatory requirements. As a result, there is little competition for hospital care. This can lead to "lowballing," whereby after a government or health authority gives up its own hospitals, it is at the mercy of the provider when the initial contract expires.
- *High complexity* means that the service has multiple (and perhaps conflicting) goals, which are best attained when the service is embedded within an overall system of care. For example, long-term institutional care is a very complex service with multiple goals. Even a blood test requires professional interpretation, including the implications for future care, but it is far less complex than most kinds of health care services.
- *Low measurability* means that it is difficult to quantify the quality of service. For example, how would one measure the quality of palliative care, that is, the quality of a death? And if you can't measure quality, how do you know what you're buying?
- *Cream skimming* means that a provider can choose the easiest patients but be paid at the same average rate. If a for-profit hospital does all its knee replacements on middle-aged athletes but is paid at the same rate as would apply to a complicated patient (such as a seventy-eight-year-old with heart disease and a bleeding disorder), then it is being overpaid for its services.

There are some health care goods and services for which markets do work. There is no need for crown corporations to build hospital beds. Many companies can manufacture beds. It's not difficult to get into this market. It's not hard to determine whether a hospital bed has met specifications. Cream skimming doesn't apply.

Some claim that the for-profit sector is more innovative than the public and non-profit sectors. Camille Orridge, executive director of Toronto's home care agency (Community Care Access Centre), says that for-profits are more flexible. She claims that in particular, smaller, owner-operated agencies are more likely to adjust care to the patient's needs. For example, she maintains that originally she couldn't get non-profit nursing agencies to see AIDS patients, so she went to a for-profit firm.

There is no doubt that some for-profit providers are very innovative. But, overall, the non-profit sector adds more value. Non-profits are much more likely than for-profits to

- expend resources on linking different organizations together to plan community networks,[33]
- engage their communities and enlist volunteers,[34] and
- provide continuing education and training to their staff.[35]

Private markets are still the best way to ensure the efficient manufacture of medical equipment and pharmaceuticals. But the for-profit sector appears to offer little but headaches for patient care. The private sector is no panacea for the problems medicare faces. Up close it looks a lot more like snake oil.

On the other hand, non-profit delivery is only one part of the solution. Recent reports from the Canadian Institute for Health Information indicate that patients in the Canadian hospitals with the best outcomes have 50 per cent lower death rates from stroke or heart attack than patients in hospitals with the worst records.[36] This difference is much larger than differences reported in studies of for-profit vs. non-profit care. Retaining non-profit care is a very important step in preserving quality and access and reducing costs, but we have to do a lot more to ensure Canadians the high-quality health care they deserve.

Conclusions

Overall, this review of the evidence on public vs. private health care concludes the following:

- Public finance increases equity of care and efficiency of financing.
- Non-profit care is, in general, less costly and of better quality.
- Public-private partnerships (P3s) cost more money. The private partner borrows the money to front the project but has to pay higher interest rates than if government put up the cash. The public sector still retains most of the risk.
- Permitting for-profit providers to enter a new sector or allowing the growth of for-profit providers in sectors in which they already operate means that it will be more difficult for Canada to maintain that health care is a public service in negotiations with our international trade partners.

It is understandable that some Canadians believe that private profit can save medicare—private markets are generally the best way to distribute goods and services. But they're not the best way for everything. In the next two chapters we'll look at the real solutions to medicare's woes—re-engineering for quality.

Chapter 13

Re-engineering for Excellence

Dr. Kizer Does Surgery on the
US Veterans Administration System

When retired businessman Ronald Kulka started attending the US Veterans Administration (VA) outpatient clinic in Brick, New Jersey, he already had cancer and heart disease. His physician, Richard Stark, follows these problems closely. But Kulka was surprised how much attention his doctor paid to his diabetes. It's not a surprise to Dr. Ken Kizer, the VA health system's former director. To a great extent because of Kizer's vision and energy, the VA provides some of the world's best-quality health care.

In the past, the VA system was maligned for its long waits and questionable quality. The VA was often the last choice for someone who had lost his or her private insurance. Today the Veterans Administration still has its problems.[1] But thanks to advanced access, waits are plummeting. The VA health system has clear, measurable goals for quality and is making rapid progress toward their attainment. Canadians need to be cautious about unthinkingly importing other countries' putative successes, but health systems anywhere could certainly emulate the principles of the VA's transformation.

The US Veterans Administration traces its roots to 1636, when the Plymouth colony voted to provide care for colonists who were injured and disabled during war. During the Civil War, Abraham Lincoln extended pensions to widows and orphans—the War Between the States created lots of them.* Now, the Department of Veterans Affairs is one of the world's largest providers of health care and pension benefits, with a bigger budget than the Province of Ontario.

In the 1980s and '90s, VA officials and veterans realized that their health care program was failing. Most VA hospitals and staff were located in the US northeast, but many of the veterans from these states had retired to the warmer southern states. And while other health organizations were restructuring to substitute ambulatory care for institutional care, the VA was still providing almost all of its care from hospitals. The VA's endemic problems were similar to those faced by other health systems, including those in Canada. The VA poorly managed chronic illness, frailty, and death and dying. There was a lot of inappropriate prescribing and long waits and delays for most care.

In the old days, Ronald Kulka's VA doctors probably would have been treating his diabetic complications, but now Dr. Stark and his team focus their care on *preventing* complications. Dr. Stark treats Kulka according to clinical practice guidelines that are established by panels of doctors, scientists, and other health professionals. Like Group Health Cooperative in Seattle and the Group Health Centre in Sault Ste. Marie, the VA keeps track of all its diabetic patients, the services they receive, and their outcomes. Furthermore, once the lab technician enters lab results into the electronic health record, the result is immediately available to the physician. It is also available in a secure, encrypted form to epidemiologists and program planners.

Now 93 per cent of diabetics have their diabetic control measured

---

* As of July 2003, there were still six children of Civil War veterans receiving pensions.

at least once a year, 66 per cent have had a recent eye examination, and 78 per cent have had a recent foot examination.[2] There are very few individual practices in Canada that could beat this performance.

Opening the Door to Access and Quality in Buffalo

By the late 1990s, Buffalo physician John Sanderson had seen a lot of changes in his job as primary care medical director for the Western New York Veterans Administration.[3] He welcomed the enhancement of primary health care. He enjoyed working in teams with nurses, pharmacists, dietitians, and social services. But the pressure to perform more ambulatory care conspired with increased numbers of patients to lengthen wait times. Patients also complained that when they were sick, they could seldom see their main provider. Dr. Sanderson felt like Dr. Frazzle, whom we met in chapter 11.

Fortunately, in 1999 the Institute for Healthcare Improvement conducted a workshop on advanced access for Buffalo VA staff. Like Sault Ste. Marie's Dr. David Crookston, Dr. Sanderson found the journey to open access arduous, but the rewards immense. Wait times are down dramatically. In 1999, only 10 per cent of urgent patients saw their regular provider, but after three years it was 80 per cent. Sanderson claims that staff and patients had to make quite a few adjustments. But he notes that the "moment of truth" for his own patients was when they first phoned about an urgent problem and were given an appointment with him that day: "Once that happened, you had a convert."

Dr. Ken Kizer: Leadership by Example

One of the keys to the VA's renewal was hiring Dr. Ken Kizer as undersecretary for health in 1994. A former US Navy diver, Kizer hit the VA health system like a one-man army. In truth, Kizer had a great deal of help, but the reform of the VA indelibly bears his stamp.

Kizer started his professional career as a California emergency-room physician and rapidly progressed up the line to chief of public health for the state and then director of the California Department of

Health Services, the state's chief health official. Along the way, he became certified in six medical specialties, a fellow of the International Explorers Club, and a founding member of the International Wilderness Medical Society. Eventually the Clinton administration appointed him undersecretary.

Kizer explains that the VA tried to make the patient's perspective the focus of all planning. And patients, especially sick patients, want a seamless system of care. One of Kizer's first decisions was to replace 173 autonomous hospitals with 22 regional integrated service networks. The networks put a network of hospitals and outpatient facilities under one management structure. This is very similar to the way that Saskatchewan and some other provinces have created regional health authorities to integrate their hospitals with home care, long-term care, mental health, and public health.

Previously, the VA had funded its facilities on the basis of what it had received the year before, with some sort of across-the-board increase. Now funding is based upon the number of patients served.* This meant that the VA moved dollars from the northeast, where the patients used to live, to the Sunbelt, following the veterans who retired there. As the budget moved south, so did much of Kizer's political support. Eventually, some of the most discontented senators from northeastern states delayed his renomination process, forcing him out in 1999. But he had accomplished more in his nearly five years as CEO than most managers do in a lifetime.

During the first four years of Kizer's mandate, from 1994 to 1998, the VA decreased hospital utilization by 62 per cent.[4] At the same time, it increased the overall number of patients treated by 18 per cent, increased ambulatory visits by 35 per cent, and instituted

---

* To compensate VISNs for highly complex and costly patients, the capitated annual rate has two levels: basic care ($2,604), which covers 96 per cent of patients and accounts for 62 per cent of funds, and complex care ($36,460), which covers 4 per cent of patients and accounts for 38 per cent of funds. This year, the VA instituted a third category for patients seen just once—$66 for a single visit.

universal primary care. Kizer says with pride that by 1998, "most patients could name the person responsible for their primary care." From 1994 to 2000, the proportion of patients receiving appropriate colorectal cancer screening increased from 34 per cent to 74 per cent and the proportion of heart patients with management of their cholesterol levels increased to nearly 100 per cent.[5] Kizer also notes that the VA discontinued 72 per cent of its forms.

A key part of the strategy was the development of quality indicators. For example, the VA routinely measures the functional ability of all patients.[6] The VA was also the first large health system to routinely measure pain as the "fifth vital sign." Kizer set firm goals for the system, but he decentralized its management from Washington to the twenty-two network administrators. He and his central managers provided clear direction and overall strategies to the network managers. Knowing what was expected of them, by and large they delivered.

In 2003, Kizer and others published an article in the *New England Journal of Medicine* comparing VA care to that delivered by the US Medicare* fee-for-service system.[7] From 1997 to 2000, the VA system did better than Medicare on twenty-three of twenty-four indicators measured.

Network 2 includes forty-seven counties in upstate New York and two in Pennsylvania. From 1996 to 2000, Network 2 had the biggest improvement in patient satisfaction. The number of patients treated increased by 42 per cent while the cost per patient decreased by 23 per cent, also the best in the system. The network's scores for most indicators are above the 90th percentile of organizations published by the National Committee on Quality Assurance. In 2002, Network 2 won the Kizer Quality Award, recognizing organizational quality and effectiveness. This means that western New York veterans, many

---

* The US Medicare program provides universal public coverage for those over 65 or for those who suffer from certain conditions, such as end stage renal disease. Patients have to pay substantial user fees for services.

of modest means, get some of the best health care in the United States. How's that for a fire in Tonawanda!

Lessons from the VA's Transition

The VA system isn't perfect,[8] but health policy students and planners from around the world see many lessons from its radical restructuring and performance improvement. Dr. Kizer says the most important lesson he has learned is that effective cost control and increased patient satisfaction are possible only through improvements in quality. Of course, this is mainstream thinking outside of health care. If it costs $500 million for a manufacturer to re-tool its plant and retrain its employees, it's a good business decision if now there are $200 million less in annual recalls. At the personal level, it's cheaper to fix your plumbing properly the first time for $250 than incorrectly for $100 with $300 spent later to fix the problems the first plumber caused.

Kizer backs up his argument going through the categories of poor quality—waste, errors, overuse, and underuse. Waste is, by definition, costs without benefit, such as drugs being prescribed but not taken. Almost all errors, except immediately fatal ones, require more work and resources. Kizer claims that overuse is much more prevalent than underuse, although he does admit that most of his experience is in his own country.

Kizer notes that better management of chronic illness improves quality and reduces costs. Advanced access improves patient satisfaction while reducing costs. Patients really like seeing their regular primary health care providers when they're sick and this cuts the extra costs usually associated with walk-in clinics and emergency rooms.

Kizer says that almost any change in the health care workplace that improves patient satisfaction and provider satisfaction will also decrease overall costs of care. He laments that this is the hardest message to sell.

Dr. Kizer claims that the VA is proof that a public-sector health care organization can transform itself even under budgetary pressure and intense political scrutiny—he has some familiarity with the British and Canadian systems and understands that they face similar issues. Dr. Kizer notes that the VA had to decide whether it was in the hospital business or the health care business. Funding had largely been focused on hospitals, while community care was a separate budget category. The integrated service network was the structure that reflected the agency's determination to see health care, not just hospitals, as its true mission.

In an ongoing study of the VA, interviews with managers and clinicians repeatedly identified leadership—specifically Dr. Kizer's leadership—as the key factor in the transformation. Dr. Kizer was an outsider to the agency, which meant he was not entangled in various loyalties and intrigues. He had substantial leadership experience in the public sector and knew how to work in a politically charged environment. He knew a lot about innovation in health care. Dr. Kizer thinks that being a physician might also have been useful to him. He wryly notes, "I know where the bodies are buried." He knew how doctors, nurses, administrators, and others tended to act and respond. Dr. Kizer feels that his professional ethics may have pushed him to respond quickly to quality issues. For example, when he found out that mortality rates for elective hip surgery varied from 0 to 12 per cent in the seventy-three hospitals performing the surgery, he insisted that such surgery be stopped immediately in hospitals with death rates over 2 per cent until they could show the numbers were wrong. (Some did, and their surgical programs continued.)

The VA developed a comprehensive plan for renewal based upon clear, measurable goals. The goals were based upon clinical quality measures, but also included patient satisfaction and indicators of administrative and financial performance. The VA is a very large public agency and every day there is a crisis somewhere between Alabama and Alaska. It required an ongoing effort not to be distracted from the overall mission and goals.

Kizer says it was hard to change the structure of the VA. He still bears scars from the political battle to implement integrated service networks. With a chuckle, he claims that it was even harder to change the culture of the health care system. Professionals and administrators saw advanced access, better teamwork, telephone care, and accountability based upon clear measures as direct challenges. Senior leadership had to persevere in the face of criticism. They had to respond meaningfully to real criticism but avoid meaningless disputes.

Kizer knew from his experience in California that he had to maintain communication throughout the organization. He notes that health care is a 24/7 enterprise and many staff don't work nine to five, which presents particular communication problems. He made a point of visiting facilities after regular hours to connect with evening and night staff.

Kizer says that the public release of high-quality data had a major impact on doctors and other professionals. Professionals want better quality, and "nobody wants to be at the bottom of the list." He notes that it's important to focus on organizational and team performance and not on the performance of individuals. Some organizations release individual physician data, but Kizer says that sends the wrong message. Health care delivery is based in teams. This should be reinforced by team-based accountability measures. Furthermore, the best way to improve performance is to make the average performance excellent, not simply to eliminate individual bad apples.

Kizer says it's easy for organizations to forget the importance of training and education. Managers today talk about creating a learning organization, but few put their money where their mouths are. Typically, training is considered part of the administration budget, but the first cut always goes to administration. And the biggest administration budget item that isn't staff is, you guessed it, training. As just one example of the organization's commitment to training and education, in 1999 the VA trained Dr. Sanderson's team and 133 others in methods to deal with waits and delays.

The VA has taken full advantage of the Breakthrough Series collaborative methodology for both training and quality improvement.

The Institute for Healthcare Improvement pioneered collaboratives to facilitate rapid improvement. In an IHI collaborative, like the Calgary example cited in chapter 11, interdisciplinary teams study, test, and implement rapid improvements. Over a period of a year or more, group sessions including all the collaborative's participants and outside experts are interspersed with intervals of action back home. Audio and video conferencing are used to facilitate communication between group sessions. Long-distance relationships typically develop among the participants and promote informal sharing. The action periods use rapid "plan-do-study-act," or PDSA, cycles, which may be only twenty-four hours in duration but are typically one week to one month long. This allows organizations to make change, study its impact, and try again within a short period of time. (Appendix B describes the collaborative methodology in more detail, and more on PDSA can be found in Appendix A.)

Kizer also notes that good information systems are essential for managing modern health systems. The VA's electronic health record is critical for providing high-quality care to individuals and also for continuous quality improvement.

The final lesson Kizer and others have drawn is that it is important to balance the need for system-wide standards with operating-unit flexibility. Kizer established three categories of goals for the system. The first were mandated from head office. The individual integrated networks themselves generated the second group, while the third were mutually agreed-upon measures.

In theory, the VA had standardized care before it created the twenty-two integrated service networks. But that was not really the case in practice. After decentralization the holes became more obvious and grew. During Kizer's tenure, some networks, such as Network 2, flourished, but others were not so successful. In some regions, long-standing programs fell into disarray during the transformation. This has also been noticed during regionalization in Canada. Since Kizer's departure, there has been more focus on consolidating gains and ensuring that all regions are moving ahead.

**Lessons from the Transformation
of the Veterans Administration
Health Care System**

1. You can improve quality, patient satisfaction, and control costs at the same time.
2. Rapid improvement is possible in a publicly funded system facing budgetary pressures and harsh political scrutiny.
3. Know what you do and what "business" you're in.
4. Appoint leaders whose backgrounds and experience are appropriate for the transformation.
5. Follow a focused and coherent transformation plan, based upon a clear vision of your destination. Don't get distracted by the *crise du jour*.
6. Structural change is relatively easy and does facilitate changes in process. But you need to change the organizational culture to get different processes and better outcomes.
7. Persevere in the presence of imperfection.
8. Develop and manage communication channels from the highest to the lowest levels of the organization. Don't overlook the ability of clear communication of relevant data to improve performance.
9. Focus on organizational and team performance, not on individuals.
10. Do not overlook training and education.
11. Good information technology is absolutely essential.
12. Balance systemwide unity with operating-unit flexibility.

England's Aging NHS Gets a Facelift

Like the US Veterans Administration health system, the English National Health Service (NHS) had fallen on hard times by the 1990s. Many health care workers felt like Sue Farrington, a manager at the Lakeside Medical Centre in the West Midlands: "Everyone appeared to be running to stand still . . . There was an attitude of tried that, didn't work, things don't change."[9] But, like the VA, the NHS is undergoing renewal. Now, Bradford family doctor Graham Hillary says, "Staff are happier, the majority of patients are happier, and the doctors are less stressed . . . Visitors to the surgery remark on the tranquil, peaceful, and calm atmosphere."[10] Like the VA, the NHS is attempting to renew itself using primary health care, chronic illness management, community care, and a systematic approach to waits and delays.

The NHS Arises from Ashes of War

During the Second World War, England was an island fortress. It was the free world's unsinkable aircraft carrier maintaining the Western Front during the dark days of the war. All Britons were recruited into the war effort. Under siege, sharing was second nature. The king and queen showed their solidarity, staying in London even though the Luftwaffe bombed Buckingham Palace. Almost everyone was in uniform or working in a job critical to the war effort. How could any Briton be denied needed health care under such circumstances?

One forgotten footnote to the Second World War is that the British voters soundly thrashed Winston Churchill in the 1945 election. He was an effective wartime leader* of a coalition government, but as the war wound down, average Britons preferred the Labour party's plan for post-war reconstruction. After all, if the country had been able to provide needed health care to all when half the economy was devoted to the war effort, then it should be even easier once people stopped killing each other.†

---

* Some say that Labour leader Clement Atlee, an apparently quiet deputy prime minister from 1942 to 1945, helped moderate some of Churchill's wilder schemes.
† To be fair, Churchill's Conservatives did have a plan for their own health scheme, but it was not as broad as Labour's.

Clement Atlee's Labour government created the NHS in 1948. It quickly became as beloved to the Brits as medicare is to Canadians. But just as granny's tea service faded over the years, so the NHS's lustre also tarnished. By 1979, the NHS gave good care to urgent cases but waiting lists for elective care were growing longer and longer. Britain spent less of its economy on health care than any other developed country—5.5 per cent, compared with 7 per cent for Canada and 9 per cent for Denmark and Sweden.[11]

There was a gathering consensus that the NHS needed more money and modernization, but that was trumped by the election of Margaret Thatcher and her Conservatives. She had other plans for the public purse—tax cuts and military spending. During their term of office from 1979 to 1997, the Conservatives reorganized the NHS's structure several times, but there was little new money until John Major succeeded the "Iron Lady" as Conservative leader in 1991. By the time Tony Blair brought the Labour party back to power in the 1997 election, Britain was spending only 6.8 per cent of its GDP on health while Canada spent 8.9 per cent and the top spender, the US, paid out 13 per cent.

The NHS had been a Labour idea, and the party arrived in office with a commitment to its renewal. Blair calls the creation of the NHS in 1948 a "seminal event." Like medicare in Canada, the NHS enshrines the idea that need, not ability to pay, should determine who gets health care. In 2000, the Labour government announced a new plan for the NHS, which included a budget increase of 50 per cent over five years. The government is committed to ultimately attain the average spending of other European countries. Blair is adamant that new money needs to buy change.[12]

Organization of Health Care in England
The English Department of Health bears the overall responsibility for the management of the health and social services system, including

policy development and funding.* Twenty-eight strategic health authorities with average populations of two million are responsible for co-ordinating service development. This is the size of a large Canadian regional health authority, like Vancouver or Montreal.

Three hundred and three primary care trusts (PCTs) with average populations of 200,000 are responsible for the planning and procuring of primary and secondary health services† and for population health improvement. When fully implemented, the English PCTs will plan, directly fund, and commission health services, ultimately managing 75 per cent of the NHS budget. PCTs must ensure the provision of primary health care, hospital services, dental care, mental health care, NHS Direct (a telephone advice line), patient transport, population screening, and pharmacist and optician services. They are also responsible for the functional integration of health and social services for patients.

The UK health care landscape also features hospital trusts, mental health trusts, care trusts (providing social and personal care), ambulance trusts, walk-in centres, and special health authorities (for example, the blood service).

England has historically had strong primary health care, and the new PCTs will consolidate that sector's central position in the health service. English general practitioners have been paid on a capitation basis for decades. *Capitation* literally means "per head" funding: the NHS pays family doctors a fixed sum for every regular patient on their lists. Compared to traditional fee-for-service payment, capitation facilitates group medical practice as well as better teamwork

---

* Like Canadian provinces, the devolved governments of Northern Ireland, Scotland, and Wales are responsible for the administration of health care in their jurisdictions. Their systems are very similar to England's, but this discussion applies to England.

† This includes routine specialist and hospital care, such as pediatrics, obstetrics, orthopedics, and ear, nose, and throat.

with other providers.* In the 1950s and 1960s, grants were provided to encourage "single-handed," or solo, practices to amalgamate with each other. Over time, the NHS has also funded computers and renovation of practices. Canadian family doctors typically have no other professional staff in their offices, but the NHS has located home care and other services in general practices. As in the Calgary home care partnership described in chapter 14, the co-location of personnel facilitates the development of interdisciplinary approaches to care.

A Thoroughly Modern Agency

The reforms also established key management structures. The Commission for Health Improvement (CHI) is responsible for quality assurance. It inspects health organizations and reports on their performance. The National Institute for Clinical Excellence (NICE) is responsible for assessing pharmaceuticals and technology. In 2001, the NHS established the Modernisation Agency to co-ordinate clinical service redesign and to promote leadership development.† The agency is charged with stimulating service improvement and spreading best practices. It's really an umbrella organization. The Modernisation Agency provides a home base for existing programs, including

- The National Primary Care Development Team
- The Primary Care Leadership Programme
- The NHS Leadership Programme for Chief Executives
- Clinical Governance
- The Changing Workforce Programme
- The Capacity and Demand Management Programme

---

* To be fair, capitation can also encourage underservicing. It really depends upon the details of the individual capitation plan. The UK plan is superior to most of the pilots developed in Canada over the years.

† For more on the Modernisation Agency, see http://www.modern.nhs.uk.

- The Management Education Scheme by Open Learning
- The NHS Management Training Scheme
- Nursing Leadership
- Service Improvement

The agency's staff is drawn mostly from the NHS on secondment. One of its key strategies is to pass ownership to the rest of the system for quality improvement and re-engineering. As in Calgary, the Modernisation Agency is trying to ensure that every clinical team has the tools to conduct continuous quality improvement. Clinical staff are often seconded to the agency on a part-time basis, and agency personnel are frequently "embedded" into clinical teams.

The Agency Is Governed by the "3 Rs" of Modernisation

One of the agency's guiding rules is to attempt to see the world through patients' eyes. The agency includes patients on redesign teams and uses real patient stories to focus the teams on the right target. The agency consulted in depth with Dr. Donald Berwick and the Institute for Healthcare Improvement. And it trains personnel in IHI's plan-do-study-act rapid-cycle methodology to move change along in manageable steps.[13]

Cancer and heart disease are a particular priority for the NHS. One project involves reducing the time to administer thrombolytic, or so-called clot-busting, drugs to patients with heart attacks. The shorter the "door-to-needle" time in an ER, the more effective the treatment. Program manager Sally Dore, a former cardiac nurse, is responsible for the project at Sherwood Forest Hospitals Trust, not far from where Robin Hood camped with his Merry Men.[14] Dore started her study by spending time with thrombolysis nurses in the ER. A new nurse pointed out to her that it was inconvenient to find someone else to manage her heart-attack patient while she was searching for the one nurse who had keys to the medication refrigerator where the hospital stored the thrombolytic medication. The solution: Dore immediately gave keys to all thrombolysis nurses.

Dore demonstrated that the nurses' input really counted.* She was soon inundated with ideas, each one tested with the PDSA methodology. One nurse noted that it was difficult to know the accurate time because all the ER's clocks seemed to be on different schedules. The solution: Dore spent $75 on three satellite-linked clocks. Building one small change upon another, within a year the proportion of heart-attack patients whose door-to-needle time was less than thirty minutes rose from 30 per cent to 90 per cent.

The Modernisation Agency has its fingers everywhere. One project is changing the way emergency departments (in English jargon, accident and emergency departments, or A&Es) treat patients. The Idealised Design of Emergency Access Programme (IDEA) aimed to have all patients discharged from the ER within four hours of entry. IDEA has recently been renamed the Emergency Services Collaborative. Many A&Es are now using a new method for seeing patients with minor problems: See and Treat. As in Canada, A&Es almost always see really sick patients immediately. A nurse used to triage patients with minor problems, and then they waited. They could wait for twelve hours or more—wait even longer than in Canada. Usually, delay for minor problems causes no harm other than anxiety and lost time. But occasionally, patients are triaged incorrectly and disasters ensue. Sometimes a meningitis patient is alert at three o'clock, complaining of a mild headache, and comatose by six.

In November 2002, at the Royal Liverpool and Broadgreen University Hospitals A&E, the average wait time was eight hours.[15] That was when Royal Liverpool introduced See and Treat. Now a doctor or nurse practitioner sees patients with minor problems immediately. The staff triage and treat the patients at the same time. The ER also made other changes inspired by advanced access. They mapped their demand and now try to match staffing to meet the hourly estimated

---

* Readers familiar with principles of community and organizational development can now smile smugly to see these methods finally being applied to health care.

requirements. Within five months, the average wait times had fallen over 90 per cent.

The NHS service improvements have improved patient satisfaction and staff morale. "Now, we are providing a service to patients that we are really proud of," says Gerry Murphy, a Sherwood Hospital nurse practitioner. "I love my job, but I couldn't say that twelve months ago because I spent so much time apologizing to patients."

Primary Care Gets to the Heart of the Matter

Dr. John Oldham's family practice, the "Manor House," is located in historic Glossup, 15 kilometres east of Manchester. The Manor House practice includes six doctors, two nurse practitioners, three practice nurses, five home care nurses, and three midwives.*

The recently knighted Sir John Oldham and his group have always been innovators. During the early 1990s, the NHS passed some of the funding normally allocated for hospital and specialty care to family practices. This experiment was referred to as "fundholding." Oldham's group was one of the first to try out the new option.

In 1992, Oldham completed an MBA at the University of Manchester School of Business and did his dissertation on continuous quality improvement in primary health care. In the early 1990s, he heard about the Institute for Healthcare Improvement and learned about the collaborative method. He lobbied the Conservative government to start a primary care collaborative, but without success. When Labour came to power in 1997, Oldham found big ears for his ideas. The Blair government eliminated fundholding, but Blair and his health minister, Allan Millburn, were very keen on Dr. Oldham's other notions and appointed him to head up the new National Primary Care Development Team (NPDT).†

The NPDT started the Primary Care Collaborative in June 2000. It is based on the IHI collaborative model for quality improvement and

---

* For more details on Dr. Oldham's practice, see http://www.manorhousesurgery.co.uk/.
† For more on the National Primary Care Development Team, see: http://www.npdt.org/.

makes extensive use of the PDSA rapid-cycle methodology. The model was perfect for a culture where most doctors already worked in groups with other doctors and teams with other providers. Most already had computers. The NPDT provided resources, such as payment for locum physicians, so that doctors could attend meetings.

The collaborative focuses on three areas of patient care where there is consensus that significant improvements can be made: access to primary care, secondary prevention for patients with coronary heart disease (CHD), and integration of primary and secondary care.

The collaborative started with 40 practices, and has had three more enrolment periods since. As of July 2003, it included 3,500 practices representing 24 million patients, more than half the population of England. In 2002, the collaborative decentralized many of its functions to a network of 11 NPDT centres. The original collaborative projects sowed seeds locally, and now they have sprouted. Each NPDT centre

- is responsible for a local collaborative involving all PCTs within a defined geographical area,
- operates an NPDT centre helpline from nine to five dealing with questions from local PCTs and practices, and
- organizes training for PCT access facilitators.

There are access facilitators in every PCT. They teach generic quality improvement skills, including access. They also provide support for secondary prevention programs for coronary heart disease and diabetes.

The results of the collaborative have been sensational. By April 2003, practices that had enrolled in the fourth wave had reduced waits for family doctors by 82 per cent. Including all the practices involved in the initial four waves, the time to the third next available appointment with family doctor* had fallen to one day.[16]

---

* Considered the best metric of waiting.

First-wave practice Sunnybank Medical Centre in Bradford is typical.[17] It started with a third next available appointment of nine days and up to two hundred patients who didn't show up for their appointments every month. Its initial analysis showed 25 per cent to 30 per cent undercapacity. Eighteen months later, after shaping demand through telephone and group consultations and expanding the roles of nurses and other staff, there is no wait whatsoever for the third next appointment. No-shows have plummeted to fewer than forty per month, or less than 1 per cent of all patient visits.

One of the overall NHS goals is to reduce coronary heart disease deaths because England has one of the highest CHD rates in the world.[18] As of July 2002, the NPDT boasted the following results:

- More than 85 per cent of patients with CHD were on Aspirin.
- More than 70 per cent of CHD patients were on cholesterol-lowering medication.
- More than 80 per cent of patients who had a heart attack in the past twelve months were on beta blockers.
- More than 60 per cent of patients with CHD had blood pressure below 140/85.

One practice in South Stoke, south of Oxford, computerized its existing paper CHD register. The practice implemented nurse-led follow-up clinics instead of seeing patients in an ad hoc fashion. As of December 2001, the practice had increased the proportion of CHD patients taking cholesterol-reducing medications from 58 per cent to 96 per cent. They had increased beta blocker use post–heart attack from 78 per cent to 100 per cent. Aspirin use from 79 per cent to 98 per cent, and the proportion of CHD patients with blood pressures below 140/85 from 55 per cent to 74 per cent.

Healthy Communities
The NPDT recently initiated a non-clinical project, the Healthy Communities Collaborative Pilot.[19] The pilot's focus is to reduce

falls among the elderly. The collaborative sent out a request for proposals and received 147 applications, from which it selected three pilot projects. Each pilot site includes five teams that are representative of their communities. Their boundaries are coterminous with electoral constituencies or recognized neighbourhoods. The teams include staff from local health and social service organizations as well as many seniors. Boards and managers from the various statutory and voluntary organizations have committed to following through on agreed-upon strategies.

Easington is a deprived community in the northeast whose project has reduced falls by 47 per cent in the first year. Its five teams meet every month and so far have assessed elderly people's housing and remedied such risks as loose throw rugs and bath mats, reviewed prescription medications, and organized exercise groups. Other communities have paid particular attention to sidewalks heavily used by the elderly and have organized the exchange of "sloppy slippers" for safer footwear.

Lessons from the NHS Reforms

The NHS did not launch most of its reforms until 2000, six years after the Veterans Administration. It is still too early to draw firm conclusions about these reforms, but some preliminary results dovetail with those from the VA.

The first lesson is that, as in the VA, rapid improvement is possible in public health care systems. The NHS transition involves lots of new money, whereas the VA actually suffered a budget cut during Ken Kizer's tenure. These two cases offer support for the adage that you can make change only when there is too little or too much money.

You need leadership from the top to change public systems. There are a lot of different views about Tony Blair—in fact, because of the apparent shortage of Iraqi weapons of mass destruction, there might even be a different prime minister by the time you read this. But Blair has a sophisticated perspective on the NHS's problems. For one thing, he understands their systemic nature. "I believe that public servants are working flat out," he has said, "but in a system that shrieks out for fundamental change." Blair's strategic direction is strikingly similar to that of Dr. Kizer: "The key to reform is redesigning the system round the user."

Blair's first health minister, Allan Millburn, also brought considerable leadership and understanding to his portfolio. His resignation in June 2003 (to "spend more time with his family") may set back the reforms. There are concerns that his successor, John Reid, may lack the necessary background to ensure follow-through. On the other hand, the system has seen such change since 1997 that a period of custodianship might be welcome to all parties.

Lessons from the Renewal of the English National Health Service

1. Rapid improvement is possible in a publicly funded system under harsh political scrutiny.
2. Leadership is essential and is especially needed at the political level.
3. Have a coherent plan, but be prepared to be flexible in its implementation.
4. Change processes to change culture.
5. Communicate or perish.
6. Use collaborative processes to bridge the gap between the centre and operating units.

As in the case of the VA, the NHS's renewal is based upon coherent plans. First there are national service frameworks, which establish clinical standards, delineate strategies for their implementation, define service models, and establish performance measures.* External

---

* For details, see http://www.doh.gov.uk/nsf/index.htm.

reference groups, which include professionals, patients, managers, non-profit agencies, and advocacy groups, develop the service frameworks. As of September 2003, the NHS had developed frameworks for cancer, pediatric intensive care, mental health, coronary heart disease, the elderly, diabetes, and children's hospital services. The goal is to add one framework per year. The national service frameworks incorporate clear measurable objectives, which are tracked and publicized.

The Modernisation Agency aims for small changes in process to change the corporate culture of the NHS. As patients are served better, staff morale increases. The hope is that multiple small changes will eventually tip the balance toward transformation.

The NHS has successfully adopted the IHI collaborative methodology to facilitate change. However, the first attempts suffered in their transatlantic translation. The political context for reform will be different from place to place. And the NHS is a public system, whereas most of IHI's American work is with private (non-profit and for-profit) organizations. It is easier for managers to make change in private systems, where their main concern is workforce morale and customer satisfaction, to the extent that it affects the bottom line. In public systems, such as in Canada and England, public opinion is a crucial factor. Physicians also tend to be more politically powerful in public systems than in the US, where managers and private payers have usurped some of their political influence.

Helen Bevan, currently director of redesign for the Modernisation Agency, recalls a meeting of cancer doctors in Dudley at the beginning of the process. The NHS staff had carefully planned the day along with their IHI consultants, based upon successful American processes. But within a few hours, it was in a shambles, with most of the doctors walking out. Bevan still refers to the debacle as "deadly Dudley." Fortunately, a few physicians hung around and the project did get off the ground. But Bevan and others realized the importance of context and the need to redesign IHI's processes for the English political landscape. One would not expect a tropical palm tree to last a winter on the Canadian prairies, and one should not expect US-designed change processes to automatically work in a different political climate.

Communication has been a major challenge for the NHS. In England as in Canada, health care is almost always on the front page. Bad news attracts reporters, so it is an ongoing chore to highlight good news. So far, the NHS has not effectively communicated the message of improved performance, and this may endanger the future of the reforms.

The NHS's Modernization Provides Inspiration, Not Perfection
Like the renovation of the VA health system, the NHS modernization has had its problems. For example, while establishing meaningful targets can spur better performance, it can also provoke fraud. The political opposition recently revealed that some A&Es hit their targets by renaming gurneys "beds on wheels" and hallways "pre-admission units."[20]

Blair championed his Third Way as the new road between communism and unbridled capitalism. However, not all new ideas are good ones. As lamented in Chapter 12, the Labour government continued the Conservatives' Private Finance Initiative (PFI) for the construction of new facilities. The PFI makes the government's books look better in the short term but leads to higher costs overall.* The government is also tendering out some elective surgeries, allowing for-profit firms to bid against NHS trusts.[21] As a result, there are concerns about poaching of staff and pressures for higher salaries. These privatization policies are not necessary for the other reforms to succeed, and many would say they are a distraction from the main tasks at hand.

---

* See chapter 12 for a full discussion of the PFI.

Inspiration Is Needed from Abroad, but Perspiration Is Needed Back Home

In this chapter, we have examined two inspiring case studies of health care reform: the US Veterans Administration system and the UK National Health Service. These examples demonstrate that we can make radical changes in health care systems focused on quality. In the concluding chapter, we will discuss the heavy lifting necessary for a quality initiative for Canada.

Chapter 14

A Canadian Agenda for Excellence

Jocelyn Reimer-Kent is so excited that her dancing eyes seem to be doing the rumba. The cardiac clinical nurse specialist at New Westminster's Royal Columbian Hospital is talking about the hospital's rapid recovery program. Typically, after surgery in most hospitals, staff give patients injectable narcotic painkillers on a regular basis for twelve to twenty-four hours and then wait for patients to have pain before giving more. Pain leads to nausea, which causes poor nutrition and constipation. Patients don't breathe deeply, which leads to collapsed lungs and pneumonia. Up to one-sixth of cardiac patients develop delirium after surgery.[1]

In 1996, the Royal Columbia Hospital wanted to decrease the time cardiac patients stayed in hospital after surgery, and Reimer-Kent had her chance.[2] She formed a team with reps from key areas such as anesthesia and physiotherapy, and developed a new protocol based on the best scientific evidence. The planning team piloted the protocol itself, and it was an immediate success. Patients had less pain and were more alert. They were also able to go home earlier and were less likely to be readmitted. The Royal Columbian's cardiac program still has only four post-op ICU beds, but because of the faster patient flow, three times as many patients now use them.

The team continues to update the details of the protocol, but at present, nurses insert rectal suppositories of acetaminophen (brand name Tylenol) and indomethacin (a non-steroidal anti-inflammatory drug) as the patients move off the operating table. They continue to use the suppositories until patients can tolerate medications by mouth. They also give morphine, but the patients need less of it for a shorter period of time since the hospital maximized the use of non-narcotic painkillers. Now 95 per cent of patients have pain rated at less than 3 out of 10 for their *entire* hospital stay. Pain-related complications, such as nausea and constipation, are down by 80 per cent. The protocol is used for almost 90 per cent of cardiac patients.

The hospital recently asked Reimer-Kent to implement similar protocols for other surgical programs. She is keen to begin her new work with her motto, "No pain, great gain."

Yvonne Maffei is also a believer in innovation.[3] Now thirty, Maffei lost her job three years ago after being diagnosed with kidney failure. She couldn't both do her work and find the time and energy for traditional dialysis—four to six hours, three to four times per week. Fortunately, she lived in Toronto, and a nurse gave her the tip that she could try a new procedure developed here: nocturnal dialysis. She spent six weeks learning to run a dialysis machine in her home six nights a week. Now Maffei is feeling great: "My energy level is incredible."

There has been evidence for a long time that longer dialysis can improve the health of kidney patients. But it wasn't until 1994 that Dr. Robert Uldall started home nocturnal dialysis at Toronto's Wellesley Hospital.[4] Dr. Andreas Pierratos took over the program after Dr. Uldall's untimely death in 1995, and in 1998 the program moved to Humber River Regional Hospital. Research shows that nocturnal dialysis reduces blood pressure and prevents the heart enlargement that kidney patients tend to develop.[5] For patients like Maffei it has meant a lot more: "I have my life back. I own a children's clothing store. I'm busy." Nocturnal dialysis has normalized her life.

Neither Jocelyn Reimer-Kent nor Dr. Robert Uldall needed external stimulation to create. They were natural entrepreneurs.

But born innovators are unusual. What can we do to spread innovation from the truly gifted to the interested but timid and finally to the skeptical laggards? The spread of innovation has attracted increasing attention since Bruce Ryan and Neal Gross's 1944 landmark study that described the diffusion of hybrid corn through rural Iowa.[6] We tend to assume that good ideas spread themselves, but they usually need help.

Canadian Malcolm Gladwell's bestseller from a few years ago, *The Tipping Point*, provides a popular update on diffusion theory.[7] Gladwell, whose day job is with the *New Yorker*, refers to social trends as "epidemics." He claims that we can analyze the resurgence of Hush Puppies shoes with the same techniques that scientists use to study infectious diseases such as AIDS and syphilis. Gladwell contends that once a new trend reaches critical mass, it will take off quickly. AIDS was an almost unknown illness in 1981, and then it became a worldwide epidemic in the next few years. Hush Puppies, the smooth suede shoes with the crepe sole, had been an icon of the sixties. But by 1994, overall sales were down to 30,000 pairs and Wolverine, their manufacturer, contemplated discontinuing production. In 1995, they sold 430,000 pairs, and the next year almost 2 million. Hush Puppies spread through hip New York communities like a communicable disease.

Everett Rogers is the guru of diffusion theory. His classic text *Diffusion of Innovation* is still the most widely quoted work on the subject.[8] Rogers claims that only one person in forty is a true innovator. Roughly one-eighth are "early adopters," who implement innovations quickly. About one-third are the "early majority," one-third are the "late majority," and one-sixth are laggards who resist innovation. Typically an innovation will reach its "tipping point" after the early adopters have jumped on board. This works out to roughly one-sixth of the potential market.

Rogers claims that people's choice to adopt an innovation is based upon five attributes:

1. *Trialability*. Can it be tried on a limited basis before final adoption?
2. *Observability*. Can you see the results, preferably nearby?
3. *Relative advantage*. Does it have an advantage over the status quo?
4. *Complexity*. Does it seem overly complex?
5. *Compatibility*. Does it fit with existing practices and values?

We need to make it easy for health care providers to dip their toes into the water of innovation. We need to ensure that there are good models to see, as nearby as possible. It's nice when innovations show themselves to be obviously better—when penicillin cured pneumonia patients, a hero was born. But most innovations need more detailed research to ensure that they do more good than harm. Complicated innovations need to be strong in the other four areas to be given a chance. Finally, innovations need to fit into a social context. As we saw in the previous chapter, the Institute for Healthcare Improvement's methods needed revising for the English context; they will need further retrofitting for Canada.

Plan-do-study-act cycles and the collaborative methodology fit right into Rogers's framework. The PDSA methodology allows people to try out simple, small changes. Collaboratives usually start with true innovators and help them consolidate their gains, then these practices became the demonstration models for others.

However, if we want to re-engineer our health care system by spreading good ideas, we have to deal with a major underlying problem. At present, we grossly underutilize the talents of patients and providers. This chapter outlines how to maximize the contributions of both. It closes with a series of recommendations to help lift Canada's quality initiative off the ground.

Putting the Patient at the Centre

It would be a bad joke if it weren't true. A few years ago, Montreal building contractor Chuck Page called together his four sons to tell them he was dying.[9] When he started handing out copies of his will, his youngest son, then a McGill University pre-med student, asked the nature of the fatal illness. Page said it was trichophyton and his son happily informed him it was only athlete's foot. His doctor had told him he had a bad case of trichophyton, and "you've got six weeks, seven at the most." Page didn't realize that he had a benign illness that his doctor thought would take six or seven weeks *to cure*. Page and his family got to laugh in the end, but bad communication and services plague our system and promote poor quality.

A substantial body of evidence indicates that patients who take an active part in their care have better outcomes than those who don't.[10] However, our system makes it really hard for patients to play the lead role in their own health care. The US Institute of Medicine's recent landmark report *Crossing the Quality Chasm* notes that the gap between current attainment and potential performance is partly attributable to health care services' forcing patients to adapt to the usual procedures of the system, rather than services adapting to patients' needs and preferences.[11] The first four of the ten rules cited in the Institute's report relate directly to new roles for patients and new relationships with providers:

1. Care should be based upon continuous healing relationships instead of mainly upon in-person visits.
2. Care should be customized for individual patients' needs and values instead of being dictated by professionals.
3. Care should be under the control of patients not professionals.
4. Knowledge about care should be shared freely between patients and providers and between different providers. This transfer should take maximal advantage of leading-edge information technology. Patients should have unrestricted access to their records.

The US National Institutes of Health define patient-centred care as "health care that establishes a partnership among practitioners, patients and their families (when appropriate) to ensure that decisions respect patients' wants, needs and preferences and solicit patients' input on the education and support they need to make decisions and participate in their own care."[12] Patients are all too rarely offered an opportunity to fully participate in their care. One study showed that only 9 per cent of care decisions truly involve patients in the decision-making process.[13]

Some professionals worry that patient engagement is too time-consuming and costly. However, if patients are allowed to make more informed choices about their care, they often choose less expensive care. A recent English study showed that women who were given information on excessive menstrual bleeding and were then allowed a better opportunity to ask questions were 40 per cent less likely to have a hysterectomy. Their health care costs were also 43 per cent lower.[14]

Dr. Annette O'Connor is a University of Ottawa professor of nursing and the Canada Research Chair in Health Care Consumer Decision Support, but describes herself as a patient advocate. The University of Ottawa group has developed several aids to patient decision-making. O'Connor believes patients want clear information so that they can incorporate their own values into their decisions.[15] O'Connor also chaired a committee that assessed patient decision aids for the prestigious Cochrane Collaboration. O'Connor's committee concluded that aids provide greater knowledge, more realistic expectations, and lower decisional conflict, and that they increase the proportion of patients active in decision making.[16]

Getting the Patient's Agenda on the Agenda
Of course, communication difficulties between doctors and patients are not a new problem. Over one hundred years ago, Sir William Osler always counselled his students to "Listen to the patient. He is trying to tell you the diagnosis." Seeing the situation from a patient's

perspective is the key to quality of care. As a bonus, a physician who is an attentive listener is also less likely to be sued.[17]

In the 1980s, University of Rochester researchers discovered that doctors tended to interrupt patients' opening statements after only eighteen seconds, preventing patients from raising many of their important concerns.[18] In 1999, some of the original group reported on 199 patient encounters with 29 family doctors.[19] They found that doctors allowed patients to complete their initial statement of concern only 28 per cent of the time. Doctors typically interrupted their patients after twenty-three seconds, although it took only thirty-two seconds on average for the patients to complete their statements. Not surprisingly, the patients who fully expressed their concerns were less likely to raise them later in the interview.

Ruth Weins thought she knew what patients wanted when she was the manager of Edmonton's Royal Alexandra Hospital's neonatal intensive care unit.[20] When she had two preemies of her own she saw the problems through different eyes. Staff found it convenient to have lots of light and didn't worry about the noise they made. But as a parent, Weins saw that her baby was clearly disturbed by the bright lights, the perpetual babble of voices, and the background beeping of machines. There was no space for parents. There was no privacy. She always felt in the way.

Fortunately, Weins was able to make amends when she directed the renovation of the unit. Some of the changes were simple. Dimmer switches were installed over each incubator. Special ceiling tiles were used to dampen noise. There is a lounge for parents, with a courtesy phone and a microwave oven. There's even a suite where families can stay overnight. Now Weins's babies are healthy children, but she still remembers the importance of seeing the world through patients' eyes.

Physician Jane Poulson was a patient most of her life. She developed insulin-dependent diabetes when she was thirteen, and diabetic complications had blinded her by her final year of medical school. Undaunted, she became Canada's first blind doctor, trained as a

specialist in internal medicine at McGill, and then practised palliative care. She developed heart disease in her early forties and then a
particularly virulent form of breast cancer when she was forty-four.
Throughout these trials, she continued her medical practice.

Dr. Poulson found her cancer more terrifying than her other diagnoses. She thought she knew about communication and compassion.
But, like Ruth Weins, she found the experience as a patient very different from that of a provider. In a moving article she penned for the
New England Journal of Medicine, Poulson regretted that she was
now the consumer of a number of "bitter pills" that she had unwit-
tingly prescribed during her professional career.[21] She found no
comfort in bromides such as "Don't worry—your hair will grow
back." She was terrified when told, "Your procedure is cancelled
today." She felt demeaned when she overheard one of her doctors
refer to her as a "great case" for teaching. Poulson suggested that
medical students should learn more about the psychology of illness
through role-playing and, especially, listening to patients. Why not
spend a few minutes asking patients how they're really feeling
instead of just focusing on certain symptoms?

Dr. Poulson passed away on August 28, 2001. She had been hon-
oured during her life with numerous awards, including an Order of
Canada. But no greater honour could be granted Poulson, albeit
posthumously, than medical students being taught to see patients as
"real people rather than simply objects of interest for budding
physicians."*

Catching the Patient's Spirit

Anne Fadiman grew up in an upper-class family in Connecticut and
southern California. She graduated from Harvard University in 1975
and began her writing career at the *Harvard Magazine*. In the 1980s,

---

* For further information on the remarkable Dr. Jane Poulson, see http://www.ibc
memorial.org/232a.html#obit and http://collection.nlc-bnc.ca/100/201/300/cdn_medical
_association/cmaj/vol-165/issue-10/poulson.asp.

an old college friend, who was a resident in family practice at the Community Medical Center in Merced, California, captivated her with stories of the Hmong, a group who had been part of the late 1970s wave of refugees from southeast Asia. The Hmong have been persecuted for thousands of years since they were flooded out of their ancestral homes in northern Siberia. After this catastrophe, these fiercely independent people migrated to China, always living in the mountains for security. The Chinese military finally chased them south in the eighteenth century. The Hmong established their new home in the mountains of Laos.

During the decades of warfare that plagued Southeast Asia after the Second World War, the Hmong were major US supporters. In return they believed that the US had promised them protection and, if necessary, sanctuary. After the communist victories in 1975, the Hmong, with great persistence, held the US government to that promise. Over 150,000 immigrated to the United States. Many eventually made their way to Merced, a sleepy community in the heart of California's agricultural heartland, the Central Valley.

Through her friend, Fadiman met Lia, a young Hmong girl born in Merced who had lost most of her brain function from uncontrolled epileptic seizures. She documented Lia's story in an award-winning book, *The Spirit Catches You and You Fall Down: A Hmong Child, Her American Doctors, and the Collision of Two Cultures.*[22] Fadiman followed Lia, her mother, Foua, and father, Nao Kao, for nine years and documented the clashes between Lia's family and the Merced health care system.

Despite Foua and Nao Kao's being superlative parents who sincerely wanted the best for their child, at one point children's welfare officials removed Lia from her family. By the end of the book, Lia is back with her family and still alive despite the pessimistic predictions of her doctors. Several medical schools are using *The Spirit Catches You* to promote sensitivity to the role of culture and religion in health care.

Toward the end of the book, Fadiman suggests that Dr. Arthur

Kleinman's patient explanatory model might help avoid these and other patient–provider conflicts. Kleinman is a professor of medical anthropology and psychiatry at Harvard University and has done pioneering work on cross-cultural health care. During the 1980s, he developed a list of eight simple questions that could be used to discern a patient's perception of his or her illness.

Dr. Arthur Kleinman's Eight Questions for Eliciting the Patient's Explanatory Model of His/Her Illness

1. What do you call the problem?
2. What do you think has caused the problem?
3. Why do you think it started when it did?
4. What do you think the sickness does? How does it work?
5. How severe is the sickness? Will it have a short or a long course?
6. What kind of treatment do you think you should receive? What are the most important results you hope to receive from this treatment?
7. What are the chief problems the sickness has caused?
8. What do you fear most about the sickness?[23]

If the Merced hospital staff had asked Kleinman's questions, they would have been surprised with the answers. They would have found that the family believed that: Lia's sister had caused her illness by slamming a door and frightening Lia's soul out of her body; when Lia had a seizure, a spirit called a "dab" caught her; and epilepsy connotes nobility. Lia's family believed that because of her seizures, she might grow up to become a shaman, a position of great respect. Finally, if the health care system had asked these simple questions, they would have discovered that the family's major concern was that Lia's soul would never return.

These eight simple questions could help health care providers deliver better care to anyone. Illness is almost always experienced as a metaphor.[24] For example, a heart attack is often interpreted as the result of an emotional crisis or as a penalty for overwork. And illnesses are sometimes defined differently in different cultures.[25] Despite advances in epidemiology, which has exposed the epistemology of many diseases, we still experience illness as our movie.

Let's Heal the Healers

This book provides numerous examples of how we can re-engineer our health care system for quality while simultaneously eliminating waste and enhancing sustainability. Attaining this goal requires highly motivated people working in a safe environment, performing tasks replete with professional fulfillment. But this utopian vision does not define many Canadian health care workplaces today. In fact, health care providers are some of the unhealthiest workers in Canada.

Health care workers' injury rates are 56 per cent higher than the average for other occupations.[26] Nurses' absenteeism rates are nearly double those of other occupations. Over one-third of Canadian nurses are so emotionally exhausted that they score above burnout.[27] It's of little consolation that nurses from the US, England, and Scotland are just as fed up.[28] It doesn't have to be this way—German nurses are much happier than their colleagues in other countries. The total number of hours that Canadian nurses are off the job is the equivalent of 5,500 full-time positions—more than an entire Canadian graduating class of nurses.

The high rates of absenteeism cause remaining nurses to put in a lot of overtime. Nursing overtime in Canada amounts to the equivalent of 7,000 full-time jobs. At the same time, nurses spend up to three-quarters of their time doing non-nursing work. They're giving out meals, portering patients or lab tests, and filling out dozens of forms. Management guru Peter Drucker notes that when ward clerks are hired to do paperwork for nurses, nurse productivity soars.[29]

A key part of any overall nursing strategy must be the retention of those nurses who are working now and the recruitment of other nurses who have taken jobs outside of the profession. Elizabeth Hand, a nurse at the Oklahoma Heart Institute in Tulsa bemoans, "I meet skilled registered nurses every day who have left nursing and long to return but will not. It seems to me that there is no shortage of nurses, but rather a shortage of nurses prepared to put up with the state of affairs in hospital nursing."[30]

Governments tend to cut health care budgets in bad years and to increase funding in good. Because salaries are 75 to 80 per cent of budgets, this fiscal instability creates cyclical unemployment for health care workers. When governments cut funding, health care organizations lay off nurses, the largest group of health care workers. The next largest group, doctors, hardly ever face layoff notices. Most doctors are self-employed in private practice. From 1979 to 1994, the number of employed registered nurses rose from 59 to 80 per 10,000 Canadians, but it fell to 74 per 10,000 by 2001.[31]

The numbers tell the story of the increasing casualization of nursing jobs. In 1979, 63 per cent of nurses worked full-time, but twenty years later this had fallen to 51 per cent. Some nurses prefer part-time and casual work, but most are looking for full-time employment. Business models taken thoughtlessly from other sectors drove casualization. Casual workers allow employers the flexibility of a just-in-time workforce. They aren't paid benefits. Using more casual and part-time nurses provided apparent short-term financial benefits, but it aggravated the flight of nurses from Canada and drove up the costs for casual workers. It also made it more difficult to establish teams, and it decimated morale.

Changes to nursing education have complicated matters. Twenty years ago, most nurses received their training through diploma programs administered by hospitals. Now most nurses are trained in university programs and receive a baccalaureate degree. Many jurisdictions now require nurses to have university degrees. Unfortunately, cutbacks in traditional training programs were not matched by increases in university programs. The number of new admissions to nursing schools fell by 27 per cent from 1990 to 2000.

During the mid-1990s, Canadian nursing graduates faced a gloomy future, with senior nurses being laid off and few new job prospects. In 1996, McMaster nursing grad Laurie Horricks saw few prospects in her native country. She looked to the US.[32] "The farther south you go, the better it is," she claimed. Megan Burns found herself buttering bagels at Tim Hortons after being laid off from the Toronto Hospital.[33] Marie Louise Wallace nursed for thirty years but she's also now in the nutrition business, behind the counter at Bow Wow Express, a Toronto pet-food emporium.

Extra, Extra! Researchers Discover the Obvious! Nurses Are Good for Your Health!

Ontario premier Mike Harris was sanguine about the nursing situation, claiming that public-sector restructuring was long overdue.[34] When Ernie Eves became premier in 2001, he briefly attempted to play the anti-Harris. He claimed that Ontario was hiring more nurses. However, the 2003 graduating class faced similar slim job prospects. New grad Tirzah Chung tried to maintain a brave face but lamented, "Sadness and resignation have hit me as I find the lack of entry-level opportunities for nurses persists throughout the Greater Toronto Area."[35]

If Harris is still listening, it turns out that nurses do matter. Hospitals with more nurses provide higher quality of care.[36] University of Toronto nursing professor Anne Tourangeau's research team recently published a study of seventy-five Ontario hospitals and nearly fifty thousand patients.[37] The result: hospitals with more registered nurses or more experienced nurses had lower mortality rates.

Magnet Hospitals Pull Nurses into Practice

It's not only the number of nurses that is important, it's also how they feel about their jobs. Twenty years ago, American researchers noticed that some hospitals maintained their staff during the nursing shortage of the early '80s.[38] They nicknamed these "magnet hospitals" because they were able to retain staff and even attract new staff despite the general shortage. The American Nurses Association wanted to promote the nurse-friendly aspects of these institutions, so it established a formal certification program for magnet hospitals in 1994, administered by the American Nurses Credentialing Center. As of May 2003, there were sixty-nine magnet-designated organizations. The key features of magnet hospitals include increased numbers of nurses, flexible hours with self-scheduling, a participative management style, an emphasis on professional autonomy, collaborative team relationships, and—very importantly—a nurse executive at the board level.[39] Nursing leadership within the institution seems to be particularly important in establishing a nurse-friendly environment.[40]

Research on magnet hospitals indicates that a hospital that is nurse-friendly is probably patient-friendly as well.[41] Magnet hospitals have higher staff morale, better patient satisfaction, and 5 per cent lower death rates.

Magnetic North
No Canadian hospital has formal magnet designation because of the substantial investment required to translate the concept to the Canadian context. But Vancouver's Children's and Women's Health Centre has tried to model itself on the magnet model. Heather Mass, the chief of nursing, had long been interested in magnet hospitals, and when her board expressed concern about nurse retention, she saw her opportunity. In 2001, the turnover rate of nurses reached 9 per cent— low compared with other hospitals, but high for Children's and Women's. The board decided to accelerate the development of the hospital's nurse-friendly culture. The hospital established a nursing council to advise management on nursing policies. It developed a document on principles of nursing practices and helped craft retention policies. Half of the council members are staff nurses, paid for their attendance, with replacements provided to their units.

Nurses tend to be keen on further education both to increase their skills and to advance their careers. The Children's and Women's Health Centre's foundation pays for the tuition and the time for nurses to take certain programs. All new maternity nurses take a twelve-week course, which can be used for credit toward a master's degree. Nurses even have the opportunity to write a paper under supervision and get a UBC credit. There are nurse educators on each unit to ensure that young nurses are supported and that all nurses continue to learn. Scheduling is left to the units so that nurses can sort out these issues themselves.

In fact, a lot of implementation of policy is left to the unit level—another recommendation from the nursing advisory council. Nurses can close their units to new admissions if they think there are not enough staff to provide safe care. They rarely take this action (once or twice per year), but just being given this authority greatly enhances their professional status. Children's and Women's also raised the profile of ward managers, who don't have to be nurses. The Genetics manager is a genetics counsellor, and the Women's Health Clinic manager is a social worker.

Some nurses are concerned that the hospital is downloading senior management decisions to nursing units. But Mass responds, "We still treat bedside nurses as widgets. We don't trust them to make good decisions and use resources wisely. We should treat them as professionals and then hold them accountable."

As a result of these policies, the hospital's turnover rate is now less than 4 per cent. As of the summer of 2003, there were no vacancies when some Canadian hospitals had over 10 per cent of their positions unfilled. In fact, Children's and Women's was forty positions *overhired*.

Human Resources 101: Happier Employees
Better management practices lead to healthier health care workers.[42] And it looks as though happier health care workers provide better-quality care. That means fewer deaths, less disability. It doesn't cost extra to treat employees, including managers and professionals, with

kindness and consideration. It costs a lot more to deal with low morale and high turnover rates.

The health care system reeks of nineteenth-century labour relations. Other sectors became aware of the importance of participatory management and organizational fairness decades ago. Health care organizations still too often are run according to the military model, with a strict, hierarchical command structure. One result is that health care providers tend to work below their level of expertise. Family doctors or specialist nurses could perform much of the work of specialist physicians. Nurses could perform much of the work of family doctors. Leonard Berry, from Texas A&M's business school, comments, "When health care professionals consistently work below their level of expertise, scarce resources are wasted, care is more costly, boredom and frustration increase, and access is impaired."[43]

Organizations tend to restrict non-professionals to menial tasks, which also leads to boredom, frustration, and waste. Recall from chapter 6 how the drivers for San Francisco's innovative On Lok SeniorHealth are often the ones to engage patients in discussions about their desires for acute care for their next episode of illness. Recall from chapter 7 how Saskatoon's Sherbrooke Community Centre cross-trained its non-professional staff so they could establish meaningful relationships with their clients. It is tragic that the health care system currently wastes so much human potential. But the good side of all this waste is that it provides a bank of resources from which to fund innovation.

Teamwork Is the Key to Happier Providers and Healthier Patients

Calgary family physician Kevin Hanrahan found himself burnt out: "There is a trap in family medicine where you always feel under pressure to see more patients, work harder, and make more money."[44] Like most family doctors, he was mainly carrying these burdens himself. He's a lot happier now, but he's no longer a family doc. His new job? He's a firefighter with the Calgary fire department. He's thrilled with his new job. Like many youngsters, he always wanted to be a firefighter. But what's the best part of his new job? "My favourite thing about being a firefighter is the team approach."

Health care is a team game too, but you wouldn't know that from a peek behind the scenes at most health care facilities. There's the usual tension between doctors and nurses, the two most numerous professions. Other professionals, such as social workers and rehabilitation workers, feel left out by both larger groups. Non-professionals wonder what role they have beyond blindly following orders. Then there is the patient, too often surrounded by cacophony and discord.

But if we start delivering care in a team way, patient outcomes and staff esprit de corps improve. That's why one of *Crossing the Quality Chasm*'s ten rules is that "providers should cooperate and work in high-functioning teams instead of attempting to work in isolation. Concern for patients should drive cooperation amongst providers and drive out competition based upon professional and organizational rivalries."

Howdy Partner: Growing Teamwork in Calgary

Sue Evans started her nursing career in the UK where she spent much of her time working closely with family doctors.[45] She was disappointed when she came to Canada and found that home care nurses worked with so many different doctors they rarely ever met them. A typical Calgary Health Region community care co-ordinator (CCC) like Evans could have 20 family doctors involved with the 50 patients on her caseload. At best she would play telephone tag with several doctors as she made her rounds in the community.

Calgary family doctor Prem Lakra also missed the closer relationships he had with UK community nurses before he immigrated to Canada. For physicians like Dr. Lakra who typically have over 15 elderly patients receiving home care, it could be maddening to have to deal with 10 different nurses. The solution—a partnership.

In 2001, Evans became part of the pilot for the home care physician partnership program, which involved 17 other CCCs and 23 family doctors. The partnership program includes a blueprint for the doctor and nurse to clarify their relationship. At the beginning of the pilot, there were six hours of orientation meetings. Now there's just two. For the first, the CCC, the project co-ordinator, and a physician working with the project bring lunch to the family doctor's practice to talk informally with the doctor and his or her staff. Then the doctor and CCC meet for another hour to discuss the blueprint that delineates regular meeting times and communications for urgent situations.

Evans began by looking after all of the patients of three family doctors including Dr. Lakra. Brian Higgins and his wife, Joyce, have been very appreciative of Evans and Lakra's collaboration. Evans started visiting Higgins after he had a toe amputated because of diabetes and peripheral vascular disease. When she took on his care she discovered an infection on the other foot. Sue immediately called in the SWAT team. A nurse from the Special Wound Assessment Team saw Robert's infected ulcer with Sue and then recommended a particular treatment protocol, which slowly healed Higgins's skin.

Project doctors and nurses were pleased with their new professional relationships. The patients and caregivers were pleased with the better care. Evans says she has developed a bond with her physician colleagues. Knowing she has more support means she can provide better care. Dr. Lakra claims that "this type of care allows people to live at home longer." Joyce Higgins says that knowing that Dr. Lakra and Evans are communicating effectively with each other has taken a burden off her shoulders.

All participants identified face to face contact as one of the key success factors. Up until the pilot project it was rare for family doctors and CCCs to ever meet together to solve their problems. Familiarity bred respect. Some of the doctors were so pleased that they started to suggest more work for the nurses. The home care nurses managed very complicated patients with diabetes so why couldn't they see the less complicated ones who came to the office for follow-up? What about all the teaching they could provide to patients with high blood pressure, asthma, and other chronic conditions?

The family doctors' enthusiasm was music to the ears of Dr. Peter Sargious. Sargious is the medical director of the region's chronic disease management program. Sargious and other regional staff were just starting an expansion of the home care model to office management of chronic illness. He knew that the region would have to collaborate with family doctors to establish effective chronic disease management.

As of November 2003, over one hundred family doctors were participating in the chronic disease management program, amounting to one-quarter of all Calgary family physicians. Sargious says that he hopes to integrate specialist physicians into the projects, building on the region's experience with shared care psychiatry. A number of university-based specialists will move off fee-for-service payment in 2004, and he notes that this should ease their participation.

Evans is helping to pilot this new project. She now spends roughly half a day per week in each of eight family physicians' offices. She sees patients with diabetes, high blood pressure, and five other conditions. The latest addition to the list are patients on anti-coagulants. Evans continues to be thrilled with her work. She says that the project has greatly enhanced her job satisfaction.

This kind of teamwork improves effectiveness and efficiency. Everyone works up to his or her full potential. The home care project permitted the CCCs to delegate more tasks to licensed practical nurses and personal care aides and teach more self-care to patients and families.

Systems Thinking about Teamwork

We need to apply this teamwork thinking to health human resources. Researcher Cathy Fooks assessed Canada's sorry state of health human resources for the Romanow Commission.[46] The report's final recommendations were startlingly simple:

- Integrate health human resource (HHR) planning into the planning for system design.
- Plan HHR according to health needs.
- Plan HHR on the basis of teams.
- Stop planning on the basis of individual professions.
- Plan HHR nationally.

Part of our investment in education must include remedial training in teamwork. Then we need to ensure that health professionals learn in teams as much as possible during their undergraduate education.

Don't Forget Fairness for Doctors

Doctors don't seem to be suffering quite as much as nurses. For example, their absenteeism rate is less than 20 per cent that of nurses.* But readers will recall from chapter 9 that the system is startlingly unfair to doctors. Under the existing fee-for-service system, some doctors, such as ophthalmologists, have net incomes five times or more that of other doctors who might be working just as hard. Some doctors have onerous on-call responsibilities. Others may not have taken call for years. Some doctors do a lot of teaching, but unless you're a full-time faculty member you might not be paid for this important task. Sitting on committees and helping your organization implement the best quality improvement initiative in the province usually doesn't pay either.

In the Northwest Territories, Dr. John Morse claims that having all specialists on the same pay grid has developed a more collegial atmosphere. Dr. Rob Wedel of Taber, Alberta, notes that before his group of family doctors went off fee-for-service there were high and low billers despite the fact that all of them worked hard. Now their pay packages

---

* It is true that most doctors are self-employed and many nurses have sick-time benefits, but the nursing absenteeism rate is still twice the average for all occupations.

are within 10 per cent of each other. Equity boosted morale and made the doctors feel more a part of the same team.

As mentioned in chapter 9, the potential losers (ophthalmologists, dermatologists, and others) from any fee rejigging have effectively defended the status quo. A recent Ontario investigation, led by Dr. John Wade, sits on the shelf. Superman will buy a rock of kryptonite before the Ontario Medical Association (OMA) touches Wade's report.

On the other hand, the OMA publishes guidelines for payment to salaried physicians that could be used as a template for all physicians. As shown in the accompanying table, it has five pay levels that vary according to responsibility and seniority.

Ontario Medical Association
Suggested Grading and Remuneration
for Salaried Physicians.[47]

Level 1 $112,000
- Has a limited amount of post-graduate or practical experience.
- May be responsible to a more senior physician.
- Would be promotable to Level 2 as soon as the necessary experience and skills have been obtained.

Level 2 $154,000
- Has two to five years of post-graduate experience, including training or experience in the type of work involved.
- Has a position of responsibility that may involve supervision of the work of other health-care professionals.

Level 3 $179,000
- Has five to ten years of post-graduate experience that could include (a) a higher qualification in a related specialty, or (b) approximately five years of training or experience in the particular field of work, or (c) at least five years of experience in the organization in which he or she is working.

- • Usually has supervisory position overseeing either full-time or part-time professionals and others.
- • May work single-handed because of the highly specialized kind of work.

Level 4 $194,000

- • Has greater responsibilities than those required for Level 3.
- • Has senior administrative and/or clinical responsibilities.

Level 5 $229,000

- • Holds the most senior medical post in an organization or department, is responsible for all medical staff in the organization, and may have responsibility for other health care professionals.
- • Has senior administrative responsibility, up to and including the post of chief executive officer.

(Note: Figures quoted are for net pay and do not include benefits, typically 18 per cent of pay packages, or office overhead, which is typically 40 per cent of a private doctor's gross billings.)

While some might quibble with the exact dollar amounts, using such a grid would make doctors' pay much fairer than it is now. And the absolute amounts aren't too out of kilter either. A doctor on the top rung would receive $229,000, plus approximately $40,000 worth of benefits, which private practice doctors currently have to pay for themselves. Private practitioners also have to pay their own overhead, which typically comes to 40 per cent of gross income. That means a doctor in private practice would have to bill medicare $450,000 to match this top pay level. Very few Canadian doctors bill these amounts. Even a doctor with five to ten years' experience would make the equivalent of a private doctor who currently bills $350,000.

In other sectors of society, jobs are compared with similar jobs to establish fair remuneration. Nobody does quite the same work as doctors, but nurses' jobs also feature shift work, time on call, and stressed out "clients." Nowadays, nurses need four years of post-secondary education. Many have more. A doctor straight out of school does require more education than a nurse, but how much more should we pay her? Should we pay five times as much? Should we pay 50 per cent more? Try this with your friends and co-workers. Most people tend to say a new doctor should get around twice as much as an experienced staff nurse. The OMA's suggested pay for a Level 1 doctor is approximately twice the pay of a senior registered nurse. Then ask your friends and co-workers how much more we should pay a senior doctor than a junior doctor. Again, most people say around twice as much. The OMA Level 5 pay is approximately twice that of Level 1, or four times that of a senior nurse.

Of course, if doctors wanted to earn more than their basic pay, they could do what many do now: they could work harder. They could volunteer for more overtime, more ER shifts, and more on-call time for their group. There's always extra work available for those doctors who want to work longer hours.

We might have to make some exceptions to this scheme for certain subspecialties. But wouldn't it be nice if doctors had fair remuneration? How can doctors celebrate medicare as a symbol of our country's commitment to justice when there is no fairness for them? To quote Ontario gynecologist Dr. Richard Gruneir, "I want the respect that a salary provides . . . I no longer want a sweatshop, piecework environment."[48]

Treatment and Prevention of Second Victims

Dr. Albert Wu of Johns Hopkins University coined the use of the term "second victim" for clinicians who are "wounded" by the errors they inflict upon their patients.[49] Wu outlined the psychological tailspin that clinicians endure when they realize they have made a mistake, their symptoms being proportionate to the damage they have caused.

Classically, guilt is expunged through confession, restitution, and absolution. However, the health care system is littered with barriers to confession because it entails disclosure of harm to patients, which exposes the provider to patient anger, legal suit, and professional ridicule. Professional ethics demand disclosure, but clinicians tend to hide guilt, which then is often accompanied by dysfunctional behaviour.

We can help providers who have been at the pointy end of an error. Quebec and Saskatchewan have recently taken steps to make disclosure easier. We can also help providers deal with patients and families who, according to Wu, can be "astonishingly forgiving." We can involve them in the investigation of the accident. Helping to prevent similar problems aids healing for patients and families.

In the long run, we need to make health care a lot safer. One of *Crossing the Quality Chasm*'s other rules is that safety is the responsibility of the whole system, not only of individual providers. Dr. Peter Norton, chief of the University of Calgary's Department of Family Medicine, and Dr. Ross Baker, a professor in the University of Toronto's Department of Health Policy Management and Evaluation, are the chief investigators of the National Patient Safety Study. Their research suggests five key steps to making health care safer:[50]

1. Recognize that improving patient safety is a priority.
2. Improve the reporting of errors and near misses.
3. Increase the focus on system changes.
4. Gain greater knowledge about safer systems, much of which already exists.
5. Establish leadership at all levels.

Saskatchewan Focuses on Quality

Dr. Stewart McMillan's broad Scottish brogue still reveals his roots, thirty-one years after he immigrated to Regina. McMillan was born in Glasgow, less than 40 kilometres from Tommy Douglas's birthplace. He made his first foray to the Canadian Prairies in 1969, taking a summer job in Saskatchewan during his medical training at the University of Glasgow. He felt Canada was the land of opportunity, but he made sure he also sampled our winter before he decided to move for good.

Dr. McMillan has been practising family medicine in the same location in Regina since 1973. He has always been interested in quality improvement, and in 1992 he was tapped by the just-elected Romanow government to chair the new Health Services Utilization and Research Commission. The commission did groundbreaking work to facilitate the province's health reform. One study comprehensively assessed the condition of hospital patients throughout the province and showed that the majority did not need hospital care but rather home care or other forms of treatment. Other studies led to the more appropriate ordering of lab investigations. The commission also increased the province's capacity to conduct research and evaluation.

During this time, commission board member and long-time registrar of the Saskatchewan College of Physicians and Surgeons Dr. Dennis Kendel convinced Dr. McMillan to attend a meeting of the Institute for Healthcare Improvement. Like the UK's Dr. John Oldham, McMillan found IHI's optimistic environment intoxicating. He was hooked.

In 2001, Ken Fyke's Commission on Medicare issued its final report, *Caring for Medicare: Sustaining a Quality System*. The Fyke Commission is the only health care inquiry that has highlighted that medicare's problems relate more to lack of quality than lack of funding. McMillan, Kendel, and other quality advocates, such as Saskatoon researcher and commentator Steven Lewis, were involved in the final report. The Fyke Commission recommended that the province establish an arm's-length health quality council to "lead the country in the pursuit of a quality culture that will be the next great revolution in health care."[51]

The following year, the province appointed the Health Quality Council, and McMillan became its first chair. The council hired Toronto family physician and health services researcher Ben Chan as its first CEO in October 2003. The council has attracted some international luminaries. Dr. Ken Kizer is a member and Dr. Donald Berwick, the president of the Institute for Health Care Improvement, is a special advisor. McMillan has kept in touch with changes to Britain's NHS through his visits home. He is particularly impressed with Dr. John Oldham's work with the National Primary Care Collaborative and hopes to duplicate its successes in Saskatchewan. The council has already invested $1 million in establishing a quality improvement network and plans to train personnel in the collaborative methodology in 2004.

A Quality Initiative for Canada

This book does not provide an overall political and economic plan to fix Canada's health care system. Readers are referred to other publications for grander visions.[52] But there are a few strategic directions that are clearly indicated, and they are listed below. Most have already been discussed in this book.

Key Strategies for Reform at the System Level

1. Establish leadership at political, administrative, and clinical levels—a crucial factor.
2. Invest heavily in training and education.
3. Set clear measurable goals that are meaningful to patients and providers.
4. Focus on prevention.
5. Communicate frequently, often, and always to everyone, including patients, families, communities, providers, professional organizations, unions, administrators, and especially politicians.
6. Maximize but don't get distracted by information technology.

Leadership is crucially important, and it must come right from the top. Our prime minister and premiers should be able to offer understandable diagnoses of the system's maladies and then explain their proposed solutions in plain English. Candidates for these jobs should be able to say how they would reduce the long queues for certain procedures and provide universal coverage for pharmaceuticals—without spending a lot more money.

Administrators need to promote innovation. From the deputy minister of health to CEOs, from senior managers to team leaders, resources must be preserved for training and education. When resources are tight, it's important to spend even more on training. We tend to be slower than our American cousins to adopt innovations. This prudence sometimes works in our favour. A smaller proportion of Canadians have been exposed to dangerous drugs that were later withdrawn from market, because we take longer than the US to approve new drugs.[53] We have avoided many problems of the US health system that are related to faddish, private-sector novelties masquerading as improvement. But this book demonstrates that this country is chock full of innovators. We need loosen their shackles and let the creative juices flow.

In Lewis Carroll's *Alice in Wonderland*, Alice asks the Cheshire Cat which path she should take. When the cat inquires where she wants to go, Alice says it doesn't matter. In that case, says the cat, it doesn't matter which road she travels. This interchange characterizes the lack of direction of the Canadian health care system. Medicare, one of the most beloved symbols of our country, which consumes one-tenth of our economy, lurches from crisis to crisis without any clear sense of where it's going. Senior administrators strive to keep bad news out of the newspapers, while interest groups ensure a steady stream of unhappy stories to pressure more funding. Who's looking at the big picture?

The US Veterans Administration health system and the UK's National Health Service both developed clear goals and performance indicators to guide their revitalization. Canada is still moving far too slowly on developing national indicators, mainly because of the ongoing federal-provincial wrangling about funding. However, while national goals and indicators are desirable, this lack shouldn't excuse provinces from developing their own to guide reform.

Prevention Is the Key to the Second Stage of Medicare

In chapter 1, we noted that former Saskatchewan premier and father of medicare Tommy Douglas claimed that Canada would establish medicare in two stages. The first stage entailed public payment for a largely private, illness-oriented system. Douglas asserted that the second stage would involve changing the delivery system to place an emphasis on preventive medicine. He always claimed that despite the problems in attaining the first stage, the second would be even more difficult.

What would a health system based on prevention look like, and what's the strategy to transform the present system?

We might start our prevention strategy with hospital diversion programs like Quick Response Teams. QRTs can prevent hospital admission for patients like an eighty-year-old with a fractured pelvis. If we can help him or her heal at home, we can prevent all sorts of complications, including infections with really nasty bacteria. The hospital resources, which would have been used to provide care to these and other similar patients, can then move to community care.

Now we have the resources to ensure quality care for hospital patients being discharged who are at high risk for re-admission. Better follow-up care for congestive heart failure and other complicated conditions keeps people healthy and prevents hospital admissions. This, in turn, frees up even more personnel to allocate to community care.

Now we have the means for better management of chronic illnesses like diabetes. At present too many diabetics end up needing heart surgery and kidney dialysis. Chronic disease management programs can prevent complications and reduce the demands for these expensive acute care services. This frees up even more resources.

Now we have the wherewithal to prevent illness in the first place. The most prevalent chronic conditions—from heart disease to lung cancer to hepatitis C—are 80 to 100 per cent preventable. The causes of other illnesses such as prostate cancer are not as well understood. But even if we could implement just what we know now to prevent chronic disease, we could empty thousands of hospital beds. And we could enrich and lengthen the lives of millions of Canadians.

At this stage if everything has gone according to plan, we have a system of care with most of the resources based in primary health care and community care. The transition has naturally re-allocated resources to follow the patients.

It would be nice to have a little bit of extra funding to grease the wheels of change. But any system could kick-start this process, by freeing up the personnel for a QRT. Then just keep moving the staff to follow the patients.

Douglas suggested primary health care reforms as the key tactic in support of what he called "the practice of preventive medicine."[54] This book outlines many examples of exciting prevention programs in community health centres (CHCs) such as Ottawa's Somerset West, Montreal's CLSC Notre Dame de Grace/Montreal West, Vancouver's REACH, and the Sault Ste. Marie Group Health Centre. The Quebec CLSCs combine local public health, health care, social services, and rehabilitation therapists. They include home care and mental health services, family doctors, nurses, and social workers. Some have midwives.

These centres could be the vehicles to link private doctors with the community services system. Programs like Calgary's home care partnership, Hamilton's HSO Mental Health and Nutrition, and London's Integrating Physician Services in the Home, as well as assertive community treatment and palliative care, could be based in CHCs. If we added basic lab and diagnostic equipment, voila! A patient paradise—one-stop shopping for health care.

Public health-oriented primary health care is also the best tactic to drill down to diagnose the causes of illness and then ameliorate them. Centres like CLSC Sherbrooke and South Riverdale Community Health Centre have led their communities' campaigns against poverty and lead pollution respectively. Through their work with citizens, community health centres are a tonic for our flagging democracy. CHCs engage their communities in the democratic process. Regent Park CHC has taken on a mission to ensure that in the future, neighbourhood residents will run the centre. Just think how different our country would be if public health–oriented primary health care were the norm instead of the exception.

Communicate or Die
One of the main lessons of the US Veterans Administration's success is the key role played by communication. Organizations going through change need to communicate internally to staff and externally to their stakeholders. However, we also need an ongoing, open public debate about health care issues. Too often the key analyses and deliberations occur behind closed doors. As a result, Canadians are not equipped to deal with a number of key health policy issues.

With all the media attention to disputes about doctors' pay in the past decade, why do so few Canadians know that some doctors make five times more than others? With all the worry about waits and delays, why do so few Canadians know who allocates operating-room time? With all the fretting about our rapidly escalating pharmaceutical bill, why do so few know that we're spending billions on drugs people shouldn't take?

Bad odours accumulate in closed spaces. Let's pump some oxygen into our health policy debates. The current public discourse is sterile. Governments and health care organizations need to sponsor policy forums where the key issues can be debated, not papered over. The new Canadian Health Council could be the patron for a democratic dialogue about the future of our health system.

Information Please
Health is an information-rich field. Knowledge turnover is faster here than in almost any other sector of our society. Health organizations need to ensure that knowledge remains fresh and is incorporated into practice. In the US, nurses are typically paid to upgrade their skills. In

Canada, they're lucky to get their old jobs back after returning from courses that they have paid for themselves. Health organizations also need to invest heavily in the tools of change. At present, few Canadians are familiar with collaborative and rapid-cycle improvement methodologies.

Information technology is wonderful—when it works. Group Health Sault Ste. Marie's electronic health record is key to that centre's groundbreaking diabetes program. Unfortunately, doctors' offices and clinics operate with lots of paper. In 2002, only 17 per cent of American primary health care physicians used electronic records compared with 58 per cent in the United Kingdom and 90 per cent in Sweden.[55] In Canada, it's probably even fewer than one in six. Few Canadian doctors even use e-mail for clinical purposes.

Alberta recently announced significant strides toward the establishment of an electronic health record,[56] but we shouldn't wait for the final, perfect product before we improve our information systems. If family doctors simply used a loose-leaf binder with different sections for different chronic illnesses (diabetes, asthma, coronary heart disease, and so on), they could greatly improve the care of these patients.

Conclusion

Medicare is at a crossroads. Canadians are unhappy with waits and delays. The National Patient Safety Study demonstrates that there are other big quality problems. The right says privatize while the left says more money. Most Canadians oppose market solutions, but they are also uneasy about continuing to pump public dollars into what seems, at times, to be a bottomless pit.

Tommy Douglas was medicare's most stalwart advocate, but he was no spendthrift. Douglas ran balanced budgets when he was premier of Saskatchewan. Twenty-five years ago he warned a gathering of medicare's defenders to implement a preventive program because that was the only way to keep the costs under control. He feared that medicare's opponents would use the issue of rising costs to convince Canadians that medicare needed private medicine.

This book demonstrates that we can solve medicare's apparently intractable problems with innovation. We can modernize medicare with public finance and non-profit delivery. Let's speed up medicare's renewal by spreading the best practices across the country and encouraging everyone to do even better. As the problems wane, so will the demand that we change the basic values upon which medicare was founded.

It's not too late to save medicare. It's not too early to pitch in to help. Let's take our final direction again from Tommy Douglas— "Courage my friends. 'Tis not too late to make a better world."

Your Community, Province, and Country and High-Quality Health Services

- Do your politicians know the answers to the questions posed in this book?

Appendix A:
Plan-Do-Study-Act Basics

Plan-Do-Study-Act

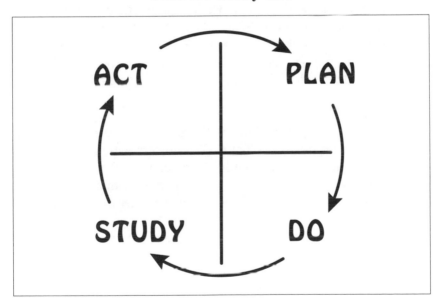

Adapted from National Primary Care Development Team, *PDSA theory & practice* (2003), http://www.npdt.org/scripts/default.asp?site_id=1&id=385.

Why Use PDSA Cycles?

Making improvements in services requires change. Change can seem threatening or overwhelming for busy people doing demanding work. The PDSA method is a way to break down change into manageable chunks and test each small part to make sure that things are improving and no effort is wasted.

What Is It?

PDSA stands for **P**lan, **D**o, **S**tudy, **A**ct. It is a model for testing ideas that you think may create an improvement. It can be used to test ideas for improvement quickly and easily based on existing ideas, research, theory, review, audit, and so on, or practical ideas that have been proven to work elsewhere. It uses simple measurements to monitor the effect of changes over time. It encourages starting with small changes, which can build into larger improvements through successive quick cycles of change.

Step 1: PLAN
Identify what change you think will create improvement and then plan the test of the change. What is your objective in introducing the change? It is important to establish the scope of the change to be introduced and how you are going to collect information about the differences that occur. How will you know whether the change made has worked or not?

The change should bring about differences that are measurable in isolation. A major change could be broken down into smaller, more manageable "chunks." Once the actual change to be introduced has been agreed upon, the following questions should be asked:

- What would we expect to see as a result of this change?

- What data do we need to collect to check the outcome of the change?
- How will we know whether the change has worked or not?
- Who, what, where, when?

Step 2: DO
Put the plan into practice and test the change by collecting the data. This stage involves carrying out the plans agreed to in Step 1. It is important that the Do stage is kept as short as possible, although there may be some changes that can be measured only over longer periods. Record any unexpected events, problems, and other observations.

Step 3: STUDY
Review and reflect. Complete the analysis of the data. Has there been an improvement? Did your expectations match the reality of what happened? What could be done differently?

Step 4: ACT
Make further changes or amendments and collect data again, after you have decided what worked and what didn't. Carry out an amended version of what happened during the Do stage and measure any differences.

An Example

A small practice is keen to increase the number of their CHD patients who are receiving cholesterol-lowering medications, as it is suspected that many are not on repeat prescriptions. A small team is set up within the practice to oversee the work, involving a family doctor, a nurse, a receptionist, and the practice manager. They decide that the first step to improving prescribing rates is to identify those patients with CHD who are not on cholesterol-lowering medications. However, they do not have a CHD register or a computer.

Step 1: PLAN—*Planning what changes you're going to make, and how you are going to measure any differences that occur. How will you know whether the change made has worked or not?*

The team decides to try to identify CHD patients though repeat prescription requests. Many CHD patients can be identified through their repeat requests by looking for patients who are receiving nitrates for angina. Patients usually come into the practice during opening hours and place their requests in a box on the reception desk.

The team's objective is to identify CHD patients by using repeat prescription requests; the change they are going to test is the monitoring of repeat prescriptions; and the data they are going to collect is the number of patients on nitrate prescriptions.

The Plan: The box will be replaced with a notice saying that patients should hand their requests to a receptionist:

- The receptionist will look at the items on the form to spot any nitrate prescriptions (a list of drug names will be printed out and stuck on the wall in reception).
- Names of patients on nitrates will be noted on a form kept on the shelf under the reception desk.
- This will be done for one week, after which the numbers of patients identified will be counted and reception staff will be asked how they found the process.

Step 2: DO—*Putting the plan into practice and doing something differently, while we measure the changes—as agreed in the plan.*

The test was carried out according to plan. The repeat prescription box was removed and a simple form produced to record patient names. A notice was put up asking patients to hand in their repeat requests to a member of the reception staff. One elderly patient had complained that the box for prescriptions was missing (he didn't have his glasses to read the notice).

Step 3: STUDY—What have the data shown us? Has there been an improvement? What could we do differently?

After one week, twenty-two patients on nitrates had been identified and their names recorded. The receptionists had no difficulties scanning the repeat requests, even when things were quite busy, but they had noticed that two drug names were missing from their list. They also thought it would be a good idea to record patient dates of birth because some patients have the same name.

Step 4: ACT—Having decided what worked and what didn't, making further changes or amendments and measuring again.

After discussion within the practice, it was decided to

- continue identifying CHD patients in this way (adding the date of birth) for another month and then study the results again;
- update the list of nitrates to include all drug names;
- increase the size of the print on the notice about the repeat prescription box; and
- start a new PDSA cycle for the practice nurses to check the notes of those patients identified in order to confirm that they have CHD.

This is the end of this particular cycle, but the strength of PDSA is that one cycle of change can lead naturally into successive cycles, building on the previous work. For example, the next PDSA cycle building on this may include:

1. PLAN: The three practice nurses decide to use a quick checklist when checking the notes in order to identify patients with CHD from the patients identified. They agree to look for the following when reviewing the notes: CHD diagnosis, MI or angina, and

blood pressure measurement. The nurses agree to each go through five sets of notes per day for two days. They decide to measure how easy it was to get the information from the notes by measuring how long it took to go through each set of notes.

2. DO: The three nurses divide the notes between them using a small checklist.

3. STUDY: The nurses find there is a variation in how long it takes to go through the notes. The time taken to get the information varies between thirty seconds and five minutes. Two of the nurses find there is no problem going through five sets of notes during a working day, but the part-time nurse finds it difficult to get through all five in the time allowed. The nurses agree that while going through the notes, it would be useful to check whether the patient had a cholesterol test in the last two years.

4. ACT: The part-time nurse reduces the number of notes she goes through each day. Cholesterol checks are added to the list of markers for CHD.

Continuing the process, the next PDSA cycle could address capturing new diagnoses for the developing CHD registry using a checklist that administrative staff could use, and the next PDSA cycle after that could address looking at the percentage of the current CHD register on statins and flagging up reviews, and so on.

PDSA cycles can build on each other as small changes lead to other changes or bigger changes and so on and so on. The sky's the limit!

PDSA cycles reduce the difficulties in getting started. Testing small changes sequentially means that design problems can be detected and amended earlier rather than later, saving huge amounts of effort put into massive change that has to be altered.

Hints and Tips

- Keep it simple.
- Keep it small and manageable to start—massive projects can be broken down into a number of small, quick PDSA cycles.
- Cycles should happen quickly—think in terms of a week, not a month.
- There is no wrong answer. If you find something that works, use it.
- Copy and adapt other people's ideas if you think they may be useful.

Appendix B:
Breakthrough Collaboratives

A collaborative in the Breakthrough Series usually consists of twenty to forty health care organizations working together for up to fifteen months to improve a specific clinical or operational area. Under the guidance of an IHI (Institute for Health Improvement) panel of experts, team members study, test, and implement the latest knowledge available in order to produce rapid improvements in their organizations. A collaborative is an intensive effort of health care professionals making significant changes that improve clinical outcomes and reduce costs.

There are eight phases to each collaborative:

1. Planning and pre-work
2. Learning Session #1
3. Action Period #1
4. Learning Session #2
5. Action Period #2
6. Learning Session #3
7. Action Period #3
8. Closing event

The Improving Chronic Illness Care Web site (http://www.improvingchroniccare.org) has dozens of materials—including planning agendas, worksheets, sample documents, and critical tools—to assist sponsors as they prepare for each phase of the collaborative.

1. Planning and Pre-Work

Months of planning precede the first learning session. During this period, collaborative sponsors establish roles for the various parties, assemble faculty, and recruit organizations to participate. Sponsors also develop materials for the pre-work session. Teams conduct extensive self-evaluations, including completion of the Assessment of Chronic Illness Care (ACIC) survey, and begin to lay the foundation for system change.

2. Learning Session #1

Learning Session #1 assembles the clinical teams and faculty for two days. It introduces the Chronic Care Model (CCM)—the model for improvement—and clinical change concepts. The sessions are interactive and include time for the teams to work together. Sponsors set the agenda, schedule action-period conference calls, and acquire faculty disclosure on conflict of interest. Learning Session #1 focuses particularly on four of the CCM components: self-management support, delivery system redesign, decision support, and clinical information systems. Teams meet to complete plans for improving care within their organizations and get ready for the "plan-do-study-act," or PDSA, cycles. The PDSA cycle is discussed in Appendix A.

3. Action Period #1

Preparation for the action period occurs before the start of the first learning session, with tasks such as scheduling conference calls and setting up an e-mail discussion list. Some of these tasks will overlap with preparation for Learning Session #2.

Senior Leader Reports
Reports filed with the senior leader inform management about participants' progress. The teams complete a report every month beginning in the first month of Action Period #1. Other teams and their senior leaders share the reports. The technical experts and the director of the collaborative track the progress of the teams during the collaborative.

4. Learning Session #2

Participants are introduced to the rest of the Chronic Care Model. They learn more about how the elements are implemented. The organizers ask some high-performing teams to prepare presentations of their work to date. Participants complete evaluations at the end of each learning session, and these are provided to presenters and used for planning of upcoming learning sessions.

5. Action Period #2

Teams continue to refine their plans for improvement within their organizations. They keep in touch with each other and consult faculty and collaborative leaders in various ways that include conference calls and an e-mail discussion list.

6. Learning Session #3

Teams begin refining plans to improve chronic illness care and implement "spread": the expansion of improvement efforts throughout a health system. Measurement of progress and filing of reports continue. The plenary sessions focus on selected clinical topics and methods for sustaining change and promoting spread. Selected teams present results from their sites. Breakout sessions focus on specific plans for testing and implementation of the innovations.

7. Action Period #3

Teams move from testing to implementing a system for better care, striving for monthly improvement. They also continue to measure their progress and are encouraged to grade the spread of innovations through their system. They continue to be in touch with each other and with leaders and faculty through conference calls and an e-mail discussion list.

Two months prior to the closing event, the teams complete a special senior leader report, which documents their entire experience with the collaborative. This report is modelled after the monthly senior leader report, but also includes a summary of changes for each component of the Chronic Care Model. The teams also complete another copy of the Assessment of Chronic Illness Care.

8. Closing Event

This is the opportunity to showcase the collaborative's success. The teams present their accomplishments to other health care professionals, the public at large, and their colleagues. The closing event highlights the Chronic Care Model and the collaborative method for implementing its components.

Since 1998, ICIC has sponsored three Breakthrough Series, year-long collaboratives to improve care for chronic conditions based on a process developed by the Institute for Healthcare Improvement in the mid-1990s. Each series has brought together twenty to sixty health care organizations, from small community clinics to large nationally recognized organizations. ICIC hopes to build on the success of the Breakthrough Series with regional collaboratives, a convenient option that promotes similar quality improvement methods among participants in a smaller geographical area.

Notes

Chapter 1: The Gathering Storm

1. S Verma, H Levy, J Quinn, No relief in sight for ERs: flu and colds adding to woes in emergency rooms, *Toronto Star*, December 29, 1999.
2. See Ontario Hansard, March 6, 1997, http://www.ontla.on.ca/hansard/house_debates/36_parl/session1/L174.htm.
3. CG Stevenson, MA McArthur, M Naus, et al., Prevention of influenza and pneumococcal pneumonia in Canadian long-term care facilities: how are we doing? *Canadian Medical Association Journal*, 2001;164:1413–1419.
4. VH Menec, C Black, L MacWilliam, et al., *The impact of influenza-like illness on the Winnipeg Health Care system: is an early warning system possible?* (Winnipeg: Manitoba Centre for Health Policy and Evaluation, 2001).
5. T Talaga, Flu bug bites thousands: havoc predicted in already feverish emergency wards, *Toronto Star*, December 22, 1999.
6. N Van Rijn, S Verma, New ER logjam as flu season hits hospitals: paramedics scramble to find beds for seriously ill patients, *Toronto Star*, December 28, 1999.
7. M Sears, Descriptive epidemiology of asthma, *Lancet*, 1997;350(suppl.), no. 2:1–4.
8. C Hoffman, D Rice, HY Sung, Persons with chronic conditions: their prevalence and costs, *Journal of the American Medical Association*, 1996;276(18):1473–1479.
9. L Papp, Asthma sufferers must take more care MDs warn, *Toronto Star*, March 20, 1996.
10. AH Anis, LD Lynd, X Wang, et al., Double trouble: impact of inappropriate use of asthma medication on the use of health care resources, *Canadian Medical Association Journal*, 2001;164:625–631.
11. C Mellor, Uncontrolled asthma worse in Nova Scotia, *Halifax Mail Herald*, May 10, 2000.

12. T Marmor, K Sullivan, Canada's burning! media myths about universal health coverage, *Washington Monthly*, July/August 2000, 15–20.

13. City of Toronto, *Moving towards cleaner air: a progress report on the air quality strategy for the City of Toronto* (2001), http://www.city.toronto.on.ca/environment/movingto_report.pdf.

14. W Marsden, Tobacco firms behind tax protest, *Montreal Gazette*, January 17, 2000; S McCarthy, Imperial boss linked to smuggling, *Globe and Mail*, February 1, 2000.

15. Physicians for a Smoke-Free Canada, *Tobacco in Canada, 2002 update*, http://www.smoke-free.ca/pdf_1/TOBACCOINCANADA2002update-inprogress.pdf.

16. S Rubec, Tobacco industry papers show efforts to target young smokers, *London Free Press*, November 23, 1999.

17. Cases from the Coroner, *College of Physicians and Surgeons Members Dialogue*, November/December 2000:30.

18. K Donovan, T Talaga, SARS: the chain of errors, *Toronto Star*, September 20, 2003.

19. A Mitchell, Preventive measures keep ERs clear, *Globe and Mail*, January 5, 2000.

20. L McLeod, WW Lau, Decreasing influenza impact in lodges: 1997–2000 Calgary Regional Health Authority, *Canadian Journal of Public Health*, 2001;92:291–294.

21. A Mitchell, Alberta's emergency-room prescription, *Globe and Mail*, January 6, 2000.

22. This section is taken largely from *Notes for remarks by Commissioner Roy Romanow, Commission of the Future of Health Care in Canada, to the conference of the Organisation for Economic Co-operation and Development (OECD)* (Ottawa, November 6, 2001).

23. B Mickelburgh, B Laghi, 88% oppose tax increase for health care, *Globe and Mail*, November 23, 2002.

24. Institute of Medicine, *Crossing the quality chasm: a new health system for the 21st century.* (Washington: National Academy Press, 2001).

25. S Elofsson, A-L Unden, I Krakau, Patient charges—A hindrance to financially and psychosocially disadvantaged groups seeking care, *Social Science and Medicine*, 1998; 46:1375–1380.

26. SED Shortt, Medical Savings Accounts in publicly funded health care systems: Enthusiasm versus evidence, *Canadian Medical Association Journal*, 2002;167:159–162.

Chapter 2: Setting the Table

1. For more on the history of medicare, see MM Rachlis, C Kushner, *Strong medicine: how to save Canada's health care system* (Toronto: HarperCollins, 1995); CD Naylor, *Private practice, public payment: Canadian medicine and the politics of health insurance* (Kingston: McGill-Queen's University Press, 1986).

2. HCFA Oral History Interview: E Berkowitz, interview with Dr. Philip Lee in his office at the Humphrey Building, Washington, DC, 27 November 1995, http://www.cms.hhs.gov/about/history/lee.asp.

3. Annual Report of Federal Auditor General, 2002, http://www.oag-bvg.gc.ca/domino/reports.nsf/html/20020903ce.html/$file/20020903ce.pdf (accessed December 29, 2002).

4. L Priest, List reveals provinces violated health act, *Globe and Mail*, December 13, 2002.

5. C Morris, NB government defends lawn tractor purchases for hospitals, Canadian Press Newswire, April 4, 2002; Provinces spend Ottawa's medical fund on saws, steamer, Canadian Press Newswire, June 10, 2002.

6. Data from the Canadian Institute for Health Information, http://secure.cihi.ca/cihiweb/dispPage.jsp?cw_page=AR31_2002sum_e (accessed December 12, 2002) and the US Department of Health and Human Services, http://cms.hhs.gov/statistics/nhe/projections-2001/t1.asp (accessed December 31, 2002).

7. US Institute of Medicine, Health insurance is a family matter (September 18, 2002), http://www.nap.edu/catalog/10503.html?onpi_newsdoc09182002 (accessed November 17, 2003).

8. A Wordsworth, Medical bills main culprit in bankruptcies: US study, *National Post*, April 27, 2000.

9. B Purchase, Health care and competitiveness. Background paper for the National Health Policy Summit, Ottawa, 1996.

10. S Woolhandler, T Campbell, DU Himmelstein, Costs of health care administration in the United States and Canada, *New England Journal of Medicine*, 2003;349:768–775.

11. WP Welch, D Verrilli, SJ Katz, et al., A detailed comparison of physician services for the elderly in the United States and Canada, *Journal of the American Medical Association*, 1996;275:1410–1416.

12. UE Reinhardt, PS Hussey, GF Anderson, Cross-national comparisons of health systems using OECD data, 1999, *Health Affairs*, 2002;21:169–181.

13. Ibid.

14. OECD data, http://www.oecd.org/EN/statistics/0,,EN-statistics-12-nodirectorate-no-no-12,00.html (accessed December 31, 2002).

15. OECD data, http://www.oecd.org/EN/statistics/0,,EN-statistics-12-nodirectorate-no-1-no-12-no-no-2,00.html (accessed December 31, 2002).

16. Canadian Institute for Health Information, Preliminary Provincial/Territorial Government Health Expenditure Estimates. From: http://secure.cihi.ca/cihiweb/products/NHEXPPT03_04_e.pdf (accessed November 9, 2003).

17. Government of Canada fiscal reference tables, http://www.fin.gc.ca/frt/2003/frt03_e.pdf (accessed October 23, 2003).

18. Canadian Centre for Policy Alternatives, *Alternate federal budget 2004: fiscal and economic update* (October 31, 2003), http://www.policyalternatives.ca/afb/afb2004 fiscal-statement.pdf.

19. S Kerstetter, *Rags and riches: wealth inequality in Canada* (Ottawa: Canadian Centre for Policy Alternatives, 2002), http://www.policyalternatives.ca.

Chapter 3: Focus on Quality

1. C Blatchford, I won't be defined by mediocre medicare, *National Post*, November 30, 2002.
2. D Naylor, *Private practice, public payment: Canadian medicine and politics of health insurance 1911–1966* (Kingston: McGill-Queen's University Press, 1986).
3. A McColl, P Roderick, J Gabbay, et al., Performance indicators for primary care groups: an evidence based approach, *British Medical Journal*, 1998;317:1354–1360.
4. Royal College of Physicians and Surgeons of Canada, *Policy regarding publication of RCPSC qualifications/specialties recognized by the RCPSC*, http://rcpsc.medical.org/english/publications/ (accessed May 13, 2003).
5. LT Kohn, JM Corrigan, MS Donaldson, eds., *To err is human: building a safer health system* (Washington, DC: National Institute of Medicine, 1999), http://www.nap.edu/books/0309068371/htm (accessed February 11, 2003).
6. TA Brennan, LL Leape, NM Laird, et al., Incidence of adverse events and negligence in hospitalized patients: results of the Harvard medical practice study I, *New England Journal of Medicine*, 1991;324: 370–376; TA Brennan, LL Leape, NM Laird, et al., The nature of adverse events in hospitalized patients: results of the Harvard medical practice study II, *New England Journal of Medicine*, 1991;324:377–384.
7. C Vincent, G Neale, M Woloshynowych, Adverse events in British hospitals: preliminary retrospective record review, *British Medical Journal*, 2001;322:517–519; RM Wilson, WB Runciman, RW Gibberd, et al., The quality in Australian health care study, *Medical Journal of Australia*, 1995;163:458–471.
8. National Institute of Medicine, *Crossing the quality chasm: a new health system for the 21st century* (Washington, DC: National Academy Press, 2001). Available free online at: http://www.nap.edu/openbook/0309072808/html/index.html (accessed November 16, 2003).
9. D Wiley, Mistakes that kill, *Maclean's*, August 13, 2001, 38–44.
10. D Hawaleshka, Claire Lewis didn't have to die, *Maclean's*, December 30, 2002, 72–76.
11. The Hamilton Health Sciences Centre has issued an apology, but the family is still pursuing the case. Lewis. JE. "Taking Exception." *Canadian Medical Association Journal*, 2003;169:13.
12. H Branswell, Diagnostic tool no benefit: study, *Hamilton Spectator*, January 2, 2003.
13. JD Sandham, RD Hull, RF Brant, et al., A randomized controlled trial of the use of pulmonary artery catheters in high-risk surgical patients, *New England Journal of Medicine*, 2003;348:5–14.
14. RJ Blendon, C Schoen, C DesRoches, et al., Common concerns amid diverse systems: health care experiences in five countries, *Health Affairs*, 2003;22(3):106–121.
15. For example, see Plexus Institute, *The heart of complexity: second annual conference on complexity and health care*, http://plexusinstitute.com/edgeware/archive/edgeplace/heart/index.html#contents (accessed February 12, 2003).
16. P Morse, Norwalk virus closes hospital wards, *Hamilton Spectator*, January 2, 2003.
17. C Fragomeni, Norwalk virus hanging in hospitals, nursing homes, *Hamilton Spectator*, January 4, 2003.
18. Saskatchewan Health Services Utilization and Research Commission, *Hospital and*

home care study (mimeo, March 1998); C DeCoster, S Peterson, P Kasian, *Alternatives to acute care* (Winnipeg: Manitoba Centre for Health Policy and Evaluation, 1996).

19. B Hutchison, C Woodward, G Norman, et al., Provision of preventive care to unannounced standardized patients, *Canadian Medical Association Journal*, 1998;158:185–193.

20. MJ Stampfer, FB Hu, JE Manson, et al., Primary prevention of coronary heart disease in women through diet and lifestyle, *New England Journal of Medicine*, 2000;343:16–22.

21. JB Cooper, RS Newbower, CD Long, et al., Preventable anesthesia mishaps: a study of human factors, *Anesthesiology*, 1978;49:399–406.

22. A Gawande, When doctors make mistakes, *New Yorker*, February 1, 1999, 40–55.

Chapter 4: Dying in Canada

1. Peggy's story is from *Closer to home: the report of the British Columbia Royal Commission on Health Care and Costs* (Victoria: The Commission, 1991).

2. P Yelaja, Rediscovering the art of dying well, *Hamilton Spectator*, December 2, 2000.

3. E Volmers, Patients do not have to suffer, *Toronto Star*, December 2, 2000.

4. Standing Senate Committee on Social Affairs, Science and Technology, Subcommittee to update "Of Life and Death," *Quality end-of-life care: the right of every Canadian* (Ottawa: The Committee, June 2000), http://www.parl.gc.ca/36/2/parlbus/commbus/senate/com-e/upda-e/rep-e/repfinjun00-e.htm (accessed February 3, 2003).

5. DK Heyland, JV Lavery, JE Tranmer, et al., The final days: an analysis of the dying experience in Ontario, *Annals of the Royal College of Physicians and Surgeons*, 2000;33:356–361; F Burge, B Lawson, G Johnston, Trends in the place of death of cancer patients, 1992–1997, *Canadian Medical Association Journal*, 2003;168:265–270.

6. A Lawlor, Pain control a right, not a luxury, group says, *Globe and Mail*, May 15, 2001.

7. PA Singer, DK Martin, M Kelner, Quality end-of-life care: patients' perspectives, *Journal of the American Medical Association*, 1999;281:163–168.

8. Anon., Decision-making for end of life care, *Members Dialogue*, College of Physicians and Surgeons of Ontario, November/December 2002, 5–9.

9. HM Chochinov, Dignity-conserving care: a new model for palliative care, *Journal of the American Medical Association*, 2002;287:2253–2260.

10. SUPPORT Principal Investigators, A controlled trial to improve care for seriously ill hospital patients, *Journal of the American Medical Association*, 1995;274:1591–1598.

11. EM Tayti, "Do not resuscitate" requests aren't always followed, *Toronto Star*, December 28, 2001.

12. NA Christakis, EB Lamont, Extent and determinants of error in doctors' prognoses in terminally ill patients: prospective cohort study, *British Medical Journal*, 2000;320:469–473.

13. H Robertson, We have lost the art of dying, *National Post*, October 21, 2002.

14. F Stone, A time for compassion, *Toronto Star*, April 6, 2000.

15. F Lowry, Does doctors' own fear of dying hinder palliative care? *Canadian Medical Association Journal*, 1997;157:301–302.

16. N MacDonald, Palliative care—an essential component of cancer control, *Canadian Medical Association Journal*, 1998;158:1709–1716.

17. E Bruera, CN Neumann, B Gagnon, et al., Edmonton regional palliative care program: impact on patterns of terminal cancer care, *Canadian Medical Association Journal*, 1999;161:290–293.

18. Inner City Health Project, *Program evaluation report* (Ottawa: The Project, 2002); Contact Inner City Health Office at 613-562-4500 for details.

19. DW Molloy, M Urbanyi, JR Horsman, et al., Two years experience with a comprehensive health care directive in a home for the aged, *Annals of the Royal College of Physicians and Surgeons of Canada*, 1992;25:433–436.

20. DW Molloy, GH Guyatt, R Russo, et al., Systematic implementation of an advance directive program in nursing homes: a randomized controlled trial, *Journal of the American Medical Association*, 2000;283:1437–1444.

21. CJ Ryan, MA Santucci, MC Gattuso, et al., Perceptions about advance directives by nurses in a community hospital, *Clinical Nurse Specialist*, 2001;15:246–252; P Angelos, C Johnston, Advance directive use among patients undergoing selected high-risk surgical procedures, *Quality Management in Health Care*, 1999;7(4):1–3.

22. LD Perry, D Nicholas, AE Molzahn, et al. Attitudes of dialysis patients and caregivers regarding advance directives, *Anna Journal*, 1995;22:457–463.

Chapter 5: A Tonic for Chronic Illness

1. C Hoffman, D Rice, HY Sung, Persons with chronic conditions: their prevalence and costs, *Journal of the American Medical Association*, 1996;276:1473–1479.

2. BG Druss, SC Marcus, M Olfson, et al., Comparing the national economic burden of five chronic conditions, *Health Affairs*, 2001;20(6):233–241.

3. HK Wolf, P Andreou, IR Bata, et al., Trends in the prevalence and treatment of hypertension in Halifax County from 1985 to 1995, *Canadian Medical Association Journal*, 1999;161:699–704; MR Joffres, P Ghadirian, JG Fodor, et al., Awareness, treatment, and control of hypertension in Canada, *American Journal of Hypertension*, 1997;10:1097–1102.

4. Vancouver Island Health Authority, *Diabetes Mellitus: frequency of investigations by physicians in British Columbia 1999–2000* (n.d.), http://cme.caphealth.org/PDFs/Diabetes.pdf (accessed December 20, 2003).

5. DE Schaubel, HI Morrison, M Desmeules, et al., End-stage renal disease in Canada: prevalence projections to 2005, *Canadian Medical Association Journal*, 1999;160:1557–1563.

6. AH Anis, LD Lynd, X Wang, et al., Double trouble: impact of inappropriate use of asthma medication on the use of health care resources, *Canadian Medical Association Journal*, 2001;164:625–631.

7. C Mellor, Uncontrolled asthma worse in Nova Scotia, *Halifax Mail Herald*, May 10, 2000.

8. B Hutchison, C Woodward, G Norman, et al., Provision of preventive care to unannounced

standardized patients, *Canadian Medical Association Journal*, 1998;158:185–193.

9. H Lee, D Garniss, R Oliver, et al., A community hospital-based heart failure program decreases readmission rates. Abstract for the meeting of the Society of General Internal Medicine, San Diego, May 2001; Vancouver/Richmond Health Board, *Evaluation of clinical paths for congestive heart failure patients: spanning the continuum of care* (Vancouver: Vancouver/Richmond Health Board, 2001).

10. Diabetes Control and Complications Trial Research Group, The effect of intensive treatment of diabetes on the development and progression of long-term complications in insulin dependent diabetes mellitus, *New England Journal of Medicine*, 1993;329:977–986; UK Prospective Diabetes Study Group, Intensive blood glucose control with sulphonylureas or insulin compared with conventional treatment and risk of complications in type 2 diabetes, *Lancet*, 1998;352:837–853.

11. MW Rich, V Beckham, C Wittenberg, et al., A multi-disciplinary intervention to prevent readmission of elderly patients with congestive heart failure, *New England Journal of Medicine*, 1995;333:1190–1195; L Blue, E Lang, JJV McMurray, et al., Randomised trial of specialist nurse intervention in heart failure, *British Medical Journal*, 2001;323:715–718; S Stewart, JE Marley, JD Horowitz, Effects of multidisciplinary, home-based intervention on unplanned readmissions and survival among patients with chronic congestive heart failure: a randomised controlled study, *Lancet*, 1999;354:1077–1083.

12. For more on the development of HMOs, see P Starr, *The social transformation of American medicine* (New York: Basic Books, 1982).

13. EH Wagner, N Sandhu, KM Newton, et al., Effect of improved glycemic control on health care costs and utilization, *Journal of the American Medical Association*, 2001;285:182–189.

14. Data from Canadian Institute for Health Information.

15. K Taggart, Co-ordinating discharge record lowers readmission, *Medical Post*, September 18, 2001.

16. For the early history of the Sault Ste. Marie Group Health Centre, see J Lomas, *First and foremost in community health centres: the centre in Sault Ste. Marie and the CHC alternative* (Toronto: University of Toronto Press, 1985).

17. JEF Hastings, FD Mott, A Barclay, et al., Prepaid group practice in Sault Ste. Marie, Ontario: Part I: Analysis of utilization records, *Medical Care*, 1973;11:91–103; FD Mott, JEF Hastings, A Barclay, Prepaid group practice in Sault Ste. Marie, Ontario: Part II: Evidence from the household survey, *Medical Care*, 1973;11:173–188; GH DeFriese, On paying the fiddler to change the tune: further evidence from Ontario regarding the impact of universal health insurance on the organization and patterns of medical practice, *Millbank Memorial Fund Quarterly*, 1975;53(2):117–148.

18. P Bragaglia, C Apostolon, T Wetzl, et al., The Health Promotion Initiative in Diabetes (HPID) outcomes management program at the Group Health Centre. Presentation to the Canadian Diabetes Association annual meeting, Edmonton, October 2001.

19. EH Wagner, LC Grothaus, N Sandhu, et al., Chronic care clinics for diabetes in primary care: a system-wide randomized trial, *Diabetes Care*, 2001;24:695–700.

20. D Fera, The diabetes group visit. Presentation to the Canadian Diabetes Association, Vancouver, October 2002.

21. SR Wilson, P Scamagas, DF German, et al., A controlled trial of two forms of self-management education for adults with asthma, *American Journal of Medicine*, 1993;94:564–576; A Lahdensuo, T Haahtela, J Herrala, et al., Randomised comparison of guided self-management and traditional treatment of asthma over one year, *British Medical Journal*, 1996;312:748–752; J Cote, DM Bowie, P Robichaud, et al., Evaluation of two different educational interventions for adult patients consulting with an acute asthma exacerbation, *American Journal of Respiratory and Critical Care Medicine*, 2001;163:1415–1419.
22. J-A Gillespie, Optimal asthma care, *Nursing BC*, December 2002, 21–23.
23. Anon., Asthma education and patient monitoring, *Canadian Medical Association Journal*, 1999;161(11 suppl):S15–18.
24. T Bodenheimer, K Lorig, H Holman, et al., Patient self-management of chronic disease in primary care, *Journal of the American Medical Association*, 2002;288:2469–2475.
25. Canadian Institute for Health Information: Dialysis patients older and sicker, September 18, 2002. http://secure.cihi.ca/cihiweb/dispPage.jsp?cw_page=media_18sep2002-e (accessed November 16, 2003).
26. DB Miller, et al., Use of a chronic care model to direct the care of persons with diabetes in the Capital Health Region of British Columbia, *Annals of the Royal College of Physicians and Surgeons*, 2002;35:495–498.
27. J Bourbeau, M Julien, F Maltais, et al., Reduction of hospital utilization in patients with chronic obstructive pulmonary disease, *Archives of Internal Medicine*, 2003;163:585–591.
28. J Cote, DM Bowie, P Robichaud, et al., Evaluation of two different educational interventions for adult patients consulting with an acute asthma exacerbation. *American Journal of Respiratory and Critical Care Medicine*, 2001;163:1415–1419.
29. SJ Katz, RC Kessler, E Lin, et al., Medication management of depression in the United States and Ontario, *Journal of General Internal Medicine*, 1998;13:77–85.
30. K Taggart, Hypertension higher in Canada than US, *Medical Post*, December 5, 2001.

Chapter 6: There's No Place Like Home

1. DL Rajacich, S Cameron, Preventing admissions of seniors into the emergency department, *Journal of Gerontological Nursing*, 1995;21:36–40.
2. CL McWilliam, M Stewart, J Sangster, et al., Work in progress: integrating physicians' services in the home, *Canadian Family Physician*, 2001;47:2502–2509; M Stewart, F Ellett, S Golding, et al., *Evaluation of an organization for integrating physician services in the home* (Ottawa: Canadian Health Services Research Foundation, 2002).
3. D Steinmetz, E Berkovits, H Edelstein, et al., Home intravenous antibiotic therapy programme, 1999, *Journal of Infection*, 2001;42:176–180.
4. AO Wai, L Frighetto, CA Marra, et al., Cost analysis of an adult outpatient parenteral

antibiotic therapy programme: a Canadian teaching hospital and Ministry of Health perspective, *Pharmacoeconomics*, 2000;18:451–457.

5. Canadian Institute for Health Information, Hospital Morbidity Database (accessed November 16, 2003).

6. M Lock, JG Ray, Higher neonatal morbidity after routine early hospital discharge: are we sending newborns home too early? *Canadian Medical Association Journal*, 1999;161:249–253; S Liu, SW Wen, D McMillan, et al., Increased neonatal readmission rate associated with decreased length of hospital stay at birth in Canada, *Canadian Journal of Public Health*, 2000;91:46–50.

7. KE Grullon, DA Grimes, The safety of early postpartum discharge: a review and critique, *Obstetrics and Gynecology*, 1997;90:860–865.

8. UR Kotagal, HD Atherton, R Eshell, et al., Safety of early discharge for Medicaid newborns, *Journal of the American Medical Association*, 1999;282:1150–1156.

9. R Walker, Alberta's newborn discharge speed top in Canada, *Medical Post*, January 26, 1999.

10. L Soderstrom, P Tousignant, T Kaufman, The health care cost effects of substituting home care for inpatient acute care: a review of the evidence, *Canadian Medical Association Journal*, 1999;160:1151–1155.

11. NE Mayo, S Wood-Dauphinee, R Cote, et al., There's no place like home: an evaluation of early supported discharge for stroke, *Stroke*, 2000;31:1016–1023.

12. M King, Comprehensive care management: a closer look, *New York Doctor*, June 1992.

13. http://www.onlok.org/stats.html (accessed May 16, 2003).

14. BA Christie, B Skinner, S Weatherill, What's new for the old, *Canadian Healthcare Manager*, October/November 1997, 23–29.

15. Inner City Health Project. *Program evaluation report* (Ottawa: The Project, 2002) (contact Inner City Health Office at 613-562-4500 for details).

16. LI Stein, MA Test, Alternative to mental hospital treatment: I. Conceptual model, treatment program, and clinical evaluation, *Archives of General Psychiatry*, 1980;37:392–397; BA Weisbrod, MA Test, LI Stein, Alternative to mental hospital treatment: II. Economic benefit-cost analysis, *Archives of General Psychiatry*, 1980;37:400–405. MA Test, LI Stein, Alternative to mental hospital treatment: III. Social cost, *Archives of General Psychiatry*, 1980;37:409–412.

17. HG Lafave, HR de Souza, GJ Gerber, Assertive community treatment for severe mental illness: a Canadian experience, *Psychiatric Services*, 1996;47:757–759.

18. M Hollander, A Tessaro, *Evaluation of the maintenance and preventive model of home care* (Victoria: Hollander Analytic Services, March 2001), http://www.hollanderanalytical.com/group/current-projects (accessed December 20, 2003).

19. N Hall, P De Beck, D Johnson, et al., Randomized trial of a health promotion program for frail elders, *Canadian Journal on Aging*, 1992;11:72–91.

20. AE Cuellar, JM Wiener, Can social insurance for long-term care work? The experience of Germany, *Health Affairs*, 2001;19:825.

21. J Tilly, JM Wiener, *Consumer-directed home and community services: policy issues* (Washington, DC: Urban Institute, January 2001), http://www.urban.org/url.cfm?ID=310065 (accessed December 20, 2003).

Chapter 7: Long-term Care

1. M Stuart, M Weinrich, Home- and community-based long-term care: lessons from Denmark, *Gerontologist*, 2001;41:474–480.
2. A Goldstein, Better than a nursing home? *Time*, August 13, 2001, 40–45; C Kauffman, Assisted living industry was hot in the '90s, then cooled, *Des Moines Register*, July 14, 2002.
3. L Reynolds, Who's caring for seniors? man's death prompts questions from daughter, *Winnipeg Free Press*, January 24, 2003.
4. W Armstrong, *Eldercare—on the auction block* (Edmonton: Alberta Chapter of the Consumers' Association of Canada, 2002).
5. L Campbell, V Doyle, E Gallagher, *The need for supportive living in BC: the case of the Capital Health Region* (Victoria: Capital Health Region, 2001).
6. G Bravo, M Charpentier, M-F Dubois, et al., Profile of residents in unlicensed homes for the aged in the Eastern Townships of Quebec, *Canadian Medical Association Journal*, 1998;159:143–148.
7. J Robinson, F Teplitsky, E Wong, et al., *Guide to supportive housing services for seniors in Toronto* (Toronto: Toronto District Health Council, 2001).
8. JP Hirdes, L Mitchell, G Ljunggren, International and regional variations in restraint use: implications for selecting benchmarks, *Canadian Journal of Quality in Health Care*, 1999;15:19–23.
9. S Morrison, 1 out of 3 patients restrained, *Hamilton Spectator*, August 7, 1999.
10. Ontario Hansard, November 1, 2002. http://hansardindex.ontla.on.ca/hansardespeaker/37-1/1099a-24.html (accessed November 16, 2003).
11. KS Dunn, The effect of physical restraints on fall rates in older adults who are institutionalized, *Journal of Gerontological Nursing*, 2001;27:40–48; R Magee, EC Hyatt, SB Hardin, et al., Use of restraints in extended care and nursing homes, *Journal of Gerontological Nursing*, 1993;19:31–39.
12. BS Rubin, AH Dube, EK Mitchell, Asphyxia deaths due to physical restraint: A case series, *Archives of Family Medicine*, 1993;2:405–408.
13. WR Proctor, JP Hirdes, Pain and cognitive status among nursing home residents in Canada, *Pain Research and Management*, 2001;6:119–125.
14. L Barder, L Slimmer, J LeSage, Depression and issues of control among elderly people in health care settings, *Journal of Advanced Nursing*, 1994;20:597–604.
15. E Cocco, M Gatti, A de Mendon, et al., A comparative study of stress and burnout among staff caregivers in nursing homes and acute geriatric wards, *International Journal of Geriatric Psychiatry*, 2003;18:78–85.
16. J Cohen-Mansfield, Turnover among nursing home staff: a review, *Nursing Management*, 1997;28(5):59–60,62,64.
17. WD Spector, HA Takada, Characteristics of nursing homes that affect resident outcomes, *Journal of Aging and Health*, 1991;3:427–454.
18. WH Thomas, *Life worth living: how someone you love can still enjoy life in a nursing home* (Acton, MA: VanderWyk and Burnham, 1996).

19. S Ransom, *Eden Alternative: the Texas project* (San Marcos: Texas Institute for Long-Term Care, Texas State University San Marcos, 2001).

20. MT Coleman, S Looney, J O'Brien, et al., The Eden Alternative: findings after 1 year of implementation, *Journals of Gerontology Series A: Biological Sciences and Medical Sciences*, 2002;57:M422–427.

21. P Schofield, Evaluating Snoezelen for relaxation within chronic pain management, *British Journal of Nursing*, 2002;11:812–821.

22. JC Chung, CK Lai, PM Chung, et al., Snoezelen for dementia, *Cochrane Database of Systematic Reviews*, 4:CD003152, 2002.

23. WJ Dahl, SJ Whiting, A Healey, et al., Increased stool frequency occurs when finely processed pea hull fiber is added to usual foods consumed by elderly long term care residents, *Journal of the American Dietitians Association*, 2003;103:1199–1202.

24. C Arnold, W Dahl, C Torgerson, et al., Prevalence of malnutrition in Saskatoon special care homes. Abstract from the annual meeting of the Canadian Society for Clinical Nutrition, Vancouver, April 24–26, 2003.

25. A Saletti, EY Lindgren, L Johansson, et al., Nutritional status according to mini nutritional assessment in an institutionalized elderly population in Sweden, *Gerontology*, 2000;46:1398–1145; C Compher, JN Kim, JG Bader, Nutritional requirements of an aging population with emphasis on subacute care patients, *American Academy of Clinical Nutritionists Clinical Issues*, 1998;9:441–450.

26. PA Gross, GV Quinnan, ME Weksler, et al., Relation of chronic disease and immune response to influenza vaccine in the elderly, *Vaccine*, 1989;7:303–308.

27. M Mallet, Refeeding syndrome, *Age and Ageing*, 2002;31:65–66.

28. C Harrington, D Zimmerman, SL Karon, et al., Nursing home staffing and its relationships to deficiencies, *Journal of Gerontology: Social Sciences*, 2000;55:S278–287

29. BR Przybylski, ED Dumont, ME Watkins, et al., Outcomes of physical and occupational therapy service in a nursing home setting, *Archives of Physical Medicine and Rehabilitation*, 1996;77:554–561.

30. O Intrator, NG Castle, V Mor, Facility characteristics associated with hospitalization of nursing home residents, *Medical Care*, 1999;37:228–237.

31. CM Stein, MR Griffin, JA Taylor, et al., Educational program for nursing home physicians and staff to reduce use of non-steroidal anti-inflammatory drugs among nursing home residents: a randomized controlled trial, *Medical Care*, 2001;39:436–445; I Schmidt, CB Claesson, B Westerholm, et al., The impact of regular multidisciplinary team interventions on psychotropic prescribing in Swedish nursing homes, *Journal of the American Geriatrics Society*, 1998;46:77–82.

32. BTB Chan, The declining comprehensiveness of primary care, *Canadian Medical Association Journal*, 2002;166:429–434.

33. Hamilton District Health Council, *Physician coverage for residents of long term care facilities* (Hamilton: Hamilton District Health Council, 2000).

34. WO Spitzer, DL Sackett, JC Sibley, et al., The Burlington randomized trial of the nurse practitioner, *New England Journal of Medicine*, 1974;290:251–256.

35. HW Chappell, D Murrell, Nursing home patients: liaison nurse visits influence recidivism, *Journal of Gerontological Nursing*, 1994;20(5):33–36; JB Burl, A Bonner, M Rao,

et al., Geriatric nurse practitioners in long-term care: demonstration of effectiveness in managed care, *Journal of the American Geriatrics Society*, 1998;46:506–510; A Joseph, C Boult, Managed primary care of nursing home residents, *Journal of the American Geriatrics Society*, 1998;46:1152–1156.

36. Canadian Institute for Health Information, *1999 hospital injury admissions report* (Ottawa: CIHI, 1999).

37. P Kannus, J Parkkari, S Niemi, et al., Prevention of hip fracture in elderly people with use of a hip protector, *New England Journal of Medicine*, 2000;343:1506–1513; G Meyer, A Warnke, R Bender, et al., Effect on hip fractures of increased use of hip protectors in nursing homes: cluster randomised controlled trial, *British Medicine Journal*, 2003;326:76–80.

Chapter 8: Prevention

1. MJ Stampfer, FB Hu, JE Manson, et al., Primary prevention of coronary heart disease in women through diet and lifestyle, *New England Journal of Medicine*, 2000;343:16–22.

2. FB Hu, JE Manson, MJ Stampfer, et al., Diet, lifestyle, and the risk of type 2 diabetes mellitus in women, *New England Journal of Medicine*, 2001;345:790–797.

3. Statistics Canada, *The Daily*, September 25, 2003. http://www.statcan.ca/Daily/English/030925/d030925c.htm (accessed November 16, 2003).

4. Organisation for Economic Co-operation and Development, *OECD health data 2003*, http://www.oecd.org/document/16/0,2340,en_2825_495642_2085200_1_1_1_1,00.html (accessed November 20, 2003).

5. J Chen, WJ Millar, Are recent cohorts healthier than their predecessors, *Health Reports*, 2000;11(4):9–23.

6. Canadian Cancer Society, Canadian cancer statistics, http://www.cancer.ca/vgn/images/portal/cit_776/437843niw_2002stats-en.pdf (accessed April 9, 2003).

7. Chen, ibid.

8. RE Anderson, The spread of the childhood obesity epidemic, *Canadian Medical Association Journal*, 2000;163:1461–1462.

9. Canadian Cancer Society, 2003 statistics, http://www.cancer.ca/vgn/images/portal/cit_776/61/38/56158640niw_stats_en.pdf (accessed September 15, 2003).

10. Statistics Canada, *The daily*, September 3, 2002, http://www.statcan.ca/Daily/English/030903/d030903a.htm (accessed September 15, 2003).

11. Federal/Provincial/Territorial Advisory Committee on Population Health, *Strategies for population health* (Ottawa: The Committee, 1994).

12. E Wood, MW Tyndall, PM Spittal, et al., Impact of supply-side policies for control of illicit drugs in the face of the AIDS and overdose epidemics: investigation of a massive heroin seizure, *Canadian Medical Association Journal*, 2003;168:165–169.

13. JF Anderson, Interpreting the relation between injection drug use and harm: a cautionary note, *Canadian Medical Association Journal*, 2000;162:1695–1696.

14. B Fischer, Prescriptions, power and politics: the turbulent history of methadone maintenance in Canada, *Journal of Public Health Policy*, 2000;21:187–210.
15. KL Sees, KL Delucchi, C Masson, et al., Methadone maintenance vs 180-day psychosocially enriched detoxification for treatment of opioid dependence: a randomized controlled trial, *Journal of the American Medical Association*, 2000;283:1303–1310; MJ Kreek, Methadone-related opioid agonist pharmacotherapy for heroin addiction: history, recent molecular and neurochemical research and future in mainstream medicine, *Annals of the New York Academy of Science*, 2000;909:186–216.
16. DR Gibson, NM Flynn, JJ McCarthy, Effectiveness of methadone treatment in reducing HIV risk behavior and HIV seroconversion among injecting drug users, *AIDS*, 1999;13:1807–1818.
17. For a copy of the Vancouver Agreement see: http://www.city.vancouver.bc.ca/commsvcs/planning/dtes/agreement.htm.
18. McCreary Centre Society, *No place to call home: a profile of street youth in British Columbia* (Burnaby, BC: McCreary Centre Society, 2001).
19. F Bula, Safe site still draws mixed reviews: unsanctioned injections continue in Vancouver, *Vancouver Sun*, July 7, 2003.
20. A O'Brien, F Bula, Injections site gets go ahead, *Vancouver Sun*, July 25, 2003.
21. T Jordan-Knox, Drug users file in as injection site opens, *Vancouver Sun*, September 22, 2003.
22. P Millson, Abstract session 5: Effective interventions, 1st International Conference on Inner City Health Improving the Health of the Disadvantaged, *Daily Briefings*, October 6, 2002.
23. M Tyndall, C Johnston, K Craib, et al., HIV incidence and mortality among injection drug users in Vancouver, 1996–2000, *Canadian Journal of Infectious Diseases*, 2001;11(Suppl B):69B.
24. JF Anderson, Client retention in BC methadone program, *Canadian Journal of Public Health*, in press.
25. S Cameron, The big fix, *Elm Street*, April 2003, 31–45.
26. R Taylor, A Rieger, Medicine as social science: Rudolf Virchow on the typhus epidemic in Upper Silesia, *International Journal of Health Services*, 1985;15:547–559.
27. S Josey, Report on methadone clinic backfires on Oshawa council, *Toronto Star*, March 3, 2003.
28. G Bush, State of the Union speech, January 28, 2003. http://www.whitehouse.gov/news/releases/2003/01/20030128-19.html (accessed April 12, 2003).
29. C Hamlin, S Sheard, Revolutions in public health: 1848, and 1998? *British Medical Journal*, 1998;317:587–591.
30. N Krieger, A-E Birn, A vision of social justice as the foundation of public health: commemorating 150 years of the spirit of 1848, *American Journal of Public Health*, 1998;88:1603–1606.
31. T Corocran, Never mind SARS, what's on your lawn? *National Post*, April 5, 2003.
32. CBC News Online, Walkerton report highlights (January 2002), http://www.cbc.ca/news/features/walkerton_report.html (accessed April 12, 2003).
33. M McQuigge, Water: a clear and present danger, *Canadian Journal of Public Health*, 2002;93:10–11.

34. Commission of Inquiry on the Blood System in Canada, *Final report* (Ottawa: The Commission, 1997).

35. P Sullivan, Canada's public health system beset by problems: report, *Canadian Medical Association Journal*, 2002;166:1319.

36. Public health on the ropes, *Canadian Medical Association Journal*, 2002;166:1245.

37. CD Naylor, *Learning from SARS: renewal of public health in Canada*, a report prepared for the federal minister of health, October 2003, http://www.hc-sc.gc.ca/english/ protection/warnings/sars/learning.html (accessed October 7, 2003).

38. JW Frank, Presentation to the Commission on the Future of Health Care in Canada, April 2002.

39. M Enserink, Clues to the animal origins of SARS, *Science*, 2003;300:1351.

40. A Uppaluri, M Naus, N Heywood, Effectiveness of the immigration medical surveillance program for tuberculosis in Ontario, *Canadian Journal of Public Health*, 2002;93:88–91; J Barber, Efforts against tuberculosis not good enough, *Globe and Mail*, April 24, 2002.

41. B Sibbald, One country, 13 immunization programs, *Canadian Medical Association Journal*, 2003;168:598; M Naus, DW Scheifele, Canada needs a national immunization program: an open letter to the Hon. Anne McLellan, federal minister of health, *Canadian Medical Association Journal*, 2003;168:567–568.

42. C Fragomeni, Halton spotlight on West Nile virus, *Hamilton Spectator*, March 7, 2003.

43. West Nile virus data from US Centers for Disease Control, http://www.cdc.gov/ ncidod/dvbid/westnile/index.htm, and Ontario Ministry of Health, http://www. health.gov. on.ca/english/public/program/pubhealth/westnile/wnv_mn.html (accessed September 15, 2003).

44. Auditor General for Canada, Annual Report 1999, from http://www.oag-bvg.gc.ca/domino/reports.nst/html/$File/9914ce.pdf (accessed September 15, 2003).

45. MS Tremblay, PT Katzmarzyk, JD Willms, Temporal trends in overweight and obesity in Canada, 1981–1996, *International Journal of Obesity*, 2002;26:538–543.

46. MS Tremblay, JD Willms, Is the Canadian childhood obesity epidemic related to physical inactivity? *International Journal of Obesity*, 2003;27:1100–1105.

47. Statistics Canada, *The Daily*, September 3, 2002, http://www.statcan.ca/Daily/English/ 030903/d030903a.htm (accessed September 15, 2003).

48. GreenHouse Gases Online, About carbon dioxide, http://www.ghgonline.org/about carbondioxide.htm (accessed October 6, 2003).

49. M McQuigge, Water: a clear and present danger, ibid.

50. C van Netten, R Pereira, R Brands, Drinking water supply and management practices in British Columbia, 1997–98. *Canadian Journal of Public Health*, 2002;93:14–18.

51. I Urquhart, Safe water: who's going to pay? *Toronto Star*, October 30, 2002.

52. City of Toronto, *Moving towards cleaner air: a progress report on the air quality strategy for the City of Toronto*, http://www.city.toronto.on.ca/environment/movingto_ report.pdf (accessed November 23, 2002).

53. G Guyatt, Newly developed drugs pose more dangers for patients, *Straight Goods*, October 28, 2002, http://goods.perfectvision.ca/ViewFeature.cfm?REF=704 (accessed November 23, 2002).

54. World Health Organization, *Impacts of antimicrobial growth promoter termination in Denmark: the WHO international review panel's evaluation of the termination of the use of antimicrobial growth promoters in Denmark*, November 2002, http://www.who.int/salmsurv/en/Expertsreportgrowthpromoterdenmark.pdf (accessed December 20, 2003).
55. R Harvey, A silent danger still unheeded, *Toronto Star*, April 13, 2003.
56. MR Anderson, S Peacock, J Nelson, et al., Worry about ovarian cancer risk and use of ovarian cancer screening by women at risk for ovarian cancer, *Gynecologic Oncology*, 2002;85:3–8.
57. Task Force on the Use and Provision of Medical Services (Chair Graham Scott), *1989–1990 annual report*. (Toronto: Ontario Ministry of Health, 1990).
58. HK Wolf, P Andreou, IR Bata, et al., Trends in the prevalence and treatment of hypertension in Halifax County from 1985 to 1995, *Canadian Medical Association Journal*, 1999;161:699–704; AH Anis, LD Lynd, X Wang, et al., Double trouble: impact of inappropriate use of asthma medication on the use of health care resources, *Canadian Medical Association Journal*, 2001;164:625–631.
59. A McColl, P Roderick, J Gabbay, et al., Performance indicators for primary care groups: an evidence based approach, *British Medical Journal*, 1998;317:1354–1360.
60. Canadian Public Health Association, *Survey of public health capacity in Canada* (report to the Deputy Ministers of Health from the Federal/Provincial/Territorial Advisory Committee on Population Health) (Ottawa: Canadian Public Health Association, 2001).
61. Ontario Medical Association, *Health policy report* (1998), http://www.oma.org/phealth/hpolrep/feb98.htm (accessed April 12, 2003).
62. T Hancock, Public policies for healthy cities: involving the policy makers, in BC Flynn, ed., *Proceedings of the inaugural conference of the World Health Organization Collaborating Center on Healthy Cities* (Indianapolis: Institute of Action Research for Community Health, Indiana School of Nursing, 1992).
63. TK Young, J Reading, B Elias, et al., Type 2 diabetes mellitus in Canada's First Nations: status of an epidemic in progress, *Canadian Medical Association Journal*, 2000;163:561–566.
64. FB Hu, JE Manson, MJ Stampfer, et al., Diet, lifestyle, and the risk of type 2 diabetes mellitus in women, *New England Journal of Medicine*, 2001;345:790–797.
65. LT Montour, AC Macaulay, N Adelson, Diabetes mellitus in Mohawks of Kahnawake, PQ: a clinical and epidemiological description, *Canadian Medical Association Journal*, 1989;141:549–552.
66. AC Macaulay, T Delormier, AM McComber, et al., Participatory research with Native community of Kahnawake creates innovative code of research ethics, *Canadian Journal of Public Health*, 1998;89:105–108.
67. AC Macaulay, G Paradis, L Potvin, et al., The Kahnawake Schools Diabetes Prevention Project: intervention, evaluation, and baseline results of a diabetes primary prevention program with a Native community in Canada, *Preventive Medicine*, 1997;26:779–790.
68. Comparison of the dietary intakes of two different groups of children (grades 4 to 6) before and after the Kahnawake Schools Diabetes Prevention Project. MM Jimenez, O Receveur, M Trifonopoulos, et al., *Journal of the American Diabetic Association*, 2003;103:1191–1194.

69. AG Walker, Mohawks take charge to prevent type 2 diabetes, *Medical Post*, January 15, 2002.
70. M Daniel, LW Green, SA Marion, et al., Effectiveness of community-directed diabetes prevention and control in a rural Aboriginal population in British Columbia, Canada, *Social Science and Medicine*, 1999;48:815–832.
71. H Markel, Diagnosis supersize, *New York Times*, March 24, 2002.
72. SA French, RW Jeffrey, M Story, Pricing and promotion effects on low-fat vending snack purchases: the CHIPS study, *American Journal of Public Health*, 2001;91:112–117.
73. WJ Rogan, JA Ware, Exposure to lead in children—how low is low enough, *New England Journal of Medicine*, 2003;348:1515–1516.
74. HJ Geiger, Community-oriented primary care: as path to community development, *American Journal of Public Health*, 2002;92:1713–1716.
75. Data from personal interviews with Carolyn Acker and Norman Rowen, January 21, 2003, and subsequent written material. For more information, see http://www.regentparkchc.org.
76. C Byrne, G Browne, J Roberts, et al., Surviving social assistance: 12-month prevalence of depression in sole-support parents receiving social assistance, *Canadian Medical Association Journal*, 1998;158:881–888.
77. G Browne, C Byrne, J Roberts, et al., When the bough breaks: provider-initiated comprehensive care is more effective and less expensive for sole-support parents on social assistance, *Social Science and Medicine*, 2001;53:1697–1710.
78. G Browne, J Roberts, A Gafni, et al., Economic evaluations of community-based care: lessons from twelve studies in Ontario, *Journal of Evaluation in Clinical Practice*, 1999;5:367–385.
79. LL Roos, D Traverse, D Turner, Delivering prevention: the role of public programs in delivering care to high-risk populations, *Medical Care*, 1999;37:JS264–278.
80. BJ Morrison, AJ Coldman, DA Boyes, et al., Forty years of repeated screening: the significance of carcinoma in situ, *British Journal of Cancer*, 1996;74:814–819.
81. G Rosen, *A history of public health* (New York: MD Publications, 1958).
82. J-P Fortin, G Groleau, V Lemieux, et al., *Intersectoral action for health* (Mimeo; Quebec City: Laval University, 1994).
83. T Citrin, Topics for our times: public health—community or commodity? reflections on healthy communities, *American Journal of Public Health*, 1998;88:351–352.
84. R Beaglehole, R Bonita, Public health at the crossroads: which way forward? *Lancet*, 1998;351:590–592.
85. MM Rachlis, Paper prepared for a workshop on intersectoral action and health sponsored by Health Promotion and Programs Branch Alberta/NWT/Nunavut Region, Health Canada, available from the author at http://www.michaelrachlis.com.
86. Quebec Public Health Act (updated September 1, 2003) http://publications duquebec.gouv.qc.ca/dynamicScarch/telecharge.php?type=2&file=/S_2_2/S2_2_A.html (accessed September 26, 2003); National Institute of Public Health Act http://publi cationsduquebec.gouv.qc.ca/dynamicSearch/telecharge.php?type=2&file=/I_13_1_1/I13 _1_1_A.html (accessed September 26, 2003).

87. "Primary health care is essential health care made universally accessible to individuals and families in the community by means acceptable to them, through their full participation and at a cost that the community and the country can afford. It forms an integral part of the country's health care system of which it is the nucleus . . . it is the first level of contact of individuals, the family and community within the national health system bringing health care as close as possible to where people live and work and constitutes the first element of a continuing health care process . . . Primary Health Care addresses the main health problems in the community, providing promotive, preventive, curative, supportive and rehabilitative services accordingly." (World Health Organization 1978)

Chapter 9: What's Up, Doc?

1. M-J Egan, Doctors turning away new patients, *London Free Press*, October 10, 2000.
2. College of Physicians and Surgeons of Ontario, http://www.cpso.on.ca/Doctor_Search/ez_srch.asp (accessed February 16, 2003).
3. A Derfel, Province short 500 GPs study says, *Montreal Gazette*, October 8, 1999.
4. J Ougler, Northern hospitals found cures for frail ERs, *Sault Star*, January 18, 2002.
5. A Smith, NS offers new rural MDs cash, *Halifax Herald*, February 3, 2001.
6. Canadian Institute for Health Information, Supply, distribution, and migration of Canadian physicians 2002, http://secure.cihi.ca/cihiweb/dispPage.jsp?cw_page=statistics_results_source_smdb_e (accessed November 12, 2003).
7. Ibid.
8. BTB Chan, *From perceived surplus to perceived shortage: what happened to Canada's physician workforce in the 1990s?* (Canadian Institute of Health Information, 2002), executive summary available at http://secure.cihi.ca/cihiweb/dispPage.jsp?cw_page=AR181_2000sum_e.
9. These data were compiled from a series of reports published by Health Canada and the Canadian Institute for Health Information.
10. G Maté, The death of the family doctor, *Globe and Mail*, December 26, 2000.
11. From OHIP fee schedule Web sites, http://www.gov.on.ca/health/english/program/ohip/sob/physserv/a_consul.pdf (accessed November 11, 2002).
12. OHIP fee schedules, http://www.gov.on.ca/health/english/program/ohip/sob/physserv/s_digest.pdf (accessed November 11, 2002).
13. OHIP fee schedules, http://www.gov.on.ca/health/english/program/ohip/sob/physserv/y_specia.pdf (accessed November 11, 2002).
14. OHIP fee schedules, http://www.gov.on.ca/health/english/program/ohip/sob/physserv/v_female.pdf (accessed November 11, 2002).
15. BTB Chan, The declining comprehensiveness of primary care, *Canadian Medical Association Journal*, 2002;166:429–434.
16. S Benady, CIHI comparison of nationwide earnings holds few surprises, *Medical Post*, February 18, 2003.

17. J Warick, Pediatricians seek changes to fee schedule, *Saskatoon Star Phoenix*, June 21, 2000.

18. M Ross, Geriatricians fed up with shortages, low pay, *Medical Post*, April 17, 2001.

19. M Blumberg, Medical society regulation of fees in Boston 1780–1820, *Journal of the History of Medicine and Allied Sciences*, 1984;39:303–331.

20. A Paul, Thirty-one MDs in "Fortune 500" of medicare billers, *Winnipeg Free Press*, December 16, 2002.

21. L Erlick, *Annual Report to District #11*, Ontario Medical Association, December 2002.

22. T Blackwell, Fee cuts will drive specialists away, doctors warn, *National Post*, September 11, 2001.

23. J Ayanian, P Hauptman, E Guadagnoli, et al., Knowledge and practices of generalist and specialist physicians regarding drug therapy for acute myocardial infarction, *New England Journal of Medicine*, 1994;331:1136–1142; M Ward, J Leigh, J Fries, Progression of functional disability in patients with rheumatoid arthritis: associations with rheumatology subspecialty care, *Archives of Internal Medicine*, 1993;153:2229–2237.

24. CH MacLean, R Louie, B Leake, et al., Quality of care in patients with rheumatoid arthritis, *Journal of the American Medical Association*, 2000;284:984–992.

25. DA Redelmeier, SH Tan, GL Booth, The treatment of unrelated disorders in patients with chronic medical diseases, *New England Journal of Medicine*, 1998;33:1516–1520.

26. JZ Ayanian, MB Landrum, E Guadagnoli, et al., Specialty of ambulatory care physicians and mortality among elderly patients after myocardial infarction, *New England Journal of Medicine*, 2002;347:1678–1686.

27. RM Richman, P Webster, AR Salgo, et al., A shared care approach in obesity management: the general practitioner and hospital-based service, *International Journal of Obesity and Related Metabolic Disorders*, 1996;20:413–419.

28. PI Hoskins, PM Fowlere, M Constantino, et al., Sharing the care of diabetic patients between hospital and general practitioners: does it work? *Diabetic Medicine*, 1993;10:81–86.

29. JB Burl, A Bonner, M Rao, Demonstration of the cost-effectiveness of a nurse practitioner/physician team in long-term care facilities, *HMO Practice*, 1994;8:157–161.

30. MW Rich, V Beckham, C Wittenberg, et al., A multi-disciplinary intervention to prevent readmission of elderly patients with congestive heart failure, *New England Journal of Medicine*, 1995;333:1190–1195; S Stewart, JE Marley, JD Horowitz, Effects of multidisciplinary, home-based intervention on unplanned readmissions and survival among patients with chronic congestive heart failure: a randomised controlled study, *Lancet*, 1999;354:1077–1083.

31. S Banerjee, K Shamash, AJD MacDonald, et al., Randomised trial of effect of intervention by psychogeriatric team on depression in frail elderly people at home, *British Medical Journal*, 1996;313:1058–1061.

32. HA Herinckx, RF Kinney, GN Clarke, et al., Assertive community treatment versus usual care in engaging and retaining clients with severe mental illness, *Psychiatric Services*, 1997;48:1297–1306.

33. M Ahlmen, M Sullivan, A Bjelle, Team versus non-team outpatient care in rheumatoid arthritis, *Arthritis and Rheumatism*, 1988;31:471–479.

34. J Shaffer, LF Wexler, Reducing low-density lipoprotein cholesterol levels in an ambulatory care system: results of a multidisciplinary collaborative practice lipid clinic compared with traditional physician-based care, *Archives of Internal Medicine*, 1995;155:2330–2335.

35. DD Meltzer, S Pels, WG Payne, et al., Decreasing amputation rates in patients with diabetes mellitus: an outcome study, *Journal of the American Podiatric Medical Association*, 2002;92:425–428.

36. N Bent, A Tennant, T Swift, et al., Team approach versus ad hoc health services for young people with physical disabilities: a retrospective cohort study, *Lancet*, 2002;360:1280–1286.

37. P Berger, Shifting attitudes/shifting power: breaching the barricades. Presentation to Frontiers in Life and Health: Pioneering Interprofessional Teamwork, Ontario Institute for Studies in Education, Toronto, November 7, 2001.

38. B Kermode-Scott, Physicians see MD role as team captain, *Medical Post*, May 28, 2002.

39. RM Leipzig, K Hyer, K Ek, et al., Attitudes toward working on interdisciplinary health care teams: a comparison by discipline, *Journal of the American Geriatrics Society*, 2002;50:1141–1148.

40. A Picard, Nurses angered by alleged operating room attack in Montreal, *Globe and Mail*, October 1, 2001.

41. N Kates, A-M Crustolo, L Nikolaou, et al., Providing psychiatric backup to family physicians by telephone, *Canadian Journal of Psychiatry*, 1997;42:955–959.

42. N Kates, M Craven, A-M Crustolo, et al., Integrating mental health services within primary care: a Canadian program, *General Hospital Psychiatry*, 1997;19:324–332.

43. N Kates, A-M Crustolo, S Farrar, et al., Mental health and nutrition: integrating specialists' services into primary care, *Canadian Family Physician*, 2002;48:1898–1903.

44. N Kates, A-M Crustolo, S Farrar, et al., Integrating mental health services into primary care: lessons learnt, *Families, Systems and Health*, 2001;19:5–12.

45. Canadian Psychiatric Association and the College of Family Physicians of Canada. Position paper on shared mental health care in Canada, April 5, 1997.

46. AG Walker, Shared care: bringing mental health treatment model to FP offices. *Family Practice*, May 17, 2000.

47. J Wasson, C Gaudette, F Whaley, Telephone care as a substitute for routine clinic follow-up, *Journal of the American Medical Association*, 1992;267:1788–1793.

48. V Lattimer, S George, F Thompson, et al., Safety and effectiveness of nurse telephone consultation in out of hours primary care: randomised trial, *British Medical Journal*, 1998;317:1054–1059.

49. L Hagan, G Garon, Info-Santé CLSC: un service efficace? *Canadian Journal of Public Health*, 1998;89:125–128.

50. GWS Scott, *Report of the fact finder on the issue of small/rural hospital emergency department physician service* (Toronto: Ontario Ministry of Health, Ontario Hospital Association, Ontario Medical Association, 1995).

51. AG Walker, PEI community has all its physicians on salary—and loving it, *Medical Post*, August 22, 2000.

Chapter 10: Canada on Drugs

1. S Scott, In the name of the daughter, *Chatelaine*, October 2002, 149–156; G Guyatt, Newly developed drugs pose more dangers for patients, *Straight Goods*, October 28, 2002.
2. SG Morgan, Issues for Canadian pharmaceutical policy, in *Canada health action: building on the legacy: papers commissioned by the National Forum on Health*, vol. 4 (Ottawa: Health Canada, 1998).
3. Canadian Institute for Health Information, *National health expenditures 2002*, http://secure.cihi.ca/cihiweb/dispPage.jsp?cw_page=media_18dec2002_2_e (accessed October 3, 2003).
4. Ibid.
5. J Lazarou, BH Pomeranz, PN Corey, Incidence of adverse drug reactions in hospitalized patients, *Journal of the American Medical Association*, 1998;279:1200–1205.
6. C Abraham, P Taylor, Drug reactions kill thousands: researchers, *Globe and Mail*, April 15, 1998.
7. JH Gurwitz, TS Field, LR Harrold, et al., Incidence and preventability of adverse drug events among older persons in the ambulatory setting, *Journal of the American Medical Association*, 2003;289:1107–1116.
8. TK Gandhi, SN Weingart, J Borus, et al., Adverse drug events in ambulatory care, *New England Journal of Medicine*, 2003;348:1556–1564.
9. CM Hohl, J Dankoff, A Colacone, et al., Polypharmacy, adverse drug-related events, and potential adverse drug interactions in elderly patients presenting to an emergency department, *Annals of Emergency Medicine*, 2001;38:666–671.
10. RM Tamblyn, PJ McLeod, M Abrahamowicz, et al., Questionable prescribing for elderly patients in Quebec, *Canadian Medical Association Journal*, 1994:150:1801–1809.
11. R Mickleburgh, Seniors overdrugged, study finds, *Globe and Mail*, June 1, 1994.
12. DB Hogan, NRC Campbell, R Crutcher, et al., Prescription of nonsteroidal anti-inflammatory drugs for elderly people in Alberta, *Canadian Medical Association Journal*, 1994;151:315–322.
13. HK Wolf, P Andreou, IR Bata, et al., Trends in the prevalence and treatment of hypertension in Halifax County from 1985 to 1995, *Canadian Medical Association Journal*, 1999;161:699–704.
14. WR Proctor, JP Hirdes, Pain and cognitive status among nursing home residents in Canada, *Pain Research & Management*, 2001;6(3):119–115.
15. Families USA. Profiting from pain: where prescription drug dollars go. http://www.familiesusa.org/site/DocServer/PPreport.pdf?docID=249 (accessed November 11, 2003).
16. GM Anderson, J Lexchin, Strategies for improving prescribing practice, *Canadian Medical Association Journal*, 1996;154:1013–1017.
17. R Moynihan, Who pays for the pizza? redefining the relationships between doctors and drug companies, 1: entanglement, *British Medical Journal*, 2003;326;1189–1192; RK Schwartz, SB Soumerai, J Avorn, Physician motivations for nonscientific drug prescribing, *Social Science and Medicine*, 1989;28:577–582.

18. D Ornish, Avoiding revascularization with lifestyle changes: the multicenter lifestyle demonstration project, *American Journal of Cardiology*, 1998;82(10B):72T–76T; LM Mynors-Wallis, DH Gath, AR Lloyd-Thomas, et al., Randomized controlled trial comparing problem solving treatment with amitryptiline and placebo for major depression in primary care, *British Medical Journal*, 1995;310:441–445.

19. KA Galt, Cost avoidance, acceptance, and outcomes associated with a pharmacotherapy consult clinic in a Veterans Affairs Medical Center, *Pharmacotherapy*, 1998;18:1103–1111; WDE Wells, Having a practice pharmacists can reduce prescribing costs, *British Medical Journal*, 1998;317:473.

20. J Robinson, *Prescription games: money, ego, and power inside the global pharmaceutical industry* (Toronto: McClelland & Stewart, 2001); A Derfel, "Free Trade Area of the Americas" experts: prescription drug costs will soar, *Montreal Gazette*, April 19, 2001.

21. J Lexchin, Prescriptions for profit, *Literary Review of Canada*, March 2001, 14–17; J Gerth, SG Stolberg, Drug firms reap profits on tax-based research, *New York Times*, April 23, 2000.

22. ALLHAT Officers and Coordinators for the ALLHAT Collaborative Research Group, Major outcomes in high-risk hypertensive patients randomized to angiotensin-converting enzyme inhibitor or calcium channel blocker vs diuretic, *Journal of the American Medical Association*, 2002;288:2981–2997.

23. S Morgan, *Price and productivity measurement in a pharmaceutical sector sub-market: the real cost of treating hypertension* (Vancouver: Centre for Health Services and Policy Research, University of British Columbia, 2001).

24. Patented Medicine Prices Review Board, *1998 annual report* (Ottawa: PMPPRB, 1999).

25. Food and Drug Administration, *List of drug products that have been withdrawn or removed from the market for reasons of safety or effectiveness* (1998), http://www.fda.gov/ohrms/dockets/98fr/100898b.txt.

26. RE Ariano, SA Zelenitsky, Ketorolac (Toradol): a marketing phenomenon, *Canadian Medical Association Journal*, 1993;148:1686–1688.

27. FE Silverstein, G Fiach, JL Goldstein, et al., Gastrointestinal toxicity with celecoxib versus nonsteroidal anti-inflammatory drugs for osteoarthritis and rheumatoid arthritis: the CLASS study, *Journal of the American Medical Association*, 2000;284:1247–1255.

28. C Bombardier, L Laine, A Reicin, et al., Comparison of upper gastrointestinal toxicity of refecoxib and naproxen in patients with rheumatoid arthritis, *New England Journal of Medicine*, 2000;343:1520–1528.

29. JM Wright, TL Perry, KL Bassett, et al., Reporting of 6-month vs. 12-month data in clinical trial of celecoxib, *Journal of the American Medical Association*, 2001;286:2398–2399.

30. P Juni, AWS Rutjes, PA Dieppe, Are selective COX 2 inhibitors superior to traditional non-steroidal anti-inflammatory drugs? *British Medical Journal*, 2002;324:1287–1288.

31. JP McCormack, R Rango, Digging for data from the COX-2 trials, *Canadian Medical Association Journal*, 2002;166:1649–1650.

32. M Mamdini, P Rochon, A Laupacis, et al., Initial patterns of use of COX-2 inhibitors by elderly patients in Ontario: findings and implications, *Canadian Medical Association Journal*, 2002;167:1125–1126.

33. H Fallding, Pricey drugs driving up health costs: Chomiak, *Winnipeg Free Press*, October 1, 2001.

34. PA Dieppe, SJ Frankel, B Toth, Is research into the treatment of osteoarthritis with non-steroidal anti-inflammatory drugs misdirected? *Lancet*, 1993;341:353–354.

35. D Henry, J Lexchin, The pharmaceutical industry as medicines provider, *Lancet*, 2002;360:1590–1595.

36. L Wayne, M Petersen, A muscular lobby rolls up its sleeves: drug makers gain remarkable access in Washington, *New York Times*, November 4, 2001.

37. G McGregor, Drug makers' war on generics: how powerful lobbyists help brand-name firms fight competition, *Ottawa Citizen*, October 14, 2001.

38. R Moynihan, Who pays for the pizza?

39. K Foss, Drug firms' freebies entice doctors, *Globe and Mail*, January 2, 2001.

40. M-M Chren, CS Landfield, Physicians' behavior and their interactions with drug companies, *Journal of the American Medical Association*, 1994;271:684–689.

41. HT Stelfox, G Chua, K O'Rourke, et al., Conflict of interest in the debate over calcium channel antagonists, *New England Journal of Medicine*, 1998;338:101–106.

42. Stelfox, ibid.

43. D Cauchon, FDA advisors tied to industry, *USA Today*, September 25, 2000.

44. D Nebenzahl, Do drug firms call the tune? *Montreal Gazette*, April 9, 2003.

45. D Wong-Rieger, Antiquated drug advertising laws need to get with the times, *Globe and Mail*, June 2, 2000.

46. B Mintzes, ML Barer, RL Kravitz, et al., Influence of direct to consumer pharmaceutical advertising and patients' requests on prescribing decisions: two site cross sectional survey, *British Medical Journal*, 2002;324:278–279; B Mintzes, Direct to consumer advertising is medicalising normal human experience, *British Medical Journal*, 2002;324:908–909.

47. A Picard, Charities "thank God" for drug firms' money, *Globe and Mail*, January 4, 2001.

48. D Hailey, Scientific harassment by pharmaceutical companies: time to stop, *Canadian Medical Association Journal*, 2000;162:212–213; M Munko, Drug makers harassing their critics: US Journal, *National Post*, July 9, 1999.

49. SM Frame, We're the only producers of Losec in the country, *Hamilton Spectator* (Letter), November 22, 1999.

50. S Morrison, Drugmaker can't stomach MD's findings, *Hamilton Spectator*, November 18, 1999.

51. J Lexchin, *A national pharmacare plan: combining efficiency with equity* (Ottawa: Canadian Centre for Policy Alternatives, 2001).

52. PK Whelton, LJ Appel, MA Espeland, et al., Sodium reduction and weight loss in the treatment of hypertension in older persons, *Journal of the American Medical Association*, 1998;279:839–846.

53. LM Mynors-Wallis, DH Gath, AR Lloyd-Thomas, et al., Randomized controlled trial comparing problem solving treatment with amitryptiline and placebo for major depression in primary care, *British Medical Journal*, 1995;310:441–445.

54. EL Hurwitz, H Morgenstern, P Harber, et al., A randomized trial of medical care with and without physical modalities for patients with low back pain. *Spine*,

2002;27:2193–2204; P Manga, D Angus, C Papdopoulos, et al., *Chiropractic management of low-back pain* (Richmond Hill, ON: Kenilworth, 1993); IBC Korthals de Bos, JL Hoving, MW Tulder, et al., Cost effectiveness of physiotherapy, manual therapy, and general practitioner care for neck pain: economic evaluation alongside a randomised controlled trial, *British Medical Journal*, 2003;326:911–916.

55. RD Feldman, N Campbell, P Larochelle, et al., 1999 Canadian recommendations for the management of hypertension, *Canadian Medical Association Journal*, 1999;161(12 suppl):S1–22; LA Leiter, D Abbott, NRC Campbell, et al., Recommendations on obesity and weight loss, *Canadian Medical Association Journal*, 1999;160(9 suppl):S7–12.

56. WR Proctor, JP Hirdes, Pain and cognitive status among nursing home residents in Canada, *Pain Research and Management*, 2001;6(3):119–125.

57. WA Katz, Musculoskeletal pain and its socioeconomic implications, *Clinical Rheumatology*, 2002;21(Suppl 1):S2–4.

58. N McManus, From quackery to respect, *Medical Post*, January 30, 2001.

59. JM Helms, *An overview of medical acupuncture*, http://www.medicalacupuncture.org/acu_info/articles/helmsarticle.html (accessed April 26, 2003).

60. DH Lein, JA Clelland, CJ Knowles, et al., Comparison of effects of transcutaneous electrical nerve stimulation of auricular, somatic, and the combination of auricular and somatic acupuncture points on experimental pain, *Physical Therapy*, 1989;69:671–678.

61. JG Lin, SJ Ho, JC Lin, Effect of acupuncture on cardiopulmonary function, *Chinese Medical Journal*, 1996;109:482–485.

62. R Haslam, A comparison of acupuncture with advice and exercises on the symptomatic treatment of osteoarthritis of the hip: a randomised controlled trial, *Acupuncture in Medicine*, 2001;19:19–26.

63. YH Lee, WC Lee, MT Chen, et al., Acupuncture in the treatment of renal colic, *Journal of Urology*, 1992;147:16–18.

64. K Taggart, Pain program benefits from MD's own experience, *Medical Post*, February 4, 2003.

65. S Morley, C Eccleston, A Williams, Systematic review and meta-analysis of randomized controlled trails of cognitive therapy and behaviour therapy for chronic pain in adults, excluding headache, *Pain*, 1999;80:1–13.

66. D Ornish, Avoiding revascularization with lifestyle changes, *American Journal of Cardiology*, 1998;82(10B):72T–76T; D Ornish, LW Scherwitz, JH Billings, et al., Intensive lifestyle changes for reversal of coronary heart disease, *New England Journal of Medicine*, 1998;280:2001–2007.

67. J Cleroux, RD Feldman, RJ Pterella, Recommendations on physician exercise training, *Canadian Medical Association Journal*, 1999;160(9 suppl):S21–28.

68. T Kavanagh, MG Myers, RS Baigrie, et al., Quality of life and cardiorespiratory function in chronic heart failure: effects of 12 months' aerobic training, *Heart*, 1996;76:42–49.

69. Ontario Cardiac Care Network, Project profile, http://www.ccn.on.ca/rehabpublic/ocrppprofile.html (accessed April 25, 2003).

70. N Lurie, EC Rich, DE Simpson, et al., Pharmaceutical representatives in academic medical centers: interaction with faculty and housestaff, *Journal of General Internal Medicine*, 1990;5:240–243.

71. G Guyatt, Academic medicine and the pharmaceutical industry: a cautionary tale, *Canadian Medical Association Journal*, 1994;150:951–953; J Breckenridge, Drug official made threat, doctor says, *Globe and Mail*, March 15, 1994.

72. BB McCormick, G Tomlinson, P Brill-Edwards, et al., Effect of restricting contact between pharmaceutical company representatives and internal medicine residents on posttraining attitudes and behavior, *Journal of the American Medical Association*, 2001;286:1994–1999.

73. A Chakrabati, WP Fleischer, D Staley, et al., Interactions of staff and residents with pharmaceutical industry: a survey of psychiatric training program policies, *Annals of the Royal College of Physicians and Surgeons of Canada*, 2002;35:541–546; Trainees need help facing drug industry, *Medical Post*, November 26, 2002.

74. J Lexchin, Enforcement of codes governing pharmaceutical promotion: what happens when companies breach advertising guidelines, *Canadian Medical Association Journal*, 1997;156:351–356; J Lexchin, PMAC code of marketing practices, *Canadian Medical Association Journal*, 1999;160:1556; K Foss, Drug firms' freebies entice doctors, *Globe and Mail*, January 2, 2001.

75. P Sullivan, Freebies to MDs targeted as drug industry starts publishing CME fines, *Canadian Medical Association Journal*, 2000;163:749.

76. RG Schlienger, TF Luscher, RA Schoenenberger, et al., Academic detailing improves identification and reporting of adverse drug events, *Pharmacy World and Science*, 1999;21(3):110–115.

77. SG Morgan, Issues for Canadian Pharmaceutical Policy, in *Canada Health Action: Building on the Legacy*. (Ottawa: Health Canada, 1998) 4:677–735.

78. JE Hux, MP Melady, D DeBoer, Confidential prescriber feedback and education to improve antibiotic use in primary care: a controlled trial, *Canadian Medical Association Journal*, 1999;161:388–392.

79. LA Allery, PA Owen, MR Robling, Why general practitioners and consultants change their clinical practice: a critical incident study, *British Medical Journal*, 1997;314:870–874.

80. R Gonzales, JF Steiner, A Lum, et al., Decreasing antibiotic use in ambulatory practice: impact of a multidimensional intervention on the treatment of uncomplicated acute bronchitis in adults, *Journal of the American Medical Association*, 1999;281:1512–1519; PA Gross, D Pujat, Implementing practice guidelines for appropriate antimicrobial usage: a systematic review, *Medical Care*, 2001;39(8 suppl. 2):55–69.

81. J Avorn, SB Soumerai, Improving drug therapy decisions through educational outreach: a randomized controlled trial of academically based "detailing," *New England Journal of Medicine*, 1983;308:1457–1463.

82. SB Soumerai, A Avorn, Economic and policy analysis of university-based drug "detailing," *Medical Care*, 1986;24:313–331.

83. B Nakagawa, The community drug utilization program. Presentation to the Second National Conference on Cost-Effective Drug Therapy, November 27–28, 1997, Toronto.

84. J Bajcar, R Vaillancourt, Integrated delivery of pharmaceutical care in family practice: a case example, *Pharmacy Connection*, Sept/Oct 1996, 26–33.

85. Personal communication with Stan Rice, acting CEO Five Hills Regional Health Authority. November 6, 2002.
86. R Cooperstock, P Parnell, Research on psychotropic drug use: a review of findings and methods, *Social Science and Medicine*, 1982;16:1180.
87. R Lagnaoui, B Begaud, N Moore, et al., Benzodiazepine use and risk of dementia: a nested case-control study, *Journal of Clinical Epidemiology*, 2002;55:314–318.
88. MT Smith, ML Perlis, A Park, et al., Comparative meta-analysis of pharmacotherapy and behavior therapy for persistent insomnia, *American Journal of Psychiatry*, 2002;159:5–11.
89. DA Charney, AM Paraherakis, KJ Gill, The treatment of sedative-hypnotic dependence: evaluating clinical predictors of outcome, *Journal of Clinical Psychiatry*, 2000;61:190–195.
90. JM Borel, KL Rascati, Effect of an automated, nursing unit-based drug-dispensing device on medication errors, *American Journal of Health-System Pharmacy*, 1995;52:1875–1879.
91. C Meyers, Barcode technology makes good medication system, *ABC News*, June 26, 2002, http://abclocal.go.com/ktrk/health/62602_health_barcode.html.
92. PL Doering, WL Russell, WC McCormick, et al., Therapeutic substitution in the health maintenance organization outpatient environment, *Drug Intelligence and Clinical Pharmacy*, 1988;22:125–130.
93. M Maclure, TM Potashnik, What is direct evidence-based policy making? experience from the drug benefits program for seniors in British Columbia, *Canadian Journal on Aging*, 1997;16(suppl 1):132–146.
94. Personal communication with BC Ministry of Health, March 3, 2000.
95. S Schneeweiss, AM Walker, RJ Glynn, et al., Outcomes of reference pricing for angiotensin-converting-enzyme inhibitors, *New England Journal of Medicine*, 2002;346:822–829.
96. M Cardwell, Quebec drug plan backfires, *Medical Post*, April 13, 1999.
97. SB Soumerai, D Ross-Degnan, J Avorn, et al., Effects of Medicaid drug-payment limits on admission to hospitals and nursing homes, *New England Journal of Medicine*, 1991;325:1072–1077.

Chapter 11: Waiting for This, Waiting for That

1. A Santin, Woman trapped in surgery nightmare, *Winnipeg Free Press*, February 12, 2003.
2. RJ Blendon, C Schoen, C DesRoches, et al., Common concerns amid diverse systems: health care experiences in five countries, *Health Affairs*, 2003;22:106–121.
3. Conference Board of Canada, Canadians' values and attitudes on Canada's health-care system: an analysis of survey results, *Ontario Medical Review*, November 2000, 30–48.
4. P McDonald, S Shortt, C Sanmartin, et al., *Waiting lists and waiting times for health care in Canada: more management!! more money??* (Ottawa: Health Canada, July 1998);

C Sanmartin, SED Shortt, ML Barer, et al., Waiting for medical services in Canada: lots of heat, little light, *Canadian Medical Association Journal*, 2000;162:1305–1310.

5. CJ Wright, G Wright, K Chambers, et al., Evaluation of indications for and outcomes of elective surgery, *Canadian Medical Association Journal*, 2002;167:461–466.

6. Canadian Institute for Health Information, *Health care in Canada 2002*, http://www.cihi.ca.

7. P McDonald, S Shortt, C Sanmartin, et al., ibid.

8. Canadian Institute for Health Information, *Health care in Canada 2002*.

9. S Lewis, ML Barer, C Sanmartin, et al., Ending waiting-list mismanagement: principles and practice, *Canadian Medical Association Journal*, 2000;162:1297–1300.

10. A Skelly, Long knee replacement waits permanently lower function, *Medical Post*, February 18, 2003.

11. S Yusuf, D Zucker, P Peduzzi, et al., Effect of coronary artery bypass graft surgery on survival: overview of 10-year results from randomised trials by the Coronary Artery Bypass Graft Trialists Collaboration, *Lancet*, 1994;344:563–570.

12. CD Morgan, K Sykora, CD Naylor, Analysis of deaths while waiting for cardiac surgery among 29,293 consecutive patients in Ontario, Canada, *Heart*, 1998;79:345–349.

13. CD Naylor, JP Szalai, M Katic, Benchmarking the vital risk of waiting for coronary artery bypass surgery in Ontario, *Canadian Medical Association Journal*, 2000;162:775–779.

14. R Sainsbury, C Johnston, B Haward, Effect on survival of delays in referral of patients with breast-cancer symptoms: a retrospective analysis, *Lancet*, 1999;353:1132–1135; O Vujovic, F Perera, AR Dar, Does delay in breast irradiation following conservative breast surgery in node-negative breast cancer patients have an impact on risk of recurrence? *International Journal of Radiation Oncology, Biology, Physics*, 1998;40:869–874.

15. MA Richards, AM Westcombe, SB Love, et al., Influence of delay on survival in patients with breast cancer: a systematic review, *Lancet*, 1999;353:1119–1126.

16. Quebec medicare challenge reaches top court: patient wants to pay for surgery, province violating his rights, he says, *Toronto Star*, May 9, 2003.

17. D Smith, Market-based reforms are the only real health guarantee, *Calgary Herald*, May 3, 2003.

18. J McGurran, T Noseworthy, Improving the management of waiting lists for elective services: public perspectives on proposed solutions, *Hospital Quarterly*, spring 2002, 28–32.

19. JST Barkun, Waiting lists for surgery, *Canadian Journal of Surgery*, 2002;45:328–329.

20. M Murray, DM Berwick, Advanced access: reducing waiting and delays in primary care, *Journal of the American Medical Association*, 2003;289:1035–1040; M Murray, T Bodenheimer, D Rittenhouse, et al., Improving timely access to primary care: case studies of the advanced access model, *Journal of the American Medical Association*, 2003;289:1042–1046.

21. Ibid.

22. N Kates, A-M Crustolo, S Farrar, et al., Mental health care and nutrition: integrating specialist services into primary care, *Canadian Family Physician*, 2002;48:1898–1903.

23. D Kosub, The new family practice, *Medical Post*, January 28, 2003.

24. TC Douglas, We must go forward, in *Medicare, the decisive year*, ed. L Soderstrom (Ottawa: Canadian Centre for Policy Alternatives, 1984).
25. IA Olivotto, MJ Borugian, L Kan, et al., Improved time to diagnosis after an abnormal screening mammogram, *Canadian Journal of Public Health*, 2001;92:366–371.
26. P Rasuli, Breast cancer diagnosis: what are we waiting for? *Canadian Medical Association Journal*, 2001;165:303–304.
27. From the Case Management Society of America, http://www.cmsa.org.
28. M Wente, Buy your own doctor, *Globe and Mail*, June 17, 2003.
29. H Buhang, Long waiting lists in hospitals, *British Medical Journal*, 2002;324:252–253.
30. Cambie Surgical Corporation, http://www.csc-surgery.com/services.html.
31. W Flemons, Disease focused quality improvement methods to change clinical practice (n.d.), http://www.crha-health.ab.ca/qihi/qi/resources/qiforum2002/a3b3_flemons.pdf (accessed June 23, 2003).
32. MM Rachlis, J Olak, CD Naylor, The vital risk of delayed coronary surgery: lessons from the randomized trials, *Iatrogenics*, 1991;1:103–111.
33. Canadian Care Network of Ontario, Outcomes of coronary artery bypass surgery in Ontario (2002), http://www.ccn.on.ca/access/outcome1.html (accessed June 25, 2003).
34. S Lewis, WRC Blundell, R Cashin, et al., Striking a Balance Working Group synthesis report, in The National Forum on Health, *Canada health action: building on the legacy*, vol. 2 (Ottawa: National Forum on Health, 1997).
35. H Scully, MA Vimr, N Jutte, et al., Planning for cardiac surgical services: advice from an Ontario consensus panel, for the Consensus Panel on Cardiac Surgical Services in Ontario and the Steering Committee of the Cardiac Care Network of Ontario, *Canadian Journal of Cardiology*, 2000;16:765–775.
36. RJ Novick, SA Fox, LW Stitt, et al., Effect of off-pump coronary artery bypass grafting on risk-adjusted and cumulative sum failure outcomes after coronary artery surgery, *Journal of Cardiac Surgery*, 2002;17:520–528.
37. JV Tu, CD Naylor, Coronary artery bypass mortality rates in Ontario: a Canadian approach to quality assurance in cardiac surgery (Steering Committee of the Provincial Adult Cardiac Care Network of Ontario), *Circulation*, 1996;94:2429–2433.
38. S Gallivan, M Udey, T Treasure, et al., Booked inpatient admissions and hospital capacity: mathematical modelling study, *British Medical Journal*, 2002;324:280–282.
39. D Light, Betrayal by the surgeons, *Lancet*, 1996;347:812–813.
40. W Hilliard, Wait times reduced for CT scans, *St. John's Telegram*, March 15, 2002.
41. M Robson, Heart surgery overhaul, *Winnipeg Free Press*, August 19, 2003.

Chapter 12: Beware of Snake Oil

1. S Woolhandler, T Campbell, DU Himmelstein, Costs of health care administration in the United States and Canada, *New England Journal of Medicine*, 2003;349:768–775.
2. See MM Rachlis, C Kushner, *Strong medicine: how to save Canada's health care system*, chapter 6 for more details on the user fee debate.

3. RG Beck, JM Horne, Study of user charges in Saskatchewan 1968–1971, in *User charges for health services* (Toronto: Ontario Council of Health, 1979).

4. RH Brook, JE Ware, WH Rogers, et al., Does free care improve adults' health? *New England Journal of Medicine*, 1983;309:1426–1434.

5. AL Siu, FA Sonnenberg, WG Manning, et al., Inappropriate use of hospitals in a randomized trial of health insurance plans, *New England Journal of Medicine*, 1986;315:1259–1266; B Foxman, RB Valdez, KN Lohr, et al., The effect of cost sharing on the use of antibiotics in ambulatory care: results from a population-based randomized controlled trial, *Journal of Chronic Diseases*, 1987;40:429–437.

6. P Clarke, User fees: experts call them failed idea, *Medical Post*, November 19, 2002.

7. S Elofsson, A-L Unden, I Krakau, Patient charges: a hindrance to financially and psychosocially disadvantaged groups seeking care, *Social Science and Medicine*, 1998;46:1375–1380; R Andersen, B Smedby, D Vagero, Cost containment, solidarity and cautious experimentation: Swedish dilemmas, *Social Science and Medicine*, 2001;52:1195–1204.

8. P Clarke, User fees.

9. RG Evans, ML Barer, GL Stoddart, User fees for health care: why a bad idea keeps coming back, *Canadian Journal on Aging*, 1995;360:360–390.

10. Romanow remedies find wide support, *Toronto Star*, December 6, 2002.

11. RG Evans, *Strained mercy: the economics of Canadian health care* (Toronto: Butterworths, 1984).

12. S Rice, Lessons Learned from De-privatization: A submission to the Commission on the Future of Health Care in Canada, March 4, 2002.

13. PJ Devereaux, PTL Choi, C Lacchetti, et al., A systematic review and meta-analysis of studies comparing mortality rates of private for-profit and private not-for-profit hospitals, *Canadian Medical Association Journal*, 2002;166:1399–1406.

14. LH Aiken, SP Clarke, DM Sloane, et al., Hospital nurse staffing and patient mortality, nurse burnout, and job dissatisfaction, *Journal of the American Medical Association*, 2002;288;1987–1993.

15. PJ Devereaux, HJ Schunemann, et al., Comparison of mortality between private for-profit and private not-for-profit hemodialysis centers: a systematic review and meta analysis, *Journal of the American Medical Association*, 2002;288:2449–2457.

16. MM Rachlis, The hidden costs of privatization: an international comparison of community and continuing care, in *Without foundation: how medicare is undermined by gaps and privatization in community and continuing care*, ed. M Cohen, N Pollak (Vancouver: Canadian Centre for Policy Alternatives, 2000).

17. E Shapiro, RB Tate, Monitoring the outcomes of quality of care in nursing homes using administrative data, *Canadian Journal of Aging*, 1995;14:755–768.

18. MM Rachlis, The hidden costs of privatization, ibid.

19. DU Himmelstein, S Woolhandler, I Hellander, et al., Quality of care in investor-owned vs. not-for-profit HMOs, *Journal of the American Medical Association*, 1999; 282:159–163.

20. S Woolhandler, DU Himmelstein, Costs of care and administration at for-profit and other hospitals in the United States, *New England Journal of Medicine*, 1997;336:769–774.

21. EM Silverman, J Skinner, E Fisher, The association between for-profit hospital ownership and increased Medicare spending, *New England Journal of Medicine*, 1999;341:420–426.

22. MM Hasan, Let's end the nonprofit charade, *New England Journal of Medicine*, 1996;334:1055–1057; C Leslie, The private clinic debate, *Medical Post*, May 9, 2000; RG Evans, ML Barer, S Lewis, et al., *Private highway, one-way street: the deklein and fall of Canadian medicare?* (Vancouver: Centre for Health Services and Policy Research, University of British Columbia, 2000).

23. D Brinkerhoff, Columbia/HCA in tentative settlement with US, Reuters News Agency, May 18, 2000; R Pear, US recommending strict new rules at nursing homes, *New York Times*, July 23, 2000.

24. J Johnson, How will international trade agreements affect Canadian health care? Discussion paper 22, Royal Commission Health Care, http://www.hc-sc.gc.ca/English/pdf/romanow/pdfs/22_Johnson_E.pdf (accessed November 4, 2002); M Rachlis, *A review of the Alberta private hospital proposal* (Caledon Institute for Social Policy, March 2000).

25. Ontario Provincial Auditor, *Annual report 1996*, http://www.gov.on.ca/opa/english/r96t.htm (accessed December 28, 2002).

26. AM Pollock, J Shaoul, N Vickers, Private finance and "value for money" in NHS hospitals: a policy in search of a rationale, *British Medical Journal*, 2002;324:1205–1209.

27. Ibid.

28. R Smith, PFI: perfidious financial idiocy, *British Medical Journal*, 1999;319:2–3.

29. NS Tories dump P3 schools program, *Halifax Daily News*, June 23, 2000.

30. Pastor of medicare founder using life savings for health, *National Post*, May 5, 2003.

31. J Lexchin, A national pharmacare plan: combining efficiency and equity, Canadian Centre for Policy Alternatives, Ottawa, March, 2001.

32. R Deber, Health care services: public, not-for-profit, or private? Discussion paper #17, Royal Commission on the Future of Health Care, August 2002, http://www.hc-sc.gc.ca/english/pdf/romanow/pdfs/17_Deber_E.pdf (accessed November 4, 2002).

33. J Banaszak-Holl, S Allen, V Mor, et al., Organizational characteristics associated with agency position in community care networks, *Journal of Health & Social Behavior*, 1998;39(4):368–385.

34. N Wolff, BA Weisbrod, EJ Bird, The supply of volunteer labor: the case of hospitals, *Nonprofit Management and Leadership*, 1993:4(1):23–45.

35. M Rachlis, The Hidden Costs of Privatization, ibid.

36. Canadian Institute of Health Information, *Health care in Canada 2003*, http://www.cihi.ca.

Chapter 13: Re-engineering for Excellence

1. For example:, Vets getting shorted on care? http://www.CBSNews.com/stories/2003/03/04/health/printable542658.shtml (accessed December 20, 2003).
2. Veterans Administration, *VHA/DOD guidelines for management of patients with diabetes mellitus*, http://www.oqp.med.va.gov/cpg/DM/P/DMtechmanual.htm (accessed July 24, 2003).
3. US Department of Veterans Affairs, *Vanguard*, November/December 2002, http://www.va.gov/pubaff/vanguard/novdec02vg.pdf (accessed July 25, 2003).
4. M Weinstock, Paths to recovery, *Government Executive*, September 2001, http://www.govexec.com/features/0901/0901s7.htm (accessed July 25, 2003); DP Stevens, GJ Holland, KW Kizer, Results of a nationwide Veterans Affairs initiative to align graduate medical education and patient care, *Journal of the American Medical Association*, 2001;286;1061–1066.
5. Lessons from the VA transformation: a case study, *Transition Watch*, 2000;3(3):1–4, http://www.va.gov/hsrd/publications/internal/Spring00tw.pdf (accessed July 25, 2003).
6. K Kizer, Reinventing government-provided health care: the "new VA" (Philadelphia: Leonard David Institute of Health Economics, 1999), http://www.upenn.edu/ldi/kizer.html (accessed July 25, 2003).
7. AK Jha, JB Perlin, K Kizer, et al., Effect of the transformation of the Veterans Affairs health care system on the quality of care, *New England Journal of Medicine*, 2003;348:2218–2227; CM Ashton, J Souchek, NJ Petersen, et al., Hospital use and survival among Veterans Affairs beneficiaries. *New England Journal of Medicine*. 2003;349:1637–1646.
8. S Jencks, The right care, *New England Journal of Medicine*, 2003;348:2251–2252.
9. National Health Service, *The National Primary Care Collaborative: the first two years*. (London: NHS, 2002).
10. Ibid.
11. OECD Statistics, http://www.oecd.org/EN/statistics/0,,EN-statistics-12-nodirectorate-no-1-no-12-no-no-2,00.html (accessed December 31, 2002).
12. Secretary of State for Health, *The NHS plan: a plan for investment, a plan for reform* (London: HMSO, 2000), http://www.doh.gov.uk/nhsplan/foreword.htm (accessed July 9, 2003).
13. NHS Modernisation Agency, http://www.modern.nhs.nhs.uk/scripts/default.asp?site_id=43&id=9574 (accessed July 28, 2003).
14. NHS Modernisation Agency, *Annual review 2002–2003*, http://www.modern.nhs.uk/home/11935/MAAnnualreview0203.pdf (accessed July 28, 2003).
15. NHS Modernisation Agency, Emergency Services Collaborative, See & treat for minors and majors, http://www.modern.nhs.uk/scripts/default.asp?site_id=35&id=11913 (accessed July 28, 2003).
16. National Primary Care Collaborative, *Bulletin*, April 2003, http://www.npdt.org/15/April%2003%20Bulletin.pdf (accessed July 28, 2003).
17. National Health Service, *The National Primary Care Collaborative: the first two years*.

18. H Tunstall-Pedoe, K Kuulasmaa, M Mahonen, et al., Contribution of trends in survival and coronary-event rates to changes in coronary heart disease mortality: 10-year results from 37 WHO MONICA project populations, *Lancet*, 1999;353:1547–1557.
19. National Primary Care Collaborative, *Bulletin*, April 2003.
20. A Guilland, NHS staff cheat to hit government targets, MBPS say, *British Medical Journal*, 2003;327:179.
21. C White, Next stage of NHS reforms come under fire, *British Medical Journal*, 2003;327:380.

Chapter 14: A Canadian Agenda for Excellence

1. M Leacche, M Carrier, D Bouchard, et al., Is side bite clamping a risk factor for neurological complications in off-pump surgery? Paper presented at the Canadian Cardiovascular Congress Halifax, October, 2001, http://www.ccs.ca/society/congress2001/abstracts/abs/a325.htm (accessed August 12, 2003).
2. J Reimer-Kent, From theory to practice: preventing pain after cardiac surgery, *American Journal of Critical Care*, 2003;12:136–143.
3. H Branswell, Dialysis during sleep helps kidney patients maintain healthy hearts, Canadian Press Newswire, June 6, 2002.
4. A Pierratos, M Ouwendyk, R Francoeur, et al., Slow nocturnal home hemodialysis, *Dialysis & Transplantation*, 1995;24:557, http://www.eneph.com/feature_archive/ hemodialysis/v24n10p557.html (accessed August 12, 2003); CM Kjellstrand, T Ing, Daily hemodialysis: history and revival of a superior dialysis method, *Therapy Overview*, http://www.aksys.com/ therapy/superior_method.asp (accessed August 12, 2003).
5. CT Chan, JS Floras, JA Miller, et al., Regression of left ventricular hypertrophy after conversion to nocturnal hemodialysis, *Kidney International*, 2002;61:2235–2239.
6. B Ryan, NC Gross, The diffusion of hybrid seed corn in two Iowa communities, *Rural Sociology*, 1943;8:15–24; see also W Tsang-Kosma, Rogers' diffusion and adoption research: what does it have to do with instructional technology? http://www.gsu.edu/ ~mstswh/courses/it7000/papers/rogers'.htm (accessed August 13, 2003).
7. M Gladwell, *The tipping point: how little things can make a big difference* (Boston: Little, Brown, 2000).
8. EM Rogers, Diffusion of innovations, 4th ed. (New York: Free Press, 1995).
9. B Evanson, Could you run that past me again, doctor? *National Post*, October 2, 2000.
10. II Holman, K Lorig, Patients as partners in managing chronic disease: partnership is a prerequisite for effective and efficient health care. *British Medical Journal*, 2000;320:526–527.
11. Institute of Medicine, *Crossing the quality chasm: a new health system for the 21st century* (Washington: National Academy Press, 2001).
12. MP Hurtado, EK Swift, JM Corrigan, eds., Committee on the National Quality Report on Health Care Delivery, Board on Health Care Services, *Envisioning the national health care quality report* (Washington: National Academy Press, 2000).

13. CH Braddock, KA Edwards, NM Hasenberg, et al., Informed decision making in outpatient practice: time to get back to basics, *Journal of the American Medical Association*, 1999;282:2313–2320.

14. ADM Kennedy, MJ Sculpher, A Coulter, et al., Effects of decision aids for menorrhagia on treatment choices, health outcomes, and costs: a randomized controlled trial, *Journal of the American Medical Association*, 2002;288:2701–2708.

15. Ottawa Health Research Institute, Annette O'Connor, http://www.ohri.ca/profiles/o'conner_summ.asp (accessed August 11, 2003).

16. AM O'Connor, D Stacey, V Entwistle, et al., Decision aids for people facing health treatment or screening decisions, *Cochrane Library*, 4 (2003), http://www.cochrane.org/ cochrane/revabstr/AB001431.htm (accessed August 10, 2003).

17. GB Hickson, EW Clayton, PB Githens, et al., Factors that prompted families to file medical malpractice claims following perinatal injuries, *Journal of the American Medical Association*, 1992;267:1359–1363.

18. HB Beckman, RM Frankel, The effect of physician behavior on the collection of data, *Annals of Internal Medicine*, 1984;101:692–696.

19. MK Marvel, RM Epstein, K Flowers, et al., Soliciting the patient's agenda: have we improved? *Journal of the American Medical Association*, 1999;281:283–287.

20. D Coulter, A new-born perspective, *Edmonton Journal*, May 4, 2000.

21. J Poulson, Bitter pills to follow, *New England Journal of Medicine*, 1998;338:1844–1846.

22. A Fadiman, *The spirit catches you and you fall down: a Hmong child, her American doctors, and the collision of two cultures* (New York: Farrar, Straus and Giroux, 1997).

23. A Kleinman, *The illness narratives: suffering, healing, and the human condition* (New York: Basic Books, 1988).

24. S Sontag, *Illnesses as metaphor* (New York: Farrar, Straus & Giroux, 1978).

25. For example, see L Payer, *Medicine and culture: international differences, outcomes, and values*, http://www.healthcareland.com/medculture.htm (accessed August 11, 2003).

26. Canadian Nursing Advisory Committee, *Our health, our future: creating quality workplaces for Canadian nurses* (Ottawa: Advisory Committee on Health Human Resources, 2002), http://www.hc-sc.gc.ca/english/pdf/Office-of-NursingPolicy.pdf (accessed May 17, 2003).

27. Canadian Institute of Health Information, Canada's health care providers (2002), http://www.cihi.ca.

28. LH Aiken, SP Clarke, DM Slaone, Nurses' reports on hospital care in five countries, *Health Affairs*, 2001;20(3):43–53.

29. P Drucker, *Post-capitalist society* (New York: HarperCollins, 1993).

30. Nursing burnout and patient safety, *Journal of the American Medical Association*, 2003;289:549–550.

31. Canadian Institute for Health Information. Canadian health care providers, http://secure.cihi.ca/cihiweb/dispPage.jsp?cw_page=AR_35_E (accessed November 17, 2003).

32. L Marr, Nursing grads see no future in Canada, *Hamilton Spectator*, April 9, 1996.

33. P Orwen, Nurses scramble to find new careers, *Toronto Star*, March 17, 1997.

34. Ontario Hansard, March 6, 1997, http://www.ontla.on.ca/hansard/house_debates/36_parl/session1/L174.htm (accessed December 14, 2002).

35. T Chung, Graduating nurses see a bleak future, *Toronto Star*, May 18, 2003.
36. J Needleman, P Buerhaus, S Mattke, et al., Nurse-staffing levels and the quality of care in hospitals, *New England Journal of Medicine*, 2002;346:1715–1722; LH Aiken, SP Clarke, DM Sloane, et al., Hospital nurse staffing and patient mortality, nurse burnout, and job dissatisfaction, *Journal of the American Medical Association*, 2002;288:1987–1993.
37. AE Tourangeau, P Giovanetti, JV Tu, et al., Nursing-related determinants of 30-day mortality for hospitalized patients, *Canadian Journal of Nursing Research*, 2002;33(4):51–70. A recent US report indicates that hospitals with better-educated nurses also had lower mortality rates; LH Aiken, SP Clarke, RB Cheung, et al., Educational levels of hospital nurses and surgical patient mortality, *Journal of the American Medical Association*, 2003;290;1617–1623.
38. SS Lassiter, Staff nurse retention: strategies for success, *Journal of Neuroscience Nursing*, 1989;21:104–107.
39. DS Havens, LH Aiken, Shaping systems to promote desired outcomes: the magnet hospital model, *Journal of Nursing Administration*, 1999;29:14–20.
40. C Fooks, K Duvalko, P Baranek, et al., Health human resource planning in Canada (a summary report for the Royal Commission on the Future of Health Care in Canada), http://www.hc-sc.gc.ca/english/care/romanow/hcc0231.html (accessed August 11, 2003).
41. LH Aiken, HL Smith, ET Lake, Lower Medicare mortality among a set of hospitals known for good nursing, *Medical Care*, 1994;32:771–787; LH Aiken, DM Sloane, ET Lake, et al., Organization and outcomes of inpatient AIDS care, *Medical Care*, 1999;37:760–772; SP Clarke, DM Sloane, LH Aiken, Effects of hospital staffing and organizational climate on needlestick injuries to nurses, *American Journal of Public Health*, 2002;92:1115–1119.
42. M Elovaino, M Kivimaki, J Vahtera, Organizational justice: evidence of a new psychosocial predictor of health, *American Journal of Public Health*, 2002;92:105–108.
43. LL Berry, K Seiders, SS Wilder, Innovations in access to care: a patient-centered approach, *Annals of Internal Medicine*, 2003;139:568–574.
44. C La Rocque, Life after medicine, *Medical Post*, September 10, 2002.
45. Information on the Calgary home care physician partnership from: A Taylor, B Korobek, C Slauenwhite, Innovations in Seniors' Care—Home Care/Physician Partnership. Calgary Regional Health Authority. November 30, 2002. And, Community Partnerships Unite Caregivers, *Frontlines*, 2002;64:1. And from interviews with project staff.
46. C Fooks, K Duvalko, P Baranek, et al., Health human resource planning in Canada: ibid.
47. From the *Ontario Medical Review*, May 2003, 45–46.
48. R Gruneir, The call of salary, *Medical Post*, April 29, 2003.
49. AW Wu, Medical error: the second victim, *British Medical Journal*, 2000;320: 726–727.
50. P Norton, R Baker, Creating a safer future for Canadian health care. Presentation to the fifth Joint National Conference on Quality in Health Care, February 2003, http://www.cchse.org/5thJointQuality/Baker%20Norton%20Patient%20Safety%20Feb%202003.pdf (accessed December 20, 2003).

51. KJ Fyke, *Caring for medicare: sustaining a quality system, the report of the Saskatchewan Commission on Medicare* (Regina: The Commission, 2001).
52. See MM Rachlis, C Kushner, *Strong medicine: how to save Canada's health care system* (Toronto: HarperCollins, 1995); MM Rachlis, *The federal government can and should lead the renewal of Canada's health policy* (Caledon Institute of Social Policy, 2003), http://www.caledoninst.org/pdf/55382038X.pdf (accessed December 22, 2003).
53. NSB Rawson, KI Kaitlin, Canadian and US drug approval times and safety considerations, *The Annals of Pharmacotherapy*, 2003;37:1403–1408.
54. T Douglas, speech to SOS Medicare Conference, Ottawa, November 5, 1979.
55. T Bodenheimer, K Grumbach, Electronic technology: a spark to revitalize primary care, *Journal of the American Medical Association*, 2003;290:259–264.
56. Alberta Ministry of Health, New electronic health record helps keep patients safe (press release, October 21, 2003), http://www.gov.ab.ca/acn/200310/15355.html (accessed October 26, 2003).

Index

409